WHITE SLAVE

based on the journal of James Riley;
wrecked with his crew off the coast of Africa,
enslaved and seeking redemption in the desert

David Maislish

First published in Great Britain by
Pen Press Publishers Ltd
39-41 North Road
Islington
London N7 9DP

ISBN 1-904754-98-8

Printed and bound in the UK

A catalogue record of this book is available from
the British Library

Cover design by: Peter Croft

CONTENTS

ILLUSTRATIONS, MAPS and LETTERS

* Illustrations by Peter Croft
# Reproduced by permission of the artist, Ethel Pontsler

Preface

Whilst rummaging about in an antiquarian bookshop some years ago, I found on the floor the Narrative of Captain James Riley. As I flicked through the pages, I saw enough to be drawn by this true story of a man and his crew going to sea, being shipwrecked, suffering enslavement and then encountering the desert, sandstorm, battle, murder and imprisonment; followed by escape and further perils.

Riley's Narrative was an amazing tale, but just as intriguing were the parts of the story that were silent – his origins, family, the details and histories of the places he passed through; and, vitally, what became of all the characters after Riley's account ended.

After two years of research and the re-tracing of Riley's footsteps in Morocco and the Sahara, I managed to enlarge the story, not only by describing and explaining all connected matters, but also by tracing the lives of the main characters up to their deaths; and ultimately suggesting the huge impact the story had on world history.

I hope that the result is a book that will fascinate anyone who is interested in history, religion, fascinating facts, heroism, adventure – or just a good read.

David Maislish
London
December 2004

ACKNOWLEDGEMENTS

My thanks to Lynn Ashman and her colleagues at Pen Press; to Linda Lloyd, my editor, for all the advice and the improvements to the manuscript; also to Lucy for the corrections, to Mark for the IT support, and to all who helped and encouraged me over the last four years.

DM

CREW OF THE COMMERCE

George Williams
… a tall man in his mid-thirties, with a craggy face and a large aquiline nose. He had longish light-brown hair, a crooked mouth and steely eyes.

Aaron Savage
… approaching forty years of age, with thinning light brown hair and a rugged pale complexion.

Horace Savage
… the curly-haired young man … His eyes were full of hope and earnestness … his pale pock-marked face.

Dick Delisle
… a tall black man, slim and imperious … always willing to crack his face into a large smile.

John Hogan
… a tall, thickset man, slightly overweight and in his late thirties. He had a moustache and long black hair, which he tied in a ponytail.

James Barrett
… of average height, with dark hair, dark eyes and a small goatee beard … a good-looking man in his late twenties.

William Porter
… strongly built, with black curly hair and large, dark eyes that were just a little crossed … a silent man, but a strong man.

Archibald Robbins
… in his early twenties, of medium height, and had blond hair and narrow blue eyes. He was a quiet and private person.

Thomas Burns
… of average height, and had dark curly hair. He had small narrow eyes that always seemed to be looking into the distance.

James Clark
… a rather short, muscular young man with spiky reddish-brown hair.

Antonio Michel
… a tall, older man with greying hair. He had a studious expression, dark eyes, a large pointed nose and a wide mouth.

New Orleans Saybrook Gibraltar

Bahamas Cape Verde Canary Cape Bajador
         Islands   Islands

WORLD MAP

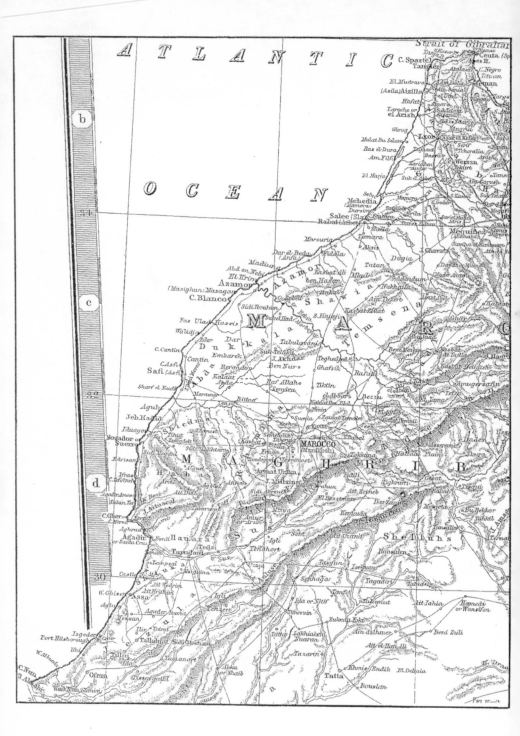

MOROCCO

TRANSLATION OF ARABIC WORDS

alcayd	……..	civil magistrate
bashaw	……..	governor
cadi	……..	judge of Muslim law
djalaba	……..	hooded robe
douhar	……..	group of tents
dourham	……..	walled village
haick	……..	blanket/robe
hajji	………	pilgrim
kasbah	……..	fortress
koubba	……..	saint house
medina	……..	main town
mellah	……..	Jewish enclave
mulay	……..	prince
rais	……..	captain/chief
salaam	………	peace
souk	……..	market
sulle	………	prayer
tabib	……..	doctor

CHAPTER ONE

Youth and the sea

How many people have said, 'As soon as I get back, as soon as I have some free time, I'm going to write this down'? Yet they never do it. But I knew I was experiencing something unique, something that a reader would wonder at, that would fill people's minds with horror and amazement. Unless I wrote down all that had happened to me, no one would believe my story, and it would eventually be as if it had never taken place.

Yet the intent to write all this down was not the only thing going through my mind as I watched the poor wretch kneeling a few yards in front of me under the blazing sun. My immediate concern was that I must not pass out; I had to think of something else and maintain my composure, and I should certainly not show cowardice by looking away from the fearful sight.

My companion, Rais bel Cossim, diverted my thoughts for a moment and explained to me in a very matter-of-fact way that you could tell a man's religion from his mode of execution. A Christian was hanged, a Jew was drowned, a Muslim was beheaded. I thought that if I had been given the choice, I would have selected the Muslim execution; so the differences suggested a favouring of the majority Muslim population in giving them a speedier and less painful death. But I was wrong; this was not death by the swift blade of the French Revolution, this was beheading by a butcher.

The executioner was a butcher on two counts, because when an execution or a judicial removal of limbs takes place in these parts, the butchers of the town are required to provide one of their number to carry out the sentences. Sometimes the man is selected by the casting of lots; but more often, as in this case, one of the town's butchers volunteers so as to claim the fee, which is calculated according to a detailed tariff offering different prices for heads, arms, hands and legs.

The kneeling man was motionless. He stared at the ground as the executioner strode towards him, blade in hand. The curved knife must have been over two feet long. It gleamed in the sun as the butcher raised it high above his head with a dramatic swing of the arm. He looked at the crowd, smiling as his gaze moved slowly from left to right, soaking in their admiration. Then he bent down a little, and with his free hand he grabbed hold of the kneeling man's beard. At the same moment the soldiers on either side of the condemned man stretched his arms out sideways. Then a shriek as the butcher began his work, cutting around the prisoner's neck with a leisurely sawing movement.

He kept on cutting until he reached bone. By then the unfortunate man was unconscious, his white *haick* spattered with blood, as was the ground. The butcher stopped, wiped the blood from the blade and put it down. Then he took the man's head in his hands and twisted it violently from side to side to widen the cut. Taking up his knife, he started to cut the neck once more so as to divide the sinews, until finally he threw the knife aside and wrenched the head clean off. Then, in triumph, he carefully placed the severed head on the mat that had been spread out to receive it, leaving plenty of room for the mutilated limbs of the other men who had come to suffer their sentences that day.

Barbaric indeed, but I could recall being told of the rules imposed in my native Connecticut by the Puritans who had governed our community little more than a hundred years ago. The death penalty had covered many offences, including witchcraft, cursing or smiting of parents and incorrigible stubbornness of children. Somewhere there is barbarism in every history. But often it is unrecognised at the time, and awaits a future generation to provide the label that will then attach to it everafter.

Connecticut was far away. Yet I could visualise my parents' house; I could see my mother; I could hear her words. How many times did my mother tell me that I should not go to sea? I think it was every time she saw me after I had told her that I wanted to leave the family farm and make a life sailing the oceans. That was a long long time ago. This was Africa in 1815. It had taken me thirty-eight years to reach this place.

I was born in Middletown on 27th October 1777, during the war between England and the Colonies - the War of Independence or the American Revolution, according to where you were standing at the time. But the war would be of little interest to me, as it was over by the time I was six years old.

I was the fourth child of Asher Riley and Rebecca Sage, and my parents gave me the name of my late grandfather, James.

My father was a farmer, and our small farm was not far from Middletown. My mother was responsible for the home and the children. She was a tall woman with shoulder-length blond hair, strongly built and slim rather than thin, with a pale complexion and angular features. Mother was a friendly and cheerful person, but she had a ready capacity for firmness and anger.

My father spent all his time working on the farm. He was assisted by my older brother, Asher, and also by hired help during harvest time and whenever else he could afford their pay.

As far as I can remember, my early childhood was happy and uneventful. But then, when I was eight years old, a second consecutive poor harvest meant that my parents' circumstances deteriorated sharply, and as a result Asher and I could no longer be supported at home. My parents had to send both of us out to neighbouring farms to earn our keep. For six years I was moved from farmer to farmer wherever work could be obtained, while at the same time continuing with limited schooling between working periods. That occasional schooling was available to me at home because of the arrangement under which the parents of schoolchildren were obliged to take turns in providing board and lodging for the teachers. With such a large family (I would eventually have eleven brothers and sisters), there was usually a teacher living in our house when I returned from a spell of work.

I had been my mother's favourite and I loved her for it, yet she let an eight-year-old child be sent from the home. I knew that it was done for financial reasons; but in my mind that justified my father's actions, not my mother's. I could never understand it. I never loved her as much again. In fact, I never loved anyone as much again.

Although I was sad to be away from my parents, at least I was well fed, and all the manual work meant that I grew quite strong. Also, it became part of my way of life to spend long periods away from home. I began to fancy myself as an adult, ready for my own life independent of my family.

The farms where I worked were small, and there were only a few hired labourers. Certainly there were no slaves working there. I wonder how I would have behaved towards slaves had I come across them. Would I have given a moment's thought to their misery? I doubt it. Oddly, I think I would have understood their resignation and acceptance of their position; an attitude I now find incredible. But my views on slavery and my recognition of its misery were only to develop as a result of the next decision I would make.

When I was at home, I could see how my father worked on the farm, his sole ambition being to feed his family. My father was quite different from any other person I have ever met. He was tall with dark hair, a nose a little too large and a chin a little too small. When it came to work, he was serious and responsible. But as to anything else, he was disinterested and relaxed.

He was a good father to all of us, even though I saw little of him during my youth. It was a shame that work and the number of children meant that he did not have much time for me. I often wished that I had been an only child, because then my relationship with him would have been fuller and I would have been a happier and different person. But I never bore any resentment towards him; he was doing what he had to do.

But what was it that he was doing? To me, his whole life seemed to be merely an attempt at survival. Surely there was more to it than that? I could not live such a stagnant existence. But how could it be avoided? Staying at home would condemn me to follow my father; or perhaps I could get some work in town. But so what? Stagnation in town was no better than stagnation on the farm. To make anything of my life, I had to leave, go somewhere else; but where? I had no knowledge of other places.

By the time I was fifteen, I had found the solution. I would go to sea. This was not a child's unrealistic fantasy for the future. I was determined to travel. I would visit foreign countries; I would make my fortune on the oceans.

There was no particular reason for making a decision at that time. It was just that you have to have some sort of ambition, some sort of view of what you want to do; and this was mine. Anyway, the sea was always one of the choices available to a boy in Connecticut. For many years the whaling industry had been one of our major employers, and trade with the Caribbean and then with other parts of the world had quickly followed.

America's international commerce had, of course, been halted during the War of Independence; but with victory the risk of capture by English ships disappeared. Now Connecticut vessels set sail freely once more, making for destinations in the Americas and Europe. I was in the right place at the right time; my ambition was available to me, and it was on my doorstep.

"Mother, I have decided to go to sea," I said proudly, expecting admiration, encouragement, at least good wishes. But nothing of the sort. My parents were horrified at my decision. They had never been involved in the sea trade, nor had my grandparents.

"But I need the adventure, the excitement," I pleaded.

"It's far too dangerous; it's out of the question," countered my mother.

"But all of us are here only because our parents or grandparents or whatever, had the courage to brave the Atlantic."

She was not impressed with my historical reasoning. Nothing would convince her that what I wanted to do was sensible. All her arguments seemed to me to be negative. To my mind, all mine were positive. Anyway, my parents offered me no acceptable alternative, and my love of the sea grew more and more, the longer we argued.

In the end, my mother and father gave up the struggle. I suppose they thought that with so many children, the loss of only one to ocean travel was something they could bear.

Nevertheless, I could not rest on my success. I knew that I must leave before my parents changed their minds. My father had to travel to New Haven on the coast to collect some equipment for the farm. I asked him to take me along to see if I could get a job on a ship, and he agreed. He said he would try to find a vessel for me, provided it was one that was not going too far away. The door was opening.

I remember that I just walked out into the fields and lay on my back staring at the sun and the sky, dreaming of where I would travel in years to come.

*   *   *

As the sun shone into my eyes, I saw the butcher throw another bloodied leg on to the mat. It was disgusting.

"Rais," I said, "how can this man continue his trade in the town tomorrow morning? Surely no one will want to have anything to do with him after they have seen this? And what of the families of the victims? Are they really going to greet him and buy raw meat in his shop?"

"No, my friend," Rais said, smiling broadly, "he will be given armed protection for twenty-four hours."

"My God, Rais, do people only remember this for one day?"

"Of course not, Riley, but twenty-four hours gives the butcher

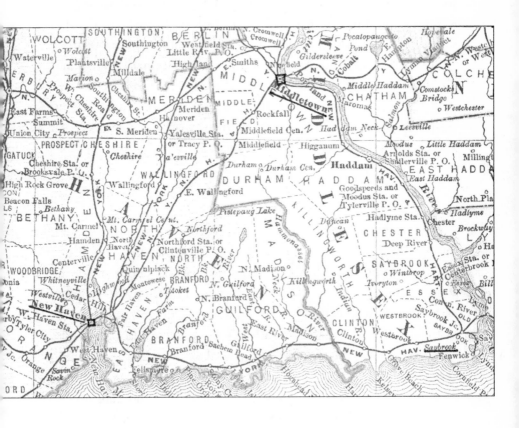

CENTRAL- SOUTH CONNECTICUT

time to collect his belongings and get out of town with his fee."

I was bewildered. In order to earn his payment, the executioner and his family would have to leave the town.

But again, Rais enlightened me. "It is our law that the wife of a butcher who has performed such a task is entitled to a divorce on the grounds that her husband is a violent and dangerous man. In this way, the family is relieved from poverty, the butcher starts a new life elsewhere, and his wife starts a new life here, usually with some part of the fee." It seemed to me that there was no nonsense on earth that humans could not work on, so as to give it the aura of sense. All perfectly dreadful.

*　　*　　*

I recall walking along the seafront in New Haven with my father; every ship seemed to be the perfect one for me, and I could see adventure wherever I looked. My father approached many of the sailors, asking if there might be employment for a fifteen-year-old boy. There was no interest, until eventually my father spoke to the master of The Carib Trader. This vessel was bound for the West Indies, and the master agreed to take me on board as a cabin boy.

But I could not believe it when he turned to me and said, "Come on James, go on board and Joe will explain your duties to you."

"But I haven't said goodbye to my mother."

"Well, we're leaving tomorrow, so either you go home to your mother, or else you board the ship now," he said rather angrily. I looked around hopefully, waiting for someone to say that I could go home for the night and report for duty the next day, but nothing was said. Nothing had to be said; this was not the time for going home, this was the time to take my chance.

I bid my father farewell, but he was surprisingly, or should I say disappointingly, unemotional. He told me to take care of myself and work hard, and said that he looked forward to seeing me at home again in a few weeks. With that, I went on board. My excitement had now turned to fear, and I felt terribly lonely.

We sailed into the ocean early the next morning. It was as though I had lost one dimension; no more than a painting on the wall watching what was happening. But soon orders started to fall on my head from every direction. I did whatever was asked of me and tried my best to impress my shipmates, who were all my seniors.

Keen for commendation and promotion from the first day, I was not held back by the subsequent realisation that regardless of my efforts, I would get nowhere until I was seventeen.

I travelled regularly on the run from the Connecticut River to the West Indies and back for the next three years. There was little adventure, just hard work. But during that time I managed to gain some knowledge of the science of navigation, as well as undertaking various duties on board ship. In between voyages I was able to go home and spend time with my family. Although there were few tales of adventure to tell, I still felt that when I came home it was a return to the world of stagnation. I enjoyed the rest for several days, but I soon yearned for the sea.

After three years on The Carib Trader, it was time to move on. I was employed on other ships on longer voyages for the next two years, and by the age of twenty had passed through the grades of cabin boy, cook, ordinary seaman, seaman, second mate and chief mate. I was now over six feet tall, strong and athletic, and it was time for the next stage of my adventure. I travelled down to New York, and obtained the captaincy of a small vessel. My endeavours led to similar commands on routes to the principal states of the world with which America engaged in commerce.

My situation advanced with every voyage. In time, I started to take a financial interest in the cargoes we were transporting; buying and selling goods whenever we reached port. As a result, I managed to save a considerable amount of money.

I was now in a position to get married and start a family. In January 1802, I married Phoebe, the daughter of Hosea and Mary Miller, who lived not far from my parents' farm. She was the first girl with whom I had ever been really close. She was slight of figure, with reddish hair; and she was, to me, very attractive. I felt then, as I feel now, that it made no difference whether or not I had known other young women; I would have liked her best if she was the only one or if she had been one of many.

We lived with Phoebe's family, although I spent a good deal of my time at sea, and my fortunes continued to prosper. Even better, in 1804 our first son, James, was born.

But the United States had by now become entangled in the European war. At the beginning we were not really affected, as both sides allowed American ships to trade freely. Then, in 1805, the English won their great victory at Trafalgar. Now they ruled the waves and could deal with the Americans who had been growing rich as neutral carriers to both belligerents. The English introduced decrees that severely limited our trade with Europe, and the French followed suit; both countries seizing and confiscating American ships that violated their rules.

When things are bad, you can always rely on the politicians to make matters worse. As a counter-measure, Congress embargoed all American exports to England and France. This completed the ruin of New England's commerce. We seamen had no alternative but to pursue our calling and hope that we would not get caught.

However, few ship-owners were willing to take that risk, and I could not find a new command despite the fact that there were many traders who wanted to transport their goods abroad. I was desperate, but I also felt that no matter how bad the situation, there must still be an opportunity somewhere. There was, for the large number of idle vessels meant that the cost of purchasing a ship had plummeted.

In 1807, I finally raised enough money to acquire a half-interest in a small vessel, the other half-share being purchased by my friend James Watson, for whom I had carried several cargoes over the years. But after two successful voyages, separated by the birth of my twin daughters Amelia and Matilda, disaster struck again. In January 1808, our ship, The Two Marys, was spotted by an English man-of-war whilst en route for Nantes. By that time the English were blockading French ports and demanding that neutral ships stop in England to pay duties before continuing, so I knew I was in for trouble.

The English sent men to board The Two Marys, and they called for our documents. Then an officer wrote in the Register, '*You are hereby forbidden to enter any port in France, any port occupied by French troops, or any port under the influence of France, under pain of confiscation*', signing as lieutenant of His Majesty's ship, Agincourt. I was lucky; in many other cases the English had seized American sailors, and thousands had been sent to prison as 'deserters'.

Once the English were out of sight, we resumed our course for France. Then, on 29th January, whilst in the Bay of Biscay, we were fired on, brought to and boarded by the English schooner, Pilchard, whose officer demanded our papers. I showed him everything except the Register, convincing him that we sailed under the protection of a sea letter only. He then wrote on the letter the same as had been written in the Register by the officer from the Agincourt, and he left us with what he believed was our first warning. Again, I waited until the English were out of sight, then we continued towards Nantes.

Having eluded several other English warships, on the morning of 30th January we took shelter in the roads of Belle Isle, within thirty miles of the River Loire, hoping to run for and enter the river that night.

We made our way to the mouth of the Loire, and took on board a pilot for Nantes. Then a French boat with a marine officer and several armed sailors on board came alongside and ordered us to go on shore with our papers. On landing, we were met by the Commissary of Marine, who examined our documents. Seeing the endorsements made by the English officers, he declared that The Two Marys and its cargo were seized as prize, as we had allowed ourselves to be visited by an English vessel of war.

They threw us in prison, where we languished without charge or court hearing. We were kept in a large dark cell. The door was opened twice a day for the delivery of food and water, but we were told nothing, and had no idea whether we would be held there for days or for years.

After six weeks, the door was unlocked, and we were advised that there was a ship in port that was heading for Lisbon, from where we might travel home. All my crew left the cell, but just as I was about to leave, I was pushed back and the door was slammed in my face. I was locked up once more.

"Get home, men!" I shouted through the grating in the door. "I'll make my own way soon."

I spent three miserable weeks alone in the cell, wondering if I would ever be released. Then one evening the door was opened briefly, and another prisoner was flung in to join me. His name was Ali; he was a Moor, and he was to keep me company for the next three months.

Ali spoke a little English, and we managed to have limited conversation. I asked him to teach me some Arabic, and he did so with considerable pleasure. With over ten hours of lessons every day, I progressed rapidly, and eventually I could speak the language quite well.

Finally, I was released, or rather cast out into the streets, without a cent in my pockets. I had no idea what to do. Should I look for a vessel to take me home, or should I try to recover my fortune in Europe? In the end, I just drifted, being happy enough if I had food to eat and a place to sleep.

For over a year, I travelled through south-west France, working on farms and moving slowly but surely towards Spain. Once in Spain, I took employment on fishing boats for several months, and then I made my way to Lisbon. There I found a ship to take me to New York, from where I travelled home, reaching Middletown in the winter of 1809.

I had lost everything I had earned and saved, but I returned wiser than when I had left, having learned to read, write and speak both French and Spanish, and more usefully, having learned to speak and understand quite a bit of Arabic. It would be some years before I discovered just how helpful that would be.

Perhaps more importantly, I had received a good education in the school of adversity, and this prepared and disciplined my mind for the hardships I was destined to undergo.

Back in Connecticut, I decided to stay with Phoebe and the children for a time. But I had to earn my keep. If it was not the sea, then all I could do was work on a farm again; and fortunately, the Millers needed help.

All seemed well, and the farm flourished. For a time, I felt part of that success. But deep in my heart I knew this must soon end. I was a sailor, not a farmer. I told Phoebe that I could not stay there much longer. Her immediate response was to agree, because she assumed that I wanted us to buy our own small farm, and she said as much. I had to tell her that a farmer's life was not for me; it was too slow, too unambitious, and it was not the sea. Phoebe cried, because she knew what was going to happen. It was time for me to stem the tide of misfortune that had threatened to overwhelm me. I was determined to start afresh. I must return to the ocean.

A few days later, I went down to New York and obtained the command of another vessel.

I traded at sea and voyaged to Spain, Portugal, Brazil and the West Indies. For two years I had modest success, and in 1811 our family increased in size with the birth of our daughter Phoebe. But she was poorly, and sadly she died six weeks later.

Then the politicians dealt me another blow. In 1812, to my utter disbelief, the United States declared war on England. Did they always have to select the most powerful enemy?

I hurried home, and joined a volunteer company composed entirely of seamen. Phoebe was actually pleased that I had exchanged trading for war. Clearly she preferred me to be fighting in America, rather than navigating on the Atlantic.

However, the war was so unpopular that our civic leaders forbade our militia from fighting outside Connecticut. As a result, our unit was disbanded and I went back to sea. But now it was hopeless, as the American export trade had been totally destroyed. After eighteen months, I gave up and returned home penniless.

Back at the Millers' farm, I grew despondent. Naturally, Phoebe and the children depended on me for support. Yet we were still living with my in-laws, and I was desperate to give my family a home and to secure their future, as well as my own.

It was apparent that unarmed commerce on the oceans, the life I had chosen, was no longer the way forward. So perhaps armed seafaring was the answer. I applied for a naval appointment, but was rejected. Very well, then perhaps armed commerce. I applied for the command of a private armed vessel, but was again rejected. The future looked bleak, but in my heart I knew there was no other life for me but the sea. I was determined to search and search until I received an appointment, however modest and seemingly unexciting. It would be the first step for me, and as long as it took, I would seek it out.

I was right. The sea and adventure were not far away.

CAPTAIN RILEY

CHAPTER TWO

A new command

At last the politicians did something useful; there was a Christmas present for all of us. On 24th December 1814, at a meeting in Belgium, terms of peace were agreed between England and the United States. Of course, the present did not arrive in Middletown until after Christmas, the news only reaching us in mid-January 1815. Elsewhere the delay was fatal; for while confirmation of peace was slowly making its way across the Atlantic, fighting continued between two nations no longer at war, as the English unsuccessfully attacked New Orleans, and hundreds were killed.

Phoebe and I sat down and discussed what immediately went through my mind. She was not surprised - she had been through all this with me before. I had to return to the sea to recover our position. It was the only way I knew to improve our standard of life; and of course, I needed to be back on board ship. Phoebe was reluctant to lose me, particularly with a new baby boy to care for and another child on the way; but she knew that having married a mariner, she would always have to share me with the ocean.

Anyway, we had both been very depressed, both spiritually and financially. It was now time to look to the future with realistic hope, because the ending of the war must mean that trade would start to grow, and that automatically meant more work for American vessels and our seamen.

We agreed that in February I would start to look for a new command. I travelled down to Saybrook on the mouth of the Connecticut River and stayed at the Liberty Inn for several weeks, discussing prospects with sailors and ship-owners alike.

Finally, in early April 1815, I obtained the post of captain of a brig that was ready to sail. The ship was nearly new, over two hundred tons, and well fitted. The owners were Messrs Riley & Brown, Josiah Savage & Co. and Luther Savage, all of Connecticut. The vessel's name: the Commerce.

Next, I needed to engage a crew. During my time at the Liberty Inn, I had met George Williams and his friend Aaron Savage, both of whom came from Middletown. Like me, they had been working on farms whilst waiting for seafaring prospects to improve. Like me, they had come to Saybrook once the war was over, hoping to find a new ship.

George Williams was a tall man in his mid-thirties, with a craggy face and a large aquiline nose. He had longish light-brown hair, a crooked mouth and steely eyes. Williams told me that he was determined to earn a successful living at sea, and he said so with such conviction that it seemed to be a statement of unavoidable fact, rather than a hope or ambition. His presence could be felt in any room; I saw him as a natural leader.

Aaron Savage was a shorter man, probably approaching forty years of age, with thinning light brown hair and a rugged pale complexion. Savage was clearly a strong man who would be invaluable on board.

I immediately engaged George as chief mate and Aaron as second mate, and told them to seek out a crew of six men. Within two days they presented me with the sailors they had selected, and I engaged them after brief interviews.

Whilst waiting at the inn, I was visited by a young man called Horace Savage. He brought with him a letter from his mother, Jerusha, whom I had known many years before. She explained that Horace was determined to go to sea, much as I had been in my youth, and she asked that I take him with me and look after him. I could not refuse the mother any more than I could refuse the curly-haired young man in front of me. His eyes were full of hope and earnestness, and his pale pockmarked face begged me to take him on board. I agreed to engage him as our cabin boy.

This boy was me returning as a youth. I entrusted Aaron with Horace's education at sea, and he treated the boy very much as a younger brother, which was appropriate as they shared the same surname, although - as far as they knew - they were unrelated.

But I still had one man to deal with. The cook at the inn, who had served me meals during my stay, had never failed to ask for tales of my life at sea. Richard Deslisle was a tall black man, slim and imperious, yet friendly and always willing to crack his face into a large smile, baring his shiny white teeth.

Now this man had something to say. "You will need a cook on board?" Of course the answer was 'yes'.

"Am I the best cook you know in this town?" Again, it had to be 'yes'.

"Please give me the job."

By the time I had gathered my few belongings and paid my account, Deslisle was waiting at the door, ready to follow me wherever I went.

With a light cargo loaded, we left the Connecticut River on 6th May, bound for the Bahamas. It was a clear day and my heart was bursting. I wanted everyone I had ever known to see me. This was it; I was back at sea and it was my command.

I set a course for the Bahama Islands. Fifteen days later, we entered the Grand Bahama Bank, an area of shallows and sandbanks. From there, with a fair wind, we steered west-south-west and then south-south-west, crossing the bank in three to four fathoms. In some places the water was so clear that an object the size of a dollar coin could easily be seen lying on the seabed when all was calm.

I remained on deck as long as we were in shallows. When we

were in deeper water and clear of danger, I ordered two of the men to keep a good lookout for land and also for white waters and breakers, while I went below to take a nap. Bliss and Carrington were both young and fairly inexperienced, but I felt that they could be trusted with the task I had given them. If not, then what use were they on board?

Later, at about 5am, then fair daylight, I was awakened. There was no need to think twice; I knew what had happened. We had struck the bottom. I leapt to my feet and raced on deck, put the helm to starboard and had all the hands called in an instant. There were breakers ahead and to the south, a sound to our right, and land in the distance to the north. Why had Bliss and Carrington not seen the danger? What had they been doing? Did I have to do everything myself?

The vessel's head was towards the south-west, and she was running at about ten miles to the hour. I immediately put her hard to port and ordered all sails to be let run, praying that we might find deeper water. Despite our efforts and my prayers, the vessel touched the bottom lightly three times; but soon we were over the reef and we found plenty of water. It was an escape, but my relief was not accompanied by any joy. This should not have happened.

I stayed at the wheel, my hands glued to its polished wood, without a muscle relaxing from my shoulders to my fingertips. By seven o'clock, we were once more in open seas, proceeding with a fresh breeze, and at last I could hand over the helm to Williams.

Bliss and Carrington were summoned to my cabin, and I asked them what had happened; why had they not seen that we were approaching such dangerous shallows? Both of them could do no more than look at each other and then the floor, and mumble an apology. There was no point in saying much, because they could see my displeasure from my face. They knew they had betrayed my trust in leaving the ship in their hands. This was the first time in the course of my navigating that any vessel I was on had struck the bottom, and it was once too often.

I admit that at first I had been so shocked that my whole frame had trembled. Now my only emotion was anger. But, angry as I was with Bliss and Carrington, I was also disappointed in myself. We must have drifted from our course during the night, as so many vessels had done before with far worse consequences. I had to make sure that this did not happen again, because next time we might not be so lucky.

The remainder of our journey was uneventful. We discharged our cargo in Grand Bahama, and took a new consignment on board for delivery to New Orleans. On our arrival in New Orleans, we unloaded and awaited a new commission. Within a few days, I had accepted a voyage. We were to take a cargo of flour and tobacco across the Atlantic to Gibraltar.

Now this might be opening up the world to me again. I knew that it would be a dangerous voyage, and we would have to be vigilant at all times. I felt that by striking the bottom, judgment had been passed on us that somehow we were too slovenly or ill-equipped; so I determined to make some changes to improve the position, fairly or not. I decided to discharge Bliss and Carrington. They may not have been at fault for our near disaster, but I no longer had confidence in them, and with such a small crew and such a large ocean to cross, I had no choice but to replace both men. But before I could do anything about them, they came to see me to announce that they did not wish to sail to Gibraltar and were leaving.

I engaged in their places John Hogan and James Barrett, both seamen and natives of Massachusetts. Hogan was a tall, thickset man, slightly overweight and in his late thirties. He had a moustache and long black hair, which he tied in a ponytail. But despite his fearsome appearance, he was very much a gentle giant, and I had no doubt that he was a hardworking and reliable man.

Barrett was very different. He was a good-looking young man in his late twenties, of average height, with dark hair, dark eyes and a small goatee beard, although he was perhaps not as strong as the other sailors on board.

With our cargo loaded, we sailed from New Orleans on 24th June. Two days later, we left the river and headed into the open sea and directly for Gibraltar. It took us six and a half weeks to cross the great Atlantic Ocean. We travelled without incident, and I hoped that my bad luck had been left behind.

On the morning of 9th August, we saw Gibraltar. "Look men, one of the Pillars of Hercules, the handgrips Hercules used when he pulled Africa and Spain apart!" I shouted in triumph to my crew. "We've come from the new world and we're now entering the old world; the former limit of navigation of the Mediterranean nations."

"No, Captain Riley," said Savage, "Gibraltar isn't part of the Mediterranean nations, it's part of England."

"You're right, Aaron," I replied. "Gibraltar is certainly owned by the English, but the name is Arabic, a language with which I am familiar. Tariq ibn Ziyad captured this peninsular a thousand years ago, and as a result it was later named Mount, or Jabal, Tariq. Over time, Jabal Tariq has become Gibraltar."

With that little history lesson, we sailed into Gibraltar, tied up and unloaded our cargo. Then we had to wait until I could find a new commission. We spent our time cleaning the Commerce and wandering around the town. I could only admire what was probably the strongest fortress in Europe, a town of small stone houses on the western face of the Rock, surrounded by batteries of heavy canon pointing in every direction.

This fortress is held by the English as the key, or rather the lock and key, to the Mediterranean. The Moors and the Spanish consider the door as their property, but they cannot open their door without the consent of the English.

As I walked about the town, I came across people from every part of the world, for Gibraltar is a free port where the vessels and subjects of all nations may enter with their goods, carry out their business, and then depart without suffering any taxes or duties. There is just one requirement - your country has to be at peace with England. Of course that kept many ships away, because the

English are always at war with one or more of the major nations of the world.

At the end of several days of rest in Gibraltar, I was sitting on board the Commerce early in the morning when I saw the schooner Louisa of New York sail into the bay and tie up not far from us. I sent Horace over to the ship with a note inviting the Louisa's captain to visit us for a meal.

After he had discharged his cargo, Captain Peter Price came on board for lunch. We talked about the trading situation, and he said that he had a consignment awaiting him in Barcelona a little further up the coast, and would leave the next day. He invited me to join him for dinner on board his ship, and said that he would give me a recent edition of the New York Price Guide, as well as several newspapers.

Late that afternoon I told Porter and Robbins to lower one of the ship's boats. I climbed down into the boat, and directed them to make for the Louisa, which was by now at anchor in the bay.

Porter was strongly built, with black curly hair and large dark eyes that were just a little crossed. He was a silent man, but a strong man - a conscientious worker and a popular member of the crew.

Archibald Robbins was in his early twenties, of medium height, and had blond hair and narrow blue eyes. He was a quiet and private person; but when he was annoyed, his anger showed immediately, and the other members of the crew treated him with care and a little distance. I thought he was probably more intelligent than the others, and he would have been more useful if only he had not been so reserved.

The wind was blowing strongly and the sea was rather choppy. Porter unfurled the small sail and we moved along briskly, soon reaching the Louisa, whose crew had seen us approaching. By the time we were alongside, Captain Price was standing at the rails. We climbed the rope ladder and went on board.

Porter and Robbins were taken below, and ate their supper with the Louisa's crew. I was invited to Captain Price's rooms, and we were served roast lamb and cooked vegetables, accompanied by fresh bread, cheese and fine Spanish wine.

We chatted about the routes we hoped to travel, and at the end of the meal my host gave me the newspapers and the Price Guide. This was a very valuable document for me, as it would be the basis for my purchases in Gibraltar and the key to the profit I hoped to make on those goods when we next reached port.

I did not overstay my welcome, as I knew Captain Price would soon have to prepare his ship for departure the next morning. It was just before sunset; Porter, Robbins and I said farewell and then climbed down into our boat. The sky was now getting dark and the sea was rougher than it had been earlier in the day, though not enough to worry about – or so it seemed.

As we sailed away from the Louisa, I suddenly saw a large wave coming towards us. In an instant it grew in size, resembling the upper jaw of a whale opening wider and wider as it bore down on us in anticipation of swallowing our boat in one gulp. I had no time to give any orders or take any action, because barely two seconds passed before this evil wave was upon us. The watery jaw of the whale closed on our boat as we sat there transfixed.

I shouted to Porter and Robbins, "Get into the sea!" in the hope that the removal of its load would allow the boat to stay afloat. All three of us jumped overboard, but it did not help. The boat went down like a rock, leaving us floundering in the murky waters about seventy yards from the Louisa.

"Are you all right?" I shouted to my men.

"Yes, Captain," each replied.

"Swim to the Louisa!"

But as quickly as we swam towards the ship, the current took us further away.

Fortunately, Captain Price had not moved from the side of his vessel, and had seen everything. He ordered his men to lower one of their boats. They rowed to us, and we were rescued and brought back on board the Louisa.

We went below to dry off, and were given new clothes. Then

we drank some alcohol to warm us and revive our spirits. I was still in shock when Captain Price came into the room. "You must have angered the sea," he said with a broad smile.

In my state of mind, I took his remark seriously. "We struck the bottom near the Bahamas some weeks ago. Perhaps the ocean intended to sink us then, and she's angry that I cheated her, I don't know."

Price laughed loudly. "No Riley, my dear friend, you've just been unlucky, don't worry."

But I was worried. Was the ocean satisfied with her revenge, or was there more to come?

With another copy of the Price Guide safely in my pocket, we were taken to the Commerce. Back at last on our own vessel, it felt as though we had come home after a long and painful journey. The other members of the crew were curious to know what had happened to us, as they could see that we had returned without our boat. I left Porter and Robbins to deal with their questions, and went below.

I stayed in my cabin until the next morning, beset by a sense of foreboding and fear. This troubled me. Although all sailors know that they must respect the sea, if that respect turns to fear, you have a problem.

When our small boat had filled with water, we had been more than half a mile from the Rock, where the current would have taken us into the Mediterranean, and we must have perished within a short time if Price's men had not come to our rescue. But had the ocean allowed us to be rescued, or had we cheated her once more?

I was now desperate to get out to sea so as to make my peace with the elements. But I had not yet received a commission, so I decided to commission myself. I would trade and transport my own goods.

In the morning I went ashore carrying the Price Guide, and I purchased a large quantity of brandies and wines, which I intended to sell at a later port of call. If this did not work, then I would take my cargo back to New Orleans and sell the alcohol there -

24

hopefully for a substantial profit.

While the brandy and wines were being brought on board, Thomas Burns and James Clark, both ordinary seamen, came to see me below deck. These were two very lively and alert young men, full of energy, keen to work and keen to please.

Burns was of average height and had dark curly hair. He was always ready to help and was very popular with the other men. He had small narrow eyes that always seemed to be looking into the distance. Even when he was speaking to you from two feet away, he appeared to be staring straight through you at something far off.

Clark was a rather short, muscular young man with spiky reddish-brown hair. He was invariably seeking opportunities to impress and asking for duties beyond those normally reserved for an ordinary seaman.

"What do you two want?" I asked. "You should be helping with the loading."

"We were helping, Sir," said Clark. "But we've been approached by an American sailor who has asked us to speak to you on his behalf. He wants to know if you would engage him, as he's looking to work his passage home. Can we take him on board?"

I told them I would speak to the man. They left and returned a few minutes later with a tall, older man with greying hair. He had a studious expression, dark eyes, a large pointed nose and a wide mouth. The man told me that all he wanted was his passage back to the United States, and he required no payment. He would be happy to work just for the reward of getting home.

"How do you come to be in Gibraltar without a ship?" I asked.

"I'm marooned here," he explained. "My ship was wrecked close to Tenerife some ten months ago. All of us managed to get ashore, and since then we've each been trying to take on work and make our way home. As one of the oldest on board, I've found it hard to find such a passage, although I did at least manage to get here; but now I wish to go home to New Orleans."

We had sufficient food and drink on board for an extra man, and I could think of no reason why we should not help our compatriot return to his family. The cost would be minimal, and he might prove to be a useful addition to the crew.

"You're welcome on board," I told him. "But you must join us immediately, because we'll be leaving at first light."

"I have all my things with me, and I'm ready," he said.

Just then I heard a loud squealing from the other side of the door. "What on earth is that?" I asked.

"Don't worry," said Antonio Michel (for that was the man's name). "It's a small gift I brought for you and your men in anticipation of being allowed on board."

I confess to having been bewildered as to what it might be, so I strode over to the door and opened it. There I saw a small pig pinned to the floor by Porter and Robbins. The creature was squirming with all its might in an effort to escape.

"You may stay, and so can your gift. When we reach our next port, we'll celebrate with a dinner and your gift will be the main course." I was sure that I would have to buy at least two more small pigs so that everyone might celebrate without suffering any hunger; but my men would be entitled to their feast, and so would I.

The loading was completed, and we made ready to leave the next morning.

CHAPTER THREE

Africa and catastrophe

At six o'clock on the morning of 23rd August, I told George Williams, my Chief Mate, to have the men assemble on deck so that I could tell them my intentions.

They soon gathered, and I informed them that in one hour we would set sail for the Cape Verde Islands.

"Where exactly is that, Captain?" asked Aaron.

"The Cape Verdes are a group of small islands in the Atlantic, about four hundred miles due west of the westernmost part of Africa," I told them, figuring that they could all see in their minds the large lump in the north-west of that great continent. "Many men from there live and work in New England on the whaling boats and on shore. Have any of you been to the Cape Verdes?" I asked.

"I have, Captain," said Hogan.

"So have I," added Clark. I saw them look at each other. They were so dissimilar: Hogan with his heavy frame and ponytail, Clark with his boyish looks and spiky hair. Yet despite that, they had managed to look at one another with the same expression, an expression which said, 'So you know of that place as well. What shall we do about it? Will you speak first?'

I helped them. "What is it, you two? What's the problem?"

Hogan stepped forward. "That place is evil," he said. "It trades in humans. I won't sail with you if you trade in people." Now I understood, for I knew that the Cape Verde Islands were a staging post for the transport of slaves from Africa to the New World.

"Nor will I go there, Captain," added Clark. "I've seen the slaves - men, women and children lined up in chains, separated from their families, branded, beaten and forced on to ships sailing across the Atlantic. For some it may be a place for trade, but for others it's hell. For me it was a vision of evil that has lived with me ever since. I will not see it again."

I decided to reassure them, as I had never had any intention of trading in slaves, nor even of transporting them. However, I knew that large numbers of slaving vessels and whaling vessels called at the Cape Verdes, and I had hoped to sell my brandies and wines there, because those ships and their black trades had turned some of the islands into centres of debauchery. I decided to emphasise to the crew the secondary purpose of the voyage.

"We're going to the Cape Verdes because I wish to purchase a cargo of salt. I have no desire to be part of the slave trade and we won't have any involvement in it."

On hearing this, the men seemed a little easier. "Those islands don't only deal in slaves," I continued. "They deal in many goods from Africa that traders bring from the mainland. They're then purchased by American and European merchants who wish to avoid the dangers of the coastal trade, even if it means paying higher prices. We may buy ivory, hides, gold and amber.

"These trades are carried on by the outcasts, the *lançados*, most of whom are Jews who had to flee from Portugal to avoid being killed or forced to become Christians. They had settled in Portugal after escaping from a similar situation in Spain; although their escape from Portugal was at a price, because all their children were taken from them and given to Christian families. We can deal with the *lançados* without any connection with the slave trade, because when the king of Portugal saw the profit that could be

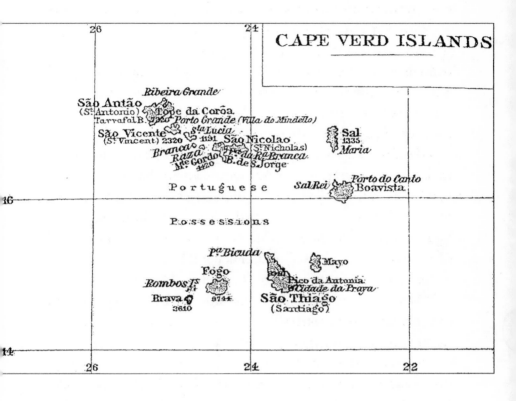

CAPE VERDE ISLANDS

made from selling slaves, he immediately made it a royal monopoly."

I looked at the men; it was clear that they were still uneasy, so I determined to take matters one step further. "We'll have nothing to do with slaves. We won't see any slaves; we won't call at any islands where slave trading takes place.

"Slave trading is carried on at Porto Grande on Sao Vicente. That island is an old volcano. Part of the crater wall has collapsed and the seawater has poured in, creating a deep-water port that can accommodate large vessels. That's why all the slave-transporting vessels go there.

"We won't pass within one hundred miles of that island," I assured them, and I saw the relief spread across their faces. "We'll go to the island of Sal where I'll purchase a cargo of salt from the salt lake inside the mouth of the old volcano at Pedra Lume, which has been breached below sea-level by the ocean, allowing the salt water to rise inside the volcano. Then we'll leave.

"Is anyone unhappy with that?" Silence. "George?"

"We're content Captain," said George. "We're all coming with you. Shall we prepare to sail?"

"Yes, George, have the men carry on." I was reassured by George, who had immediately asserted his control over the men and had spoken for them; taking the lead, rather than consulting them.

After George had set the men their various tasks, I called him over to me. "George, all that I said I'll keep to. But you should know that when we're at anchor at Sal, I'll try to sell some of our brandies and wines, and they will no doubt be bought by merchants from Porto Grande."

"There'll be no trouble, Captain," he said. "I'll deal with the men. Some wine to accompany our pork dinner might help," he added with a broad smile.

That was a good idea. What was more important, I had been encouraged by the quality and support of my Chief Mate. Anyway, now we would make for Sal.

We moved off in bright daylight. All the sails were unfurled and we picked up a firm breeze. The sun shone down on us, its heat warming us as the breeze cooled us. We said farewell to Europe, and moved out of the bay and into the Gut.

First we had to sail through the Straits of Hercules, which stretch from Cape Trafalgar in Europe to Cape Spartel in Africa. I knew that I must keep alert during this passage, because it is one of the strangest areas on the globe. The wind is generally either easterly or westerly, but at low level we had the Levanter that brought cold air streaming in from the north. Yet the real test was set by the current, so I decided to stay at the wheel with George until we had passed Cape Spartel and could safely sail south along the hump of north-west Africa.

We struggled against the sea, which surged a two-knot surface current eastwards from the Atlantic through the Straits and into the Mediterranean.

George had the helm as I stood by his side. "We should take in the sails, Captain," he said. "The current's too powerful."

"I know," I replied. Although the surface current was from west to east, I was aware that lower down there was also an east to west flow of colder salty water from the Mediterranean into the Atlantic. "We must just get to Cape Spartel, and then we'll face simpler currents."

"But Captain, I can feel the surface current is the stronger," said George.

"It has to be," I told him. "It's vital that the surface flow of water into the Mediterranean is greater than the flow of water out of the Mediterranean. Otherwise that sea would start to empty and become a shrinking salt lake. In the course of time, Europe would be joined to Africa and the Levant, and the whole nature of the world would change. But until then, they're only joined at Constantinople in the east and Gibraltar in the west. That's the significance of Gibraltar and its straits. No wonder the English defend it."

So we took in some sail and headed cautiously for the Cape

31

Verde Islands. The usual course was to go via Madeira; but to save time, I decided to run down between the Canary Islands and the African coast.

After we passed Cape Spartel, I gave the vessel more sail and we made good speed. We had a fair wind, but in the evening it became foggy, and the further we went, the foggier the night became. For another three days and nights we eased slowly forward in the mist.

As a result, we saw no land and could rely only on our latitude calculations. I spent a good deal of the time by the side of the man who had the wheel. But it was all completely pointless, as there was nothing to be seen anywhere, just fog.

On 27th August, I was standing alongside Hogan as he steered us, although there was little steering to be done. We just tried our best to keep travelling more or less in a south-south-west direction, hoping that sooner or later we would see something.

"It would have been easier a hundred years ago," said Hogan.

"What do you mean?" I asked.

"Well, Captain, when I was last in the Cape Verdes, I was told that one of the islands was a volcano which was aflame continuously for two hundred and fifty years. It served as a beacon for all mariners. Of course, by the time I was there, the fire had been out for some seventy years; but can you imagine two hundred and fifty years of non-stop flame belching out of the top of a volcano? We might have seen it even through this mist."

I must admit that I doubted whether we would have noticed the flames if the whole of Africa had been on fire.

"What is that island called?" I asked.

"It's called Fogo," said Hogan, "the Portuguese for fire, just as our destination of Sal is the Portuguese for salt."

Later on that day I calculated that we were only slightly off our course. We must have passed the Canaries without seeing them. That could have been because it was during the night, which was as dark as could be and made even more difficult by the fog. But I feared that this might be wishful thinking. I was becoming concerned about our position, but I had to make sure the crew did not notice this.

Now the darkness seemed to increase, and the fog became even thicker. I re-examined all my calculations, but could find no fault. As a precaution, I altered our course to the south-west, which ought to have carried us to the east of the Cape Verdes and directly to Sal. We sailed on at a good speed, although all the while my mind could not avoid concentrating on why we had seen no land at any time.

Some of the men mentioned that during the afternoon the seawater had been coloured, which suggested that we were not far from the shore. I disagreed, because I thought we were at least thirty miles from the coast, somewhere near Cape Bajador. But by now my fears were prevailing over my judgment. All these calculations, all these decisions, all these changes of direction meant one thing - we were lost.

By now I could hardly see the end of the jib-boom, so I rounded the vessel to and ordered the sails to be hauled in, and we eased almost to a halt. I then took a sounding; but even with a hundred fathoms of line, I could find no bottom. So for sure we must have been in deep waters and some way from land.

I therefore decided that we should continue on our present course, but slowly. I ordered the light sails to be handed and the steering sail booms to be rigged in snug.

Then it became extremely dark. We were travelling at hardly any speed at all. Our trysail boom was on the starboard side, but ready for jibing, and I ordered the helm put to port, never dreaming of danger. Yet I felt uneasy. I told the men to secure every loose thing.

We sailed slowly on for about two hours, and the mist cleared a little. Then I saw to the west huge menacing clouds, dark as coal, which were moving towards us.

The wind dropped and all was silent. There was an eerie feeling all around the ship, as if we were alone in the middle of the ocean a thousand miles from anywhere, with the elements satisfied that

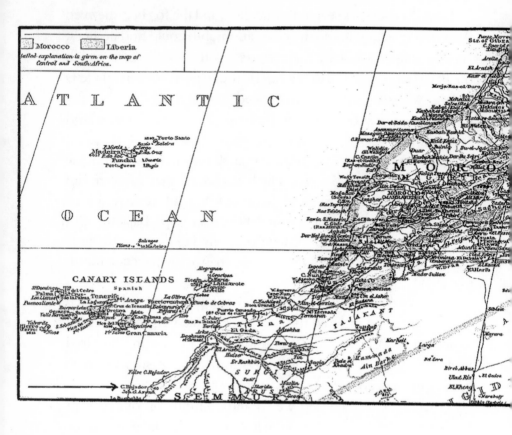

CAPE BAJADOR

they had trapped us, having conspired to give us no wind and no current.

Then a very strong breeze came, and the sea grew rough and choppy. The main boom was jibed over. At that instant I heard a roaring. The yards were braced up and all the hands were called. I realised that a squall was fast approaching us. I had two choices: either to head into the wind, which would relieve the pressure on our sails, or turn the ship and let the storm blow us from behind.

I ordered the helmsman to steer away from the squall so that we might be blown forward. But then I heard a roaring of the wind and sea together. I knew that something was very wrong, although my judgment suggested that we might ride this out quite easily. Just as I was about to order the sails to be lowered, I noticed breakers foaming at a most alarming rate under our lee. For a moment I saw a ray of hope, there were no breakers ahead.

"Forward as fast as we can go! We'll sail through this and into calmer waters."

But my hopes were destroyed as the current turned the ship a full ninety degrees and straight on to the breakers. "Turn the wheel, turn the wheel!" I cried.

"I can't," shouted Burns. "The devil's pulling it the other way. We've come too far south."

"There's no such thing as too far any more!" I shouted back. I was well aware of the belief of Portuguese sailors long ago that it was unsafe to travel beyond the dreaded Cape Bajador. Their problem had been that the wind usually blew from north to south and, having sailed south, their ships could not turn and sail home against the wind. But things had changed with the use of the lateen sail, long since invented in the East to sail into the wind.

Slowly we turned, but we could not turn enough. We were now sideways to the wind and at her mercy. Surge after surge came thundering at us. We just had to ride this out; we had to keep our calm and try to recover our direction. There should be nothing to fear, for there was no land near us.

We all hung on for dear life as the wind and rain attacked us.

We were overwhelmed by the sounds of our oppressors as the rain hissed and the wind shrieked and the sea roared. Our ship added to the nightmare of sounds as the masts creaked and the sails flapped, accompanied by the smashing of all that was below deck.

And then it happened. With a crash, she struck. We had hit rock, and the surges continued to assail us from behind, driving the ship more and more firmly on to the rocks.

She had struck with such violence that every man was thrown to the deck. I saw one of the crew slide straight past me and slam against the railings near the bow. "Help that man!" I shouted as I rose to my feet. "See to him. Get the men together!" Then, as I spoke, the vessel listed sharply to port and water began to pour in at a frightening rate.

We let go the best bower anchor; all sails were taken in as fast as possible. But I knew that the Commerce was lost. There could be no hope of saving her; we must only think of saving ourselves.

I ran out on deck. "Are all the men present?"

"Yes," said George.

"Are they all right?" I asked.

"They're fine," said George.

"Thank God for that. We're not going down yet. The ship's lost, but she's not going down. Do you all understand me? We must carry out our duties."

I knew that everything was chaos. I was shaking, but I had to appear calm in the hope that the crew would take my lead. Never had I been at such a loss as to what to do; yet never had I given so many orders.

"Get the provisions up on deck. Everything that's not been lost must be collected and tied down. We'll need the food. The coast must be much nearer than we thought.

"We can make land with our food in one of the boats," I said.

The lightning speared the sea as the rain poured down, and the waters flew over the stern and swept the decks. Every man worked without regard to the elements as if his life depended on his efforts,

36

which was indeed the truth.

They were scurrying about, holding on to the nearest fixture whenever possible, bringing barrels up on deck and tying them to the railings. The sea continued to break with tremendous power over the side and sweep across the ship. The small stern boat being in danger, we pulled it out of the water and up on board. I then instructed the men to cut the rail near the boat, so that we could launch her easily when the moment came. Then they severed the lashings of the long-boat, which was lying bottom-up on the deck.

Now, all of a sudden, the mist cleared a little, and I could see the sorry state of my vessel. She was nearly full of water, and the sea was continuing to pound her and spray over her.

Then, in the moonlight, I saw the shore. It was amazing. I had assumed that we were at least thirty miles out to sea; but to my astonishment, the coast was less than two hundred yards away.

"Throw the barrels and chests over the side and let them float to the shore. George, have the small boat prepared for launching. Time's running out." Williams immediately took two men and had the boat placed on the lee side of the vessel.

The Commerce was fixed fast on the rocks, but the ebb and flow of the breakers pulled us back and forth, and with each forward movement I heard further splintering and smashing of the ship's timbers, and all the while she filled faster and faster.

I could see that the crew had managed to bring and secure on deck barrels of water, bread and wine, as well as some salted provisions. They had also collected clothing, charts and nautical instruments. "Put those into chests," I said. "They may be vital for us." At least with the sextant we would be able to measure the sun's height every noon, which would tell us how far north or south we were.

The men did as they were told. Everyone was scrambling around working, trying to keep upright, helping one another, and carrying out my instructions. They all performed their duties without question or comment.

The skies and the waters now began to calm. It was time to act in case this was only a short break in the elements' attack.

"Porter, get into the small boat," I said. I climbed in with him. "Now men, put in some provisions and knot all those ropes together, the thick ones last, and then tie the thin end to the seat of the boat and tie the other end to the base of that mast. Right, lower us into the sea." The boat was slowly lowered until it hit the water.

We pushed ourselves away from the Commerce. For a moment, the sea seemed almost calm, and we appeared to have an easy job of rowing the hundred yards or so to the shore. Then a massive wave overwhelmed us and our boat was plunged into the foaming surges.

Somehow we managed to stay inside the boat, and driven by the current and aided by the undertow, we headed towards the shore. All the time the sea was alternately lifting us up and then plunging us deep between the waves that towered over us, filling us with terror, and then a few seconds later we were once more raised on high.

Each time we plunged, we had to hold our breath until we could draw further air once we were clear of the depths. We endured this torment for what seemed an age, as our boat went down and then up and then down again; and finally we were thrown, still inside the boat, on to a sandy beach.

We crawled out. After checking that we were uninjured, Porter and I knelt down facing one another, quite speechless. We remained there for several minutes, drawing in air and spitting out the foul salt water of the sea, which had first wrecked us and had then saved us.

"Come on Porter, we have work to do. The other men are still on the ship." First we tipped the water out of the boat and dragged it up the beach and out of the reach of the sea. We might need it again one day.

I untied the rope from the seat of the boat and we heaved the rope with all our might, until at last we had one end of the thick rope in our hands. We tied it around some rocks on the beach. The crew on board the ship pulled the rope tight and made it fast, so that we had a strong line above the water stretching from the wreck to the shore.

Now the men started heaving overboard chests, bedding, barrels and every other article that would float, and the two of us on shore collected and secured those items that drifted within our reach. This done, I could see the crew lowering the long-boat into the sea. Several barrels were passed down into the boat, and then two men jumped in.

They were similarly aided by the heavy waves, which hastened them towards the shore, and then they crashed on to the beach.

Unfortunately, the long-boat was badly damaged in the crash, but both Robbins and Burns were saved and uninjured. They had also managed to rescue three barrels of bread and two barrels of salted provisions.

We were now four men on the shore. Having picked up some clothing and other items that had floated from the vessel to the beach, we stood together wondering what we should do next. Day was now dawning. What were we to do about the men still on board?

"Captain," said Burns. "The sea is now more peaceful. Tell the men to wait until it's completely calm. Then they can swim to the shore."

It seemed a good idea to me, but then I looked once more at the ship and I could see that although the waters were calmer, she was rocking from side to side more than before, despite being stuck fast on the rocks. The men were still in danger and could not be left there much longer. I signalled and shouted to the crew to cut down the masts, as that might ease the vessel by stopping the wind blowing into the remaining sails.

Hopefully, in this way the Commerce would not be smashed to pieces at least for another day. The crew had found two axes, and I watched as the masts crashed into the sea. If there was any doubt before, there was none now; we would never sail in her again. Next it was time to find a way to get the remaining eight men to the shore.

The long-boat had been badly damaged and the small boat, which I was desperate to keep intact, could not survive journeys to and from the wreck until some repairs had been made. I therefore gestured to the crew to come one by one to the shore by using the thick rope that now reached above the sea from the vessel to where we were standing.

Hogan ventured first. He took off his jacket and grabbed the rope with both hands, his back to the shore. Next, he swung his legs up in front of him and locked one across the other at the ankles over the rope. He gradually made his way backwards in the direction of the shore by passing his hands one by one behind his head and then, with his ankles still locked over the rope, moving his knees towards his chest.

After he was clear of the vessel, every wave buried him as his weight pulled the part of the rope on which he was then hanging down towards the sea. But still he held on with a death-like grasp. As soon as the surf had passed, he proceeded a few more feet towards the shore, then halted again while being engulfed by the next wave.

Hogan continued in this manner for what seemed an age, until eventually he was within our reach, as we stood up to our waists in the sea. He collapsed into our arms, and we carried him high up the beach and revived him.

Having seen Hogan's success, the remaining seven crew members were encouraged to believe that they could save themselves in the same way, and one after another they did.

All my men were now on shore. We had lost our way and we had lost our ship, but we had all been saved from a watery grave.

CHAPTER FOUR

Discovery and confrontation

We were all alive; we were all safe. If I could have done what I wanted, I would have just lain down on the sand and rested for a few hours. But I could not allow myself such a luxury.

The men were already lying down. They deserved a rest, but I knew that I had to get them up and working straight away. We may have been safe, but it was not much use being safe on a beach hundreds of miles from civilisation with little food and no shelter. The priority was to secure the provisions and fresh water we had salvaged from our ship.

"All of you, come on now, we must do something to help ourselves. Everyone up please! Let's collect everything we've brought from the Commerce; all the barrels of food and water, and anything else you can find. Take the barrels and put them up there away from the sea," I said, pointing up the beach.

The men immediately got to their feet and started to gather all the barrels and chests that contained food, water, or wine. They carried them to a spot about fifty yards from the water's edge. Then we built a sort of tent out of the oars from our boats and some canvas that had been kept in the long-boat as small steering sails.

Now that we had collected our most important possessions,

what were we to do next? We could not just rest here and hope that someone would come along and save us. There was a distinct possibility that we would not be discovered by any human beings on this inhospitable shore, even if we stayed here for a thousand years.

The best route to safety was the way we had come: the sea. That meant that we had to repair our two boats. Then, when the waters had calmed, we could put to sea and make our way to ... but where?

Fortunately, we had rescued a compass and some nautical instruments. Using these we could perhaps sail down the coast until we were found by a friendly vessel that would deliver us to a nearby European settlement. Maybe we could even be carried to the Cape Verde Islands. We would no longer be very choosy about which of those islands we were taken to.

Whilst I was dreaming of such an unlikely rescue, I suddenly saw a figure in the distance. It was a man! As he walked towards us, he inspected a few items of our clothing that were scattered at the far end of the beach, and he began to collect some of the clothing as he advanced.

The crew all stood up, and we watched in silence as the man continued his approach. We were neither pleased nor displeased; we were just amazed that there was another human so near to us. Our minds could not comprehend what this meant; was there a city not far off, or was this some kind of hermit who lived here all alone?

I said to the men, "You all wait here. I'll go to him and try to find out whether he's friendly."

So I walked calmly towards the man, always smiling and trying to make signs of peace and friendship. But as I came within fifty yards, he started to wave me away, making it clear that he wished to approach, but I should not come any closer. He was unarmed, so I continued, only much more slowly, all the while smiling and extending my hands. I walked on until I was no more than ten yards from him, then I stopped.

The native was quite short, about five feet six inches, and he had a complexion somewhere between that of an American Indian and a negro. His chest was bare and he wore a piece of coarse woollen cloth, much like sacking, that reached from just above his waist down to his knees. The man's hair was long and bushy, dark with streaks of grey, and it stuck out in all directions to a length of about six inches. I noticed that his eyes were dark and fiery. He had a moustache, as well as a beard that reached down to his chest. His mouth, which seemed to stretch nearly from ear to ear, was lined with large shining teeth, and they seemed to be sharpened for the purpose of devouring human flesh.

Although he was rather old, he looked fierce and vigorous. He stood there with his legs apart and slightly bent, shouting at me. I tried a few words of Arabic, but either he did not understand or else he was not interested in listening to me.

He was soon joined by two old women, whom I assumed were his wives. Though their two eye-teeth stuck out like hog's tusks, they looked a little less frightful, their tanned skins hanging loosely on their faces and breasts.

Not far behind these dreadful women followed four young men, a girl of about eighteen (who was not in the least frightful or ugly) and five younger children of differing ages. The children were all entirely naked. One child had a metal hammer, another held an axe - both of which had no doubt belonged to crewmen on another unfortunate vessel wrecked on this cruel coast. They all carried knives slung on their right sides in sheaths suspended from their necks.

Having finished his shouting and snarling, the old man turned and ran back a few yards to join the others. They looked around and saw all the items we had not yet collected strewn on the beach. The old man then started giving orders to the others. They had now decided to ignore us completely. I went back to my men and told them to do nothing.

Then these people began to plunder everything they desired. Clearly they believed that they were in a strong position. Perhaps in approaching us, all they had wanted was to find out whether we had any weapons; and having discovered that we were unarmed, they felt they could do as they pleased.

They broke open the trunks and chests, and emptied the contents on to the sand. Then they picked up all the clothing and carried it to the sandhills at the back of the beach. There they laid everything out neatly to dry.

One of the trunks had contained some silk veils and handkerchiefs that I had bought in Gibraltar. They wrapped the veils around their heads like turbans and tied the handkerchiefs to their legs and arms. Some of our bedding had floated ashore; they ripped it apart and threw the feathers in the air. They seemed to be much amused, and danced across the sands surrounded by the feathers floating in the breeze. They were all delighted with their good fortune, and even the old man's stern look eased a little.

My men were incensed. We had no arms with us, but we could have driven them off with the aid of the pieces of wood on the beach and with the weight of our numbers.

"Captain," said Clark, "let's get them. We can deal with them easily."

Then our cook, Dick Deslisle, stepped forward. "Leave that old man to me," he said. "I'll break his neck." The look in his eyes was so determined that I could imagine Dick treating the old man like one of the chickens he had prepared for our meals in Gibraltar.

Next, Antonio stepped forward and took hold of Dick by the arm. "Wait," he said. "You have to decide whether to leave them or to kill all of them. If we attack and just one escapes and gets back to any others there might be behind those hills, they'll all come and massacre us."

"Nonsense," said Clark. "They've got to learn that we won't take this sort of treatment. We don't have to kill anyone; we just have to let them know that we demand respect. A few blows will soon teach that old man that we won't suffer their impudence."

44

I felt that it was time for me to take control of the situation. The last thing we needed was an argument amongst ourselves. "Stop," I insisted. "Antonio's right. These can't be the only people nearby. There must be others. We're not interested in silks and clothing; we're interested in rescue. It will have to be rescue with the help of whatever people are on the other side of those hills, or else rescue by going back to sea. Either way, it would be best to be at peace with the natives."

The men were clearly unhappy just to stand there and watch these people prancing about with our property. On the other hand, they appeared to accept that what Antonio and I had said was sensible.

I was grateful that I had Antonio to support me, for the anger amongst the crew was growing to such an extent that in the end they would have run at the natives without thought. Although my men might not have killed any of them, they would certainly have given them a good beating; a beating sufficient to make the natives run off and plot their revenge.

I was sure that restraint was the better option, even though it gave me no pleasure to see our property being stolen as we stood by. My only fear was that our passive reaction might encourage the natives to take further liberties.

So we would let them steal whatever they wanted, subject to one point. "All of you listen carefully," I said. "The barrels containing food or water - they won't take those. We will not permit that. Let them satisfy themselves with the other items, but they are not to have any of our food. We'll need our provisions in order to survive, and we'll defend those to the end. Antonio, do you agree with me?"

Antonio was reluctant. "Captain," he said, "I'd rather be hungry than dead. We may have to let them take the food, or at least some of the food."

"No, Antonio," I insisted. "We must draw a line somewhere. Not the provisions. They'll have to be happy with the rest, which is already more than they can carry away."

45

The crew gathered the barrels containing food, wine or water, and then stood in front of them while this strange family started to collect the items they had plundered. Without approaching us again, or indeed taking any notice of us at all, they picked up as much as they could and calmly strolled off in the direction from which they had come in the first place. Then they disappeared from view.

"Well, men," I said, "soon the news of our existence will pass to others over those hills, so it's time for us to prepare our escape."

We had recovered from one of the chests my two small sacks of money, mainly Spanish and American coins. I shared out the contents of one sack equally amongst the twelve of us, in the hope that the money might prove useful to the crew in procuring their return home if we were separated. Also, should we be captured, it would make all of us appear to be of equal worth. Otherwise I feared that those with money might be kept for ransom, whilst the others would be considered as being of no value and would be killed. I buried the second sack in the sand, as the men were already carrying as much money as could be concealed in their pockets.

Next we opened one of the casks and took a drink of water, and then we ate some bread. Having eaten and drunk and being once more on our own, it was time to repair the boats.

It was early afternoon. With the easing of the wind, the sea was almost smooth, so I told Porter to return to the Commerce to recover some tools and nails. Using the rope that still stretched from the shore to the wreck, he hauled himself over the water and soon returned with the items we needed.

I took the hammer and nails from him, and George Williams, Aaron, Horace, Antonio and Deslisle helped me to nail the broken pieces of each of the boats together as well as possible. It was not a perfect repair, but after an hour and a half of hammering, the boats were once more in a seaworthy condition.

I had told the other men to rest; but while the six of us had been repairing the boats, the others had been resting rather too near the wine. Unrestrained by my authority and having nothing to do, they had opened a cask of wine and drowned their sorrows to such an extent that they would be of no further use until they had slept off their drunkenness.

As we walked over the sands to join them, I saw two of the older native children running along the beach towards our makeshift tent. They grabbed hold of one of the sails and then started to untie the other one. I ran towards them, waving my fist in an attempt to stop any further theft. The two took out their knives and brandished them at me; but seeing that I would not retreat, they backed off and ran away with the sail they had managed to untie before I had reached them. These natives were getting too confident, but at least now they had seen the first sign of resistance.

It was beginning to get dark, and we all sat down next to our tent. Dick prepared a meal of salted pork and bread, accompanied by wine for those who had not already had their fill.

I gave instructions for the men to take turns on watch throughout the night, telling George that I wanted two men to keep a lookout at all times. The savages were unlikely to return before daylight, but I could take no chances, and anyway we had now seen their knives; the next time they came it might not be just for theft.

My men lay down to sleep, save for the first watch. All was now still, except for the pounding of the restless and unwearied waves that continued to dash against the deserted wreck without pity and then tumble on to the jagged rocks.

As I looked down to the end of the beach, I could see that above the rocks there were high perpendicular cliffs that jutted straight out of the sea, inviting every ill-fated vessel to crash into them. The rocks on which the Commerce had met her doom had in fact saved us, as they had halted the vessel and allowed us to escape, rather than leaving her to plough on the extra hundred yards and smash into the cliffs in a disaster that would surely have killed us all.

I lay on my back and stared at the stars in the sky. From the time when the Commerce had struck the rocks until this moment, I had been so entirely engaged by the efforts our situation demanded that there had been no time for reflection. But now thoughts rushed through my mind in a torrent, and kept me from the sleep that my weary body and mind required.

Here I was on a barren coast, a cruel sea surged in front of me and the unknown lay behind me. As if that was not enough, there were also savage beings nearby - in human form admittedly, but in its most frightening appearance - who threatened to rob us of our last resource, our provisions.

I was certain that in the morning they would return in greater numbers; numbers sufficiently strong to achieve their purpose, whatever that purpose was. What would happen then? Would they kill us, or would we be seized and doomed to slavery until relieved from our miseries by death itself?

My eyes drifted to the ocean. I had left my wife and children in Connecticut. What were they doing? Presumably they were not particularly ill at ease; there was no reason for them to think that I had been wrecked. They were not expecting me to return for several more weeks. Any news they received via Gibraltar was likely to be the good news that we had sailed off on our next voyage without any problems.

But in the end, everyone at home would realise that we were lost, unless we were rescued very soon. I could see no realistic hope of such a rescue. Would I ever return home? That was the doubt now haunting my mind.

My wife and children depended on me for their futures, and here I was, helpless and useless to them. I would give my children no instruction, no direction; I would not even be able to watch over them. Perhaps even worse, Phoebe would never know for sure whether I was alive or dead. She would be left to live without me, but she would not be released from me.

These reflections harrowed my soul. Why had such evils befallen me? Had I done something to deserve this? I had fought so hard to overcome the problems that had been put in my way. Why had I been dealt such a heavy blow? I could find no answer. Then my thoughts turned to my eleven fellow sufferers, and I sat up and looked at them. Had one of them perhaps deserved this fate, so that by chance the others had suffered with him? It was all too ridiculous.

They were a good collection of sailors, who had done nothing but work hard and support me. It was now my duty to protect them and preserve their lives. I was their captain and they would look to me in their quest for survival. I must not fail them.

But now I needed some sleep. In the morning we would decide on our first steps towards rescue and home.

I fell asleep straight away, but the night passed slowly. I awoke every hour, and on waking was bewildered by what I saw. It took me time on each occasion to work out exactly where I was and to understand my situation; only then could I go back to sleep.

When daylight began to dawn, it brought not the prospect of relief and rescue, but the threat of further problems. I could see the old man returning. He was again accompanied by his wives, but this time there were eight young men with them. The old man was armed with an iron spear, which he held in his right hand above his head, making motions all the time as if he was about to throw the weapon at us.

We stood up, not knowing what to do; whether to retreat or to advance. But when the old man and his party were about fifteen yards from us, they stopped. The old man turned to the sea and pointed to the wreck. He put his spear down and held out both hands towards our group. Then he moved his hands together to the side until they were directed at our vessel. It was obvious that he was telling us to return to the Commerce. He then waved us on in an agitated fashion, making it clear that we must leave immediately.

I said to my men, "He wants us to go to the ship, but I don't see why we should." Then the old man shouted at me and pointed to the end of the beach, where I saw a number of camels coming towards us.

The old man became more and more excited. While this was going on, the two women turned and ran towards the camels, yelling and picking up handfuls of sand, and then throwing the sand into the air. They screamed at the men with the camels, and then they screamed at us.

Next, the old man jabbed his spear at some of the crew in order to get their attention. Then he pointed his spear at the approaching camels and their keepers, shouting all the while and becoming increasingly agitated.

It would have been giving him too much credit to think that he was warning us of impending danger; rather he must have been frightened that he might have to share his spoils.

We were now all standing together, and I said to the men, "Whatever is happening here, this looks dangerous. I think the old man is right, we ought to get back to the Commerce."

"Fine," said Aaron. "But what about all our provisions, our food?"

"That's a problem," I said, "but we have no choice. We must return to the wreck. Those people coming with the camels are unlikely to be friendly. If it later turns out that they are friendly, we may be able to come back and reclaim our provisions; but I'm not willing to take any chances."

We walked down to the small boat, which was the one in better condition. The old man followed closely, continually jabbing his spear towards us. I had picked up a piece of wood and was prepared to use it to block his spear; but I did not really believe he would throw it, for fear of losing his precious implement.

The men dragged the boat into the water and positioned it underneath our rope, which still stretched to the Commerce. All twelve of us climbed in, and two men stood up and held the rope in order to pull the boat towards the wreck. We had travelled no more than fifteen yards when our combined weight resulted in water pouring over the sides of the boat, which instantly sank to the bottom. Fortunately, the water was only about four feet deep, and we scrambled back to the shore.

What were we to do now? I was well aware that I had been rushed into a decision without sufficient thought. I would have to think carefully before we took the next step. To the front lay the sea; behind stood the sandhills; to one side were men approaching with their camels. Therefore we had to go the other way.

"Listen," I said. "That way over there is the only possibility for us. Let's just go there and leave everything behind."

But the old man with his spear and the eight young men were now blocking us from going in that direction. The camels were approaching fast, and the old man then made signs to show that the men with the camels had firearms and would instantly shoot us. He used his left hand to explain this by pointing it at each of us, pretending to shoot with it.

At the same time, he and the younger men and the women were opposing our escape and insisting that we return to the wreck. And all the while the two women kept up their constant yelling.

I said to the men, "We've lost the small boat; the long-boat is not as seaworthy, but at least it's larger. We'll have to test the repairs we made yesterday." The men agreed.

"Come on, let's go," I said. We ran to the long-boat, turned it over and dragged it into the water.

I did not let anyone get into the boat until the water was about three feet deep. Then I told the men that they were to get in one at a time, and we would see at what stage it started to become overloaded.

"No!" I shouted at Horace. "Don't climb in over the side! Climb over the bow or the stern. I don't want anyone tipping the boat over." We could not afford to lose our last boat. That would really have spelled the end for us.

One by one, we climbed in, and all succeeded in getting on board. The boat lay low in the water, but not dangerously low so long as the sea remained calm.

It looked as though the repairs had been successful. Again, two men, one at either end of the boat, grabbed hold of the rope and pulled us along, until several minutes later we were beside the wreck. When I looked down, I could see that the long-boat was half-filled with water, but it had served its purpose and was still afloat.

We all climbed aboard the Commerce, save for Burns and Clark. I had told them to stay behind and bale out the boat, and then they could join us.

Once on deck, I turned to the shore and saw the savages run to our tent, where they were joined by the men who had been leading the camels. They forced the camels to kneel down, and then loaded our barrels of bread and meat and the other provisions on to them. Then the men departed with the camels and all our food.

As soon as they had left, the old man raced across the beach and smashed the remaining barrels of water and wine in a frenzy, emptying their contents on to the sand. Clearly he was angry that those men had taken what he felt was rightly his.

My men were now all on deck. "Everyone pay attention," I said. "We've lost our provisions and our fresh water. It's pointless returning to the beach. There's nothing of use left behind; only an angry savage and eight young men waiting to challenge us. And over the sandhills there are more natives, some with firearms; so we're not going back there."

"But Captain," said George, "where else can we go? The ship will never sail again and the long-boat is leaking."

"That's true, George," I said. "Our ship will never sail again, but we can take to sea in the long-boat despite the leaking. The only alternative is to return to the shore to be killed by the savages."

There was no further argument, so it was time to prepare for our departure. "All of you look around to see what there is on board that might be of use to us."

The men scurried off and managed to retrieve from the wreck several bottles of wine and a few pieces of salted pork. Then Dick returned with a great prize; it was Antonio's pig, now whimpering rather than squealing. That animal might provide a much more useful feast than had originally been foreseen.

Unfortunately there was no fresh water, and what bread we

found had been completely spoiled, having been soaked by the sea.

"Where now, Captain?" asked Aaron.

"Well," I said, "we can't sail across the ocean in the leaking long-boat, but we may at least be able to sail along the coast to a place where we can reach land without any harassment from savages. Whatever lies before us, whether it's rescue or disaster, we must go back to the sea."

CHAPTER FIVE

Capture, escape and a killing

I stood on deck at the side of the ship and looked towards the shore. The old man and four of the young men were standing together, and there was a good deal of pointing at the wreck followed by discussion and hand gestures to underline whatever they were saying.

It was impossible to guess what they might be debating. What would I be saying if I were in their position? Perhaps: 'We've taken all their goods; let's leave them. They're of no further use to us.' But no, what you hope for and what you should expect are rarely the same.

To my surprise, the natives now showed what I thought was another side to their characters. Maybe the sight of our deplorable situation had excited pity in their hearts. The five men walked down to the water's edge, slowly bowed to the ground, and then stood upright and beckoned us to return to the beach. They waved and smiled and made signs of peace and friendship.

When they saw that we had not reacted, they huddled together for another discussion. After that, they walked back several yards and the old man picked up his spear. The five of them then ran to the back of the beach. A few minutes later, they returned without the spear and their knives. Obviously they were trying to indicate that they meant us no harm and that there would be no problems if we returned.

But why should we return to the beach? There was nothing for us there, even if the natives were truly friendly; they had stolen or destroyed everything we needed. Finding that we would not come back, one of the young men ran off and disappeared from our view. About ten minutes later he returned carrying a goatskin, which he held up above his head to show to us. They then made signs to demonstrate that the goatskin was filled with water and that they wanted to give it to us.

"I don't think I'll take that bait," I said to George.

"But, Captain, we need the water," he replied. "Twelve of us drifting in a boat without fresh water; it doesn't look good."

"I know, George," I said. "But why should we trust these people?"

All the men were listening to what we were saying. Aaron spoke next. "Why don't we all go back together? Our numbers will make them behave."

"No," said Antonio, "they don't think like that. The first man on shore will get the spear in his chest."

"All right, I'll go first," said Aaron. "I'll take the chance. We need that water."

George stepped forward. "No. I'm Chief Mate, I'll go."

Then Porter made a suggestion. "One of us should be selected by chance."

Everyone agreed, even Antonio. The men prepared eleven splinters of wood, each about twelve inches long, as well as one that was only five inches long.

"Captain," said George, "hold these in your closed fist, and we'll each draw a stick. The man who draws the short stick, or you, Captain, if you're left with it, will go to the shore."

There was a general murmur of approval. I took the pieces of wood and held them tightly. I suppose we all had the same thought: eleven chances it's not me, and only one chance that it is.

Antonio stepped forward to draw first. Unbelievably, he drew the short piece. Shipwrecked, marooned, shipwrecked again and then sent to deal with savages; and he was the one most against returning to the shore. Antonio positioned himself under the rope, and reached for it with both hands. I knew what I had to do. Pushing Antonio aside, I grabbed the rope and, before a word was said, I was ten yards away from the wreck, over the sea and on my way to the beach.

I had no thoughts of what I would do when I got there. All my thoughts and strength were concentrated on passing one hand behind the other, pulling my legs along, passing one hand behind the other, pulling my legs along - until, at last, I was there.

As I stood up, gasping for breath, I realised that the old man was standing alongside me. He gave me the skin of water and I drank a little. Then, without a word being said by either of us, I once more grasped the rope and, with the skin of water partly balanced on my stomach and partly held between my thighs, I returned to the wreck.

After I was back on board, we each drank some of the water, leaving the skin half full. I looked to the shore and saw that the old man was still there. With a good deal of pointing at me, the wreck, the beach and himself, he made us understand that he wished to come on board our ship, and at the same time I should go to the shore and wait there until he returned.

My men were not enthusiastic about such an arrangement, but I told them that while the savages were being helpful, we should be conciliatory; after all, they had given me the skin of water without any problem. The men grudgingly agreed. However, I did tell them that they should hide the pig and the other items we had gathered for our voyage in the long-boat. There was no need to invite the old man to steal what little we had left.

So I returned to the rope and once more made my way to the shore. As I pulled myself backwards, the beach was out of my sight, so I was unaware of what was going on there.

When I reached the water's edge, I swung my legs down and

turned to face the natives. I was surprised to see that the old man and the four young men had been joined by the other young men and the women and children. They were all unarmed and seated on the sand, the adults nearly naked and the children entirely naked, just sitting there quietly. As they saw me approach, they started making signs of peace and welcome, looking upwards as if invoking Heaven to witness their sincerity.

The old man was sitting in the middle of the group, leading this display. He got to his feet and came towards me. When he reached me, he took my right hand in his hands and pressed me firmly. Then he let go and walked past me, grabbed hold of the rope and started his journey to the wreck.

Two of the younger children now came forward, and they led me to the place that had been occupied by the old man. I sat down with them. They all seemed very friendly, and they took turns in holding my hands and stroking me on my arms and back.

Looking to the wreck, I saw that the old man was now on board. He was wandering around, inspecting the vessel. After he had satisfied his curiosity by looking at all there was to see - which was little more than the ruined contents of the hold floating inside the wreck - he walked back to the rope. He must have been very angry to have found no weapons and no food; in fact, nothing of any use to him at all. His rare prize was a grave disappointment.

I waved to my men and tried to indicate that they should keep the old man on board until I was released; but they did not understand me. Then I shouted, but it was useless; even in the calm, the noise of the waves made vocal communication impossible.

The old man climbed on to the end of the rope and made his way to the shore. When he was almost there, I rose to take the rope, intending to start my return as soon as the old man let go. But, as I got up, I was seized by two of the young men, who by that time had furtively placed themselves either side of me. They held my arms firmly and kept me still, and the other men, the women and the children rushed towards me with daggers, knives and spears, which must have been hidden in the sand. Several of them held the points of their weapons inches from my face and chest.

To resist would surely have led to instant death. So I knelt down on the sand and tried to look calm, hoping to give the impression that I was not afraid and had no concern for my life.

I looked at these people who, only a few minutes earlier, had been so friendly. Now their faces assumed evil, malignant expressions; they showed their teeth and jabbed their weapons towards every part of my body.

The old man rushed out of the water and grabbed a scimitar from one of the women. With the young men still holding me fast, I was forced to remain kneeling on the sand as the old man grabbed the hair above the back of my neck and pulled it back, threatening to cut off my head.

I really felt as though my last moments had arrived and that I was doomed to be devoured by these beings. There was no reason to doubt that they were cannibals, and would be content if their prize at least allowed them to glut their hungry stomachs. My only wish was that the end would come quickly.

But it soon became apparent that the ridiculous conduct of the natives was purely for the purpose of frightening me. As I had remained composed and shown no sign of changing my countenance, the old man decided to end the charade with one further exhibition of his power over me. He drew his scimitar lightly across the collar of my shirt, which he cut, and then he released me.

The crew on board the Commerce had been watching what was happening. They later told me that if I had been killed - which they had expected - they would have rushed to the shore with such arms as they could find or improvise, and would have avenged my death by selling their lives as dearly as possible. It was an admirable and loyal intention; although I have often wondered why, if they were so sure that I would be killed, they did not attack immediately and give me at least a slim chance of survival.

After the old man had let go, I was allowed to stand up. He now ordered me, by producing a coin and making signs, to get the men to bring him all the money that was on board the wreck. I called to the crew, but they could not understand me. Then Hogan climbed on to the rope and crawled almost to the shore so that he could hear my instructions.

I shouted to him that I would not be released unless we gave the savages the money we had on board, and I told him to be very careful not to let the old man have any of the money until I was on the rope. Hogan understood me and hurried to the wreck. There I could see the men putting money into a bucket. Then Porter climbed on to the rope, and Aaron tied the bucket to Porter's belt so that it hung down beneath him as he pulled himself along, almost to the shore.

Seeing him so near, I screamed at Porter to come no further. He stopped crawling and just hung there. But by then one of the young men had raced into the water carrying a knife; he cut the rope by which the bucket was attached to Porter's belt, and brought the bucket with the money inside it back to the shore. Porter immediately scrambled back to the Commerce.

The savages then made me walk with them further up the beach, and there we all sat down. They were very excited at the sight of the money, and they jabbered away, smiling, laughing and growing quite animated. The old man poured the coins on to a blanket and, having counted them, he allowed the young men to take turns in feeling the coins by grasping a handful and then letting them fall between their fingers.

During this process my captors had let go of me; but they were still armed and seated around me. I thought that if I did not escape now, I might be killed within minutes. The savages had the money and probably had no further use for me. On the other hand, if I leapt to my feet and tried to dash down to the water, they would no doubt stab me. It was a cruel choice: whether to wait here to be destroyed, or try to make a run for it and expect a blade in my back within seconds.

My mind was in turmoil as I struggled to decide what to do. I did my best to justify doing nothing in the hope that something good might come of it. However, I realised that I had little to lose by trying to reach the sea, and I felt that I must make my effort soon or else it would be too late.

But before I could do anything, the savages made me get up, and they marched me down the beach and back towards the sea. That seemed to be the end. My destiny was now out of my hands. I had missed my chance, if indeed I had ever had a real chance.

But then I thought that perhaps I might be able to tempt their greed a little further. They were so excited at getting the coins, they might be equally excited at the prospect of getting some more. I made signs by pointing to the coins and to the ship, trying to explain that there was still a great deal more money on the wreck. They understood me only too well, and this information seemed to please them. I was made to sit down at the water's edge, and then they ordered me to instruct the crew to send the remaining money to the shore.

Perhaps if I could get one of my men to travel part of the way along the rope with an empty bucket, the savages might be distracted, and then I could escape.

They pushed and prodded me, pointing to the ship and hurrying me on to get my message to the crew that more money must be handed over. So I made signs to my men to have one of them crawl along the rope to listen to me. I saw them talking amongst themselves, and it was clear that none was keen to leave the wreck.

Then, at last, George climbed on to the rope and started to make his way to the beach. When he was about thirty yards from the shore, I shouted to him that he must come no further, or else he would be seized by the savages and they would then have two hostages rather than one. I must have been over-zealous in my warning, because instead of just staying where he was while I gave him instructions, George immediately swung his legs round and travelled back to the wreck with a speed that only fear could engender.

After he had left, my concern was that his return to the ship had made the natives angry. I looked at them and smiled, trying to indicate that Williams had received my instructions and would arrange delivery of the remaining money.

Of course, I had given him no instructions at all, and I was completely at a loss as to what he and the other men might do, if anything. Then I saw Antonio climb on to the rope and start to make his way towards the beach. I shouted to him to stop, but he continued and finally he swung his feet down into the sea and ran towards me. I was completely bemused as to his purpose in coming to the shore. Was he bringing something, or was he trying to rescue me? I could not work it out.

The natives were expecting Antonio to bring more money, and they ran towards him to receive it. He had no clue as to their expectations, and when he could deliver no money, the natives began to beat him with their fists and the handles of their daggers. They knocked him down and stripped him of most of his clothing. He screamed and begged for his life, but they ignored his pleas and continued to beat and kick him as he rolled on the ground.

I called to the old man, hoping to stop the assault on Antonio, at least for a few moments. Then I remembered the buried sack of coins, so I explained to the old man that we had hidden money on the beach before we had returned to the wreck, and Antonio had come to the shore to show them where it was. I pointed to what was left of our tent, and I made the old man understand that they should take me there, and I would find the hidden money for them.

The old man shouted at the others, and they stopped the beating. Then he gestured towards the tent, passing on my message. They rushed up the beach, dragging Antonio with them, leaving behind only the old man and one young man to guard me.

I shouted to Antonio, "Find the buried coins for them!" Antonio understood, and I saw him pointing to various places on the ground, showing the natives where to dig. He began to scoop away the sand, and the older children knelt down and dug with him.

While this frenzied activity was taking place, I was sitting on the sand facing the sea, with the old man on my left, his spear pointed at my breast and one of the young men on my right, holding a scimitar to my head. The only positive thought that crossed my mind was that if some buried items were discovered, the natives were bound to start shouting in celebration and my two guards might run to inspect or, at the very least, look round to see what was going on. That might be the opportunity. So I prepared my arms and legs, ready for a quick start.

The place where Antonio and the others were digging was some way behind me to my left. Unfortunately, the positioning of my guard's weapons did not allow me to turn my head to see what was happening. I only prayed that Antonio would be able to find the buried sack of coins.

Suddenly there was shouting - something had been found. My two guards turned round to see what had happened. I instantly leapt to my feet and sprinted towards the sea. "Run, Antonio!" I shouted. I was running for my life, and knew that I had to reach deep water before my pursuers.

I plunged into the sea and swam underwater until my chest was bursting, and then I swam a few yards further. It felt as though I was hardly moving as I battled against the current powering in from the sea. But I knew that having swum so many strokes, I must have covered some distance and should be well on my way to the wreck. Then I stopped and raised my head above the surface to take in air. Looking back towards the beach, I saw that Antonio had reached the water. But to my horror, the old man was directly behind me and less than twenty yards away. He raised his spear, preparing to throw it at me. I turned to dive under water, and just then, a large wave broke over me and hurled me backwards. I could not resist the wave, and had to let it take me where it would.

When the wave had passed, I once more put my head above the water-line and looked back to the beach. To my relief, I saw that the wave that had hit me had knocked the old man over and sent him tumbling back to the shore.

Now I had an advantage, but I still had some way to go; certainly over seventy yards. Swimming as fast as possible as wave after wave crashed in what seemed towering heights over me, I was able by almost superhuman exertion to reach the wreck.

George and Porter had climbed down into the long-boat, and they pulled me into it. With the assistance of some of the others, they hauled me on board the Commerce. I lay there, trying to recover my breath, spitting out the sea-water at intervals, unable to move or speak for some time.

Only when I had regained my breath did I think of asking about Antonio. I pulled myself to my knees, and the men helped me to stand up. Staggering to the side of the ship, I looked to the water to see what had become of Antonio.

"Where is he?" I said. "Where's Antonio? I can't see him."

George replied, "They caught him. We've lost him, Captain."

"But didn't he find the money for them?"

"No," said George, "he only found your hand telescope."

Looking to the shore, I saw the savages picking up all that was left on the beach, and they then started to make their way over the sand dunes, dragging Antonio's lifeless body with them. He had obviously been hurled back by the large wave.

I was stunned.

As I watched, I was conscious of my men speaking, but I could not hear a word they were saying. It was as if I was still underwater. I felt an inexpressible pang of guilt, because Antonio's death was a direct result of my escape - an escape that I had planned. But I also reflected on the fact that I'd had no other way to save my life, and if I had stayed on the beach, the chances were that both Antonio and I would have been killed. Who knows?

To be fair, none of my surviving shipmates ever suggested to me that I had done anything wrong; yet my mind and conscience were troubled.

But there was no time to dwell on such thoughts. Hostilities had now commenced.

CHAPTER SIX

To sea again

There was little doubt in my mind that the natives would soon return, and when they did so, it would be in greater numbers. Eventually they would be able to make their way to the wreck, and they would surely overpower us and massacre us with the same ferocity and heartlessness they had directed at Antonio.

The wind was now blowing fiercely, and I could see that out on the ocean there were waves ten to twenty feet high bearing down on the Commerce. Although they were smaller by the time they reached the wreck, they were still strong enough to smash against the side of the ship with a force that frightened all of us.

I had decided that we should escape by taking to sea in the long-boat, which was still tied to the side of the wreck. But breaking out into calmer water looked almost impossible. Added to this, the long-boat had taken a considerable battering, as it was constantly banging against the ship. Fortunately, whilst I had been on the shore, George had had the good sense to ensure that two men went down into the long-boat to bail it out every time it was half-filled with water.

Having resolved how to escape, the only decision left was the timing of our departure. The fierce wind and sea deterred me from leaving straight away. But, just as the delay would make our voyage in the long-boat safer, so that same delay was rendering our stay on the wreck more dangerous. The deck and sides of the Commerce had suffered terrible punishment, and in her broken state she could not hold together indefinitely.

I called the crew together and addressed them. "Men, you can see with your own eyes that we can't stay on the ship for much longer. We can't take any chances, because when she does break up it will happen very quickly, giving us no opportunity to climb down into the long-boat. So we must make sure we leave the Commerce well before that last moment."

"Captain," said George, "tell us, what are our options? Is the long-boat the only way?"

"Well, men," I said. "In all honesty there are three choices that I can see, and all of them look grim. We can return to the shore and try to climb over those dunes and escape into the interior. Of course, if we come across any of the natives, we'll be dead in minutes. We can remain on the ship, but that must mean eventual death."

"We can all see where this is leading," said Porter. "It will have to be the long-boat, and that doesn't look very hopeful."

"No, Porter. Going to sea may well result in our deaths, but unlike the other options, there is a possibility of survival, however remote. Unfortunately, we have no oars, we have no rudder, and we have no compass or quadrant to direct our course. But that boat will float for some time, so it must be our way. Does anyone disagree?"

Porter stepped forward. I thought: 'Oh dear this means trouble. Had I not explained the situation sufficiently?' But quite the opposite.

"Captain," began Porter, "I'll go to the shore and recover the two oars that are still holding up our tent."

"Well done, Porter," I said. "Go straight away. You men watch and shout to him if you see any of the savages coming on to the beach." Porter immediately set off on the rope.

"Right men," I said. "Before we get ready to leave, I'm going to have a quick look in the hold to see if there's anything that can be salvaged."

Having taken off my shirt and shoes, I jumped through the hatch. I swam underwater, and managed to come up on the starboard side of the ship. The vessel was lying at an angle on the rocks, so although the water reached the top of the hold on the port side, on the starboard side there was about three feet of air above the water level. I managed to haul myself up and hang on to the side, where I recovered my breath. In this way I dived and came up again several times, and on each occasion I tried to find something that might be of use to us amongst the floating timbers and rubbish. After a few minutes I found a cask of water that was still tightly corked. I swam back to the hatch and raised the cask so that the crew could take it from me.

I then clambered out and saw that Porter had swum back with the oars, and had also brought the money we had hidden before we left the beach, and which Antonio had been unable to find.

Now we loaded on to the long-boat a jib, small sails and a spar that we would use as a mast; and also the cask of water, some pieces of salted pork, several bottles of wine, about four pounds of figs and our live pig. We felt well provided for our voyage, although we were pathetically unprepared for what lay before us.

Everything was now ready, so I tried to encourage the crew as much as possible. I explained to them that it was better we should die together trying to survive, rather than wait around to be massacred by savages. There could be no dealing with them. When they were ferocious they would seek to kill us, and we had discovered to our cost that when they were friendly, it was mere deceit.

However, despite all my efforts, as we climbed into the long-boat the crashing of the waves caused our hearts to sink. Everyone was trembling with dreadful apprehension. The long-boat was moored on the shore side of the Commerce, and as such it was protected from the waves that were thundering on to the wreck from the ocean. Each of us feared that as soon as we sailed around the stern and into the face of the waves, we would reach our last moments.

But there was no choice. We had to try to break out. So we pushed off and rowed round the vessel and into the open sea. All of us were silent with worry. Then, as if by a miracle, the wind ceased to blow and the dreadful surges of the sea subsided, making a path for our boat through which we rowed as smoothly as if we had been on a calm river. But we could not relax, for in the distance we could still see high waves crashing with unabated fury.

I placed myself at the stern, and steered the boat with a plank of wood. We rowed on for about a mile, then raised our makeshift mast and fitted the small sail, and with a brisk wind blowing us to the south, we soon passed the point of the cape.

It was now sunset. What a day we had endured. We had started off by waking up on a deserted beach, and between that awakening and this moment when night was falling, we had encountered more problems in one day than most people would meet in a lifetime.

Night came over us as we continued to sail gently away from the shore where we had suffered so many terrors. The night was very dark, and soon it started to get foggy. We had to take care that we did not lower our guard and allow the wind to blow us back towards the coast and the rocks that must have been nearby.

I divided the men into shifts of three, plus either George or me. As each man reached his turn to sleep, he instantly fell into a deep slumber. I was hopeful that we would awaken refreshed and re-strengthened, as we would need all our mental and physical powers in the days to follow.

Daylight did not improve matters very much, as the fog was now thick and preventing us from seeing the shore for most of the time, whilst the wind, which continued to blow directly from the sea to the coast, was forcing us towards the land.

We had no compass to guide us, no instrument by which to find our latitude, and we had no rudder with which to steer our boat, except my plank. However, with occasional bailing out, our long-boat was at least seaworthy, and we continued to drift gently, keeping our distance from the shore.

All the while, my mind was burning with thoughts of what might happen to us. We had gained the open sea and managed to stand our boat off to the westward, beyond the power of the wind to drive us on shore. But to what end?

I supposed that we could reasonably hope to come across a vessel that would save us. That was the best that could happen. The worst, or so I thought, was that we should sink at sea and drown, or else gradually die one by one after our supplies ran out.

Having discussed these thoughts with my companions, I asked each of them for his opinion. No one wished to return to the shore. They had had enough of their encounters with the natives. Everyone was in favour of committing ourselves to the open sea, rather than staying close to the coast and risk being dashed against the rocks.

We decided to put ourselves on fixed daily rations of a pint of water and half a bottle of wine between the eleven of us, plus a scrap of pork and two figs for each man. It was really quite meagre, but as we had eaten nothing since the previous day, it seemed like an adequate allowance.

It was now 30th August, and I knew that we had to prepare ourselves for a lengthy period at sea.

For the moment the wind was quite gentle, but the waves still caused the occasional spray of water to fly into the boat. Clark suggested that we raise the level of the sides of the boat by fitting cloths above the gunwale. This was a good idea, and it would have the added benefit of keeping us occupied throughout the day. We tore strips from the spare sail, and spent several hours building a screen of eight to ten inches in height all around the boat, kept up by pieces of board. This small addition to our defences proved a great help in repelling the sea's spray, and consequently eased the necessity for bailing out.

A day had passed. We were no nearer rescue, but at least we had had a period of peace. As night fell, the wind blew harder and the sea became somewhat choppy. I was careful to keep the boat near the wind by her sail, and as a result we did not ship a great deal of water.

We kept the same watch arrangements as on the previous night, but we all slept much better, as time had distanced us from the horrors of our confrontations with the natives.

Now I suggested that we took turns in telling our stories. It would help us to get to know each other better, and it might make the time pass more quickly.

"Archibald," I said to Robbins, "why don't you go first?"

"Certainly, Captain," he replied. "I'd be happy to. I was born in Wethersfield, Connecticut in 1792. Do you know the town?"

"I do," I said. "It's on the Connecticut River."

"Yes," said Robbins, "on the west side. It was easy for me to get a job on board ship, because my father was part-owner of a small vessel. All our voyages were between New England and the West Indies. But during my fourth voyage, we were seized by the English; I was imprisoned for five weeks, and then released not far from home. My fifth voyage was no better; we were seized again and I was imprisoned in Halifax for two months. When I was released, I took a passage on a Swedish ship bound for New York. From there, I took another vessel, but we were immediately seized by the English yet again, and I was soon back in prison in Halifax.

"I was incarcerated for eighteen months, until peace was made with the English and I could go home. Then I travelled to Saybrook, and that is where I met Williams and Savage, who offered me employment on the Commerce as an able seaman. The rest you know."

"My God," I said. "You're entitled to some luck now! Who'll speak next?" There was no answer. I looked about me; all the others were fast asleep. Well, Robbins' story had interested me; but perhaps everyone else preferred rest.

In the morning, the weather became much more moderate, and

it was hazy all day. Our pig was now very feeble, having had no water for some time, so we killed it. We took great care to save its blood, which we then drank. Our thirst was by this time becoming unbearable, and we did not hesitate to take steps which would have disgusted us in normal circumstances.

We divided the pig's liver, intestines and some other parts between us, and we ate it raw. This satisfied our thirst to some degree, but we knew that whatever we ate and drank was not being replaced; so the greater our relief, the greater would be our problems. The sight of our resources dwindling at such a fast rate was frightening.

So, another day was passing with no vessel to be seen. When I thought of the size of the ocean, it just seemed too hopeless. It would be perfectly possible for us to drift for months without coming across a ship. But, on the other hand, with luck we might find one within hours.

We were all aware that the water situation would soon become critical. The men knew what the next step had to be, though none of us wished to mention it. In the end, I raised the subject and we agreed that from now on each of us would have to save his urine for drink. We did this by using the empty wine bottles. Repulsive as this step was, it proved vital in sustaining our lives.

Night fell swiftly and the sky was angry, threatening us with stormy weather. The wind blew from the north-east, and by midnight the spray had already half-filled the boat several times. We were all engaged in bailing out, but no one grumbled, for we knew that any relaxation would lead to disaster. I saw in the distance sharp flashes of lightning shooting across the gloom, making the scene doubly terrifying. Another storm, such as the one that had wrecked the Commerce, would deal with our small boat in minutes.

Some of the men thought that we were fighting a losing battle and it was futile trying to resist the elements. But in the end, the night passed and the storm never reached us. It must have been much further off than we had thought.

As daylight arrived, I saw the success of my exertions in encouraging the men to continue with the bailing out through the night. I reminded them of our miraculous escape from the savages, and convinced them that I still believed we would survive.

It was now 1st September, and thirst pressed upon us. We could only relieve that thirst by wetting our mouths periodically with a few drops of wine and water, and as many times with our own urine. This unpleasant routine depressed us, and we drifted on in silence.

The wind continued to blow hard, and we were worn down by the efforts of the last three days. Already suffering from hunger and thirst, we were now scorched by the burning rays of the sun. We were really getting into a parlous state. Another day and night passed as we lay there, slowly drifting out to sea.

It was the afternoon of 2nd September. There was no sign of a passing vessel that might save us. With our water and food fast diminishing, I felt it was time to consider a change of plan. I asked the men for their attention. We needed to rethink our situation. It was no good just sitting around and hoping for a miracle.

"Listen," I said, "I think we should make for the coast." The despair of floating aimlessly on the vacant sea was weakening the crew's resolve with every hour that passed, and they really did not care whether we sailed out to sea or in towards land. So they agreed to my proposal, and we immediately put about.

The prospect of actually doing something to try to secure our survival improved our mood a little. At least we now had a goal; we were not merely meandering aimlessly, hoping that someone would find us.

We continued in the general direction of the coast for four days. Each day we moistened our lips with wine and water every few hours and ate some of the flesh of our pig and its skin. But at length we became faint, and it was difficult for us to sustain our bailing-out duties. Indeed, at night no one could keep going for more than about half an hour, and I was forced to organise many short shifts.

The evening of 6th September, and we had still not found the coast. I had hoped to reach land that day, and unfortunately my disappointment showed in my demeanour. Some of the crew began to despair, for our food was gone apart from some salted pork. It was amazing how easy it was to give up, even though we knew that surrender meant death. The loss of the will to struggle on was affecting all of us.

That night was a desperate time. Matters were made even worse when some of the men, impelled by thirst, forgot what they owed to their shipmates and drank one of the two remaining bottles of wine whilst those about them slept. When I found out what had happened, I did not know what to do. It was hard to begrudge the men an extra drink. However, to have done so furtively and to have taken it without sharing with all their shipmates was wrong by any standards.

On the morning of the seventh, I mentioned the loss of wine. Of course, all the men found the strength to deny that they had been involved, adding suitable remarks such as it being an unpardonable crime, or that those who had done it deserved to be thrown overboard instantly. It was easy to guess the identity of the offenders by the strength of their admonitions. But the wine was gone, and the only remedy was calm and stricter vigilance in the future. Also, I did not wish to dwell on the subject for fear of dividing the men into two camps. Nevertheless, I was very disappointed that matters had come to this. Now the mood of the crew was very subdued - an unhealthy mixture of anger, guilt and despair.

We sailed on during the morning in complete silence. But all our misery disappeared when we saw land directly ahead in the distance. This gave us new spirit; hope again revived. The land looked perfectly smooth, without the smallest risings or hills to be seen. But my mind blackened at such a scene, because I thought that we must be viewing the coast of the desert, where our sufferings would find no relief.

Nevertheless, land it was, and the sight was most welcome. We continued our approach for some time, driven to the south by a strong current until sunset. As we drew closer, the coast appeared very different. Far from being smooth, it was formed by perpendicular and overhanging cliffs rising to a great height, with no slopes or rockfalls that we might use to climb to the top.

We came within half a mile of the shore, and I said to the men, "I think we should stay at sea for the night, and in the morning we can sail down the coast and try to find a more suitable place to land."

But every member of the crew disagreed with me. They wanted to land as soon as possible. The men all spoke at once, complaining of the miseries of being on board the boat and voicing their determination to reach land. They had been heading for the shore, and now that they had found it, they would take it.

I was the captain, and the decision was up to me; but I was well aware that these men were in such a desperate state that they would do as they wanted. If I ordered them to do otherwise, they would be likely to land the boat anyway, and my authority would be destroyed. Once we lost our discipline, our slim chances of survival would be further reduced. But the men were not interested in such a discussion, they just wanted to get to the shore. So against my better judgment, I told them that yes, perhaps it was a good idea to land straight away. Who knew what problems might arise during another night at sea?

As we neared the coast, the surf became more violent, and I saw it breaking high among the rocks near the shore. This was no place to land, so we sailed a little further down the coast until we saw a small sandy beach. Then we drank the last bottle of wine. This was partly to give us courage, but mainly because I thought the bottle was likely to be smashed during our landing anyway.

Having finished the wine, we made for the small beach, and then we were carried on the top of a large wave that deposited us on the sand and then withdrew, leaving us still in our boat on an area no more than eighty yards long and ten yards deep.

We scrambled out of the boat and carried the remains of our

water and pork up on to the rocks out of the reach of the surf. I looked back at our boat. The landing had ended its useful life. The repaired parts had broken away, and about one-third of the hull was in pieces floating out to sea. It was sad to see our boat die in such a way, having given us such service; but none of us cared too much, as we had had enough of the sea and boats.

Now I looked about and saw above me huge masses of shattered rocks extending both ways as far as the eye could see. Then I looked at my men. Our limbs had become stiff through lack of exercise whilst in the boat, and our flesh had wasted through lack of food. We were a sorry sight indeed.

"There's no point staying here," I said. "We've got to find a way of reaching the surface at the top of these cliffs. Aaron, you come with me and we'll explore down that way. The rest of you men stay here. We won't be long."

Aaron and I made our way along the beach and started clambering amongst the rocks, searching for a route upwards. But we searched in vain; there was no way we could reach the summit in that direction.

"Captain," said Aaron, "it's starting to get dark. We should get back to the men. There's no hope climbing over here."

I agreed with him, and we returned to our shipmates. They had spent the time most profitably in finding comfortable places amongst the rocks where they could sleep.

We wet our mouths with water, ate some of the fat of the salted pork, and then lay down to rest. Despite our unhappy predicament, we slept soundly until daylight. I do not know what the men's thoughts were. My only thought was that the next day would be crucial to our hopes of survival.

CHAPTER SEVEN

A distant light

I awoke the next morning shortly after daybreak to see Dick scrambling around, busily collecting a considerable quantity of mussels he had found clinging to the ridges surrounding some shallow pools at the end of our beach. He smiled when he noticed that I was watching him, and came over to me.

"Breakfast, Captain," he whispered, showing me his treasure.

"How did you find them?" I asked.

"I saw some sea birds scouring those small pools, and I thought there must be some food there."

"Well done," I said.

What an odd sight it was - all of my men apart from Dick lying asleep on ledges in the rockface. As I watched them, they began to awaken, refreshed by their undisturbed sleep. The men were very pleased with Dick's mussel breakfast, and we quickly finished off our meal.

"I think it's time for us to move on," I said to the men. "We've got to find a way of getting to the surface above these cliffs. Aaron and I tried going that way yesterday, and it was hopeless. Today we must try the other way."

"How long do you think it'll take to find a route to the top?" asked Burns.

"I don't know," I said. "It may take hours, it may take days; but the sooner we start the better. Our strength is slowly dissipating, so we must get to the top before it's completely gone. The immediate need is to find something moist, some sort of greenery we can chew on to get rid of this burning thirst."

It did not take me long to realise that our thirst had been worsened by our breakfast, for although the mussels were nourishing, they were also extremely salty.

Now it was time to move off. I told the men that we must keep together at all times, and they readily agreed. Of course no one wished to be held back by those who could not proceed any further without help; but on the other hand, each man feared that he might be the one to fail first and need support.

"What shall we carry with us?" asked George.

I told the men that food and water were all we needed, and that we should dispose of the remaining money, as I believed that money lay at the root of the troubles with the savages, and if we met any others I did not want similar problems.

"But, Captain," argued Porter, "we'll need money to pay for transport to a town where we can find a ship to take us to Europe or America."

However, I was adamant. Our only hope was to find someone, or to be found by someone, who wished to help us out of the goodness of his heart; money would not be needed.

So we buried the coins in the sand. We might as well have thrown them into the sea, for if we were to return, it would not be to collect the money - it would be to die.

"I want the food and water divided right now. Each man will carry his own share and be responsible for rationing himself." I said this with the memory of the bottle of wine fresh in my mind. As our situation deteriorated, some people, perhaps all, would do more and more desperate things to preserve their own lives.

"Take what's left of that cask of water and divide it up in those six empty wine bottles. Five of them are to have two parts, and I'll have a bottle with one part. Each of you will share a bottle with another." This was quickly done. "Now, Dick, cut the remains of the pork into eleven pieces and give every man his portion. All of you keep the clothes you're wearing and take nothing more, and let's prepare to leave."

That preparation took little time, and soon the men had lined up behind me in Indian file, each carrying a piece of salted pork wrapped in a canvas strip from our boat.

And so we started our journey. We walked slowly, keeping close to the water's edge, climbing over the rocks at the end of the beach and around the point. Now I could see that ours was one of a series of small sandy beaches separated from one another by falls of rocks from the cliffs above.

To one side was the vast expanse of the ocean, but to the other side the sight was more troublesome. The cliffs were either perpendicular or actually jutting out at an angle over our heads, and they must have risen to a height of three or four hundred feet. There seemed to be no way to reach the top, for even if there was a path to start us off, it would not be possible to climb the upper part of the precipice.

So we alternately clambered over the rocks and then wandered along the sand. The walking was easy work, as we were cooled by the breeze, and occasionally we allowed our feet and legs to be dampened by the surf. But climbing the rockfalls dividing the beaches was hard work, for these masses of sharp and craggy boulders stood in piles, which were in some cases over a hundred feet high, and we had to step from rock to rock, climbing up and then scrambling down to the sand.

We continued like this for about three hours, and then we sat down for a rest. I looked up at the precipice once more. It was as if we had not travelled at all, for the sight was exactly the same as the one on the beach where we had landed. It was clear that the beating of the ocean against the coast had undermined the precipice in such a way that these vast masses of rock had from time to time given way and tumbled to the shore. But the lower part of the precipice was all that had collapsed. If only the upper part had tumbled as well, it might have formed a route to the surface.

Each of us had a nibble of our salted pork and a mouthful of water before we continued once more on our dreary expedition.

By late afternoon we had slowed to a crawl. Our shoes were nearly all worn off; our feet were lacerated and bleeding. And still the sun's rays were beating on our bodies and heating them to what I thought was almost the point of death. Worst of all, as we wandered beneath these towering cliffs in the late afternoon, there was no longer any breeze. We needed that air to cool our burning flesh and boiling blood.

To add to my misery, as I had always led the way, at one stage I had fallen between two rocks, breaking my bottle and losing the little water it contained.

So that was how our first full day back on land passed. Finally, I called to my men, "Let's stop for the night." We sat down. No one really wanted to speak, because we all felt that although we had made progress over the ground, our situation had not improved - nor had our hopes.

"How far do you think we've travelled today?" asked Burns.

"It feels as though we've gone a long way," I said. "But I guess that we've walked only four or five miles."

"Captain," said Barrett, "at that rate, we may travel a total of no more than another twenty miles or so before we die, and twenty miles on this coast of Africa is no distance at all."

"I know, James," I said testily. "There's a strong likelihood that we won't find a way to the top, but there's also a small likelihood that we will. So what would you have me do? Say to you that because the chances are slim we should just lie down and die?"

There was no answer. I immediately regretted having snapped at him in that way.

"Men. Just rest for a while; let's gather our thoughts and talk again later."

While they were lying down, I wandered further down the beach. As I was standing by some rocks, I made a small discovery. "Over here all of you!" I shouted. The men stumbled towards me. "Look on the rocks. These are dead locusts. That means that somewhere near here there must be some greenery to eat, otherwise the locusts wouldn't have flown this way."

"Well," said Dick, "never mind the greenery, let's eat the locusts."

"No, I've already thought of that. Watch." The locusts had been in the sun for some time, and I showed my men that if I just touched the locusts, they crumbled to dust.

"I know it's not much," I said, "but it's the best news we're getting today. Now let's go over there and sleep under the cliffs. First we can each eat a very small piece of salted pork, and pass round the bottles with the urine, and we'll wet our lips with a little of it. Then take a sip of water from your bottles."

We lay down in the cool of the early evening to rest and hopefully to sleep. I looked at my shipmates. They all knew I had no water. I suppose that each man was waiting for one of the others to offer me some first. But it took several minutes before young Horace came with his bottle.

"Captain, it's for you," he said.

"Thank you, Horace. I'll just take a little." And I moistened my tongue.

I looked at him. It was not so long ago that he had come to see me at the inn with the letter from his mother. His late father, Luther, had been a prominent member of the various militias in Connecticut. When I had replied to his mother's letter, agreeing to take Horace on board with us, I had promised that I would look after him as if he were my own son.

My intentions had been good, although at this point my record did not look very impressive. But then I thought: what more could I have done if Horace had really been my son? And frankly, the answer was nothing. I had done everything possible to preserve the lives of all my men.

The next morning, 9th September, we awoke with numb and trembling limbs, the result of the change from the extreme heat of the day to the damp cold air of the night. However, the sleep had refreshed us, and though our feet were torn and our frames nearly exhausted, the men arose without complaint and set off immediately on the continuation of our march.

We wandered along the coast in the same manner as the previous day. It seemed that there would be no end to these repeated episodes of climbing up and down the piles of rocks and trudging along the sand. But then, some two hours later, we saw not far ahead of us a beach that seemed very much larger than any of the others, and what was more interesting, it sloped higher up the cliff.

Eventually, we came to within about three hundred yards of the beach. But, to our horror, it was separated from us not by fallen rock, but by the precipice that stretched far into the sea, telling us that we had made a good effort, but we could not escape. We were trapped.

Suddenly I noticed that in the waters beyond the precipice there was a large rock standing alone in the sea. It must have tumbled from above. Every time the surf roared in, that rock was covered, only to be revealed again as the waters withdrew.

"I think I have it, men," I said. "It might be our only chance. I'll tell you what I'm going to do. I'm going to swim out to that solitary rock and climb on to it. Then I'll lie down on top of the rock and hold my breath as the waters come in and cover me. When the sea withdraws, I'll jump off and try to scramble my way round and on to the next beach. What do you think?"

They all agreed - probably because I was the one who was taking the risk. Nevertheless, I was encouraged by their approval, and I prepared to put my plan into operation.

I positioned myself at the water's edge, and as soon as the surf started to move out, I raced into the sea and swam as hard as I could to the solitary rock. But it was further than I had thought, and when the waters returned I was only just alongside it, without time to climb to the top; but at least I could hang on to it.

Clinging on with every finger, I held my breath until, after what

80

seemed an age, the waters receded, allowing me to climb to the top of the rock.

I lay there panting, waiting for the water to return. In no time it came, covering the rock and me once more. Then, in the next period of safety, when the sea had once more withdrawn, I jumped down and swam to the next beach.

Having witnessed my success, each of my shipmates followed the same course, until almost two hours later we were all on the large beach. Though our limbs and bodies were much battered and bruised, we were elated by our success.

After a brief period of rest, I called the men together and told them to spread out and dig holes in the sand at differing distances from the sea. I hoped to find some water that was drinkable as a result of the sea-water filtering through the sand and coming up the hole, leaving the salt behind.

Many of us found water, but it was all as salty as the sea. Then I took the men to the back of the beach and told them to dig one large hole together as our last chance of finding drinkable water in this way.

Leaving the men to their digging, I walked about four hundred yards along the beach to an area where there was no sand, just a hard surface sloping into the sea. The collapsed rock on top of that surface reached high up the precipice, and there were some stretches that I thought I could crawl along; so I went to the best position and started my ascent.

Slowly, as I made my way upward, I climbed round the collapsed rock to its far side, out of the sight of my men. I hoped against hope that there would be a way to the top, where I might find something green to allay our burning thirst and possibly some trees that would shelter us from the scorching rays of the sun.

After about twenty minutes of crawling over the rocks, I reached the rockface itself, which was made up of many layers of different colours. I slowly zigzagged my way upward, resting now and then, until finally I managed to climb over the edge at the top.

To my horror, all I saw was a barren plain extending as far as the eye could see. There was not a single tree or shrub, not even a spear of grass. Was there any sight more desolate?

I just lay down and closed my eyes, not knowing what to do. I had used all my remaining strength to reach this place, and the dreary view was more than I could bear. We could not continue moving from disaster to disaster. At some stage we had to improve our situation or all would be lost. Despair seized me. I felt that a lingering torturous death could be avoided in only one way, and I resolved to cast myself into the sea as soon as I could reach it.

It was then that I realised that my thoughts were not really thoughts of despair - they were thoughts of self-pity. I was the captain and it was my duty to care for my crew before giving up on my own life. My subordinates on the shore were entitled to look to me as an example of courage and fortitude, not a man feeling sorry for himself.

Then I thought of Phoebe and the children, whose memory urged me to believe that our escapes since the wrecking of my ship meant that I was destined to fight on until I saw them once more.

This renewal of purpose gave me strength, and I made for the shore. I climbed down by a route similar to my ascent, the zigzagging taking me back to my starting point.

On reaching the shore, I lay in the shallow sea at the water's edge, allowing the waves to cleanse me until, once more refreshed, I walked the length of the beach back to my shipmates.

"Where have you been, Captain?" asked Robbins. "What were you doing so far along the beach?"

"Well," I said, "I've been looking for a way to the surface, and I think that the only way forward is for us to walk to the far end of the beach where the rockfall slopes higher up the cliff."

I did not tell them that I had reached the summit, because they would have been bound to ask me what I had found there.

The men told me that having dug to a depth of eight feet, they had not found any water, but had come to solid rock. Therefore, as far as they were concerned, both their search for fresh water and my search for a route to the surface had been complete failures. So, with heavy hearts, we began to stagger once more along the shore. Soon we reached the end of the beach.

"Listen," I said, "we have to climb. This is the best starting point. It won't get any easier if we wait; we'll only become weaker from lack of food."

My men lined up behind me, and we started our ascent. Again, my route led over the rocks and then to the rockface, where we moved first to the right and then to the left and then to the right again, and so on, and in time we found ourselves well on the way to the top. But now the men became despondent.

"I can't go any further, Captain," said Robbins.

Then Clark added, "I can go further, but I see no point in it. We've used nearly all our strength, and we're not much more than halfway. What happens if we get three-quarters of the way to the top, and then there's no further way up? What are we to do then? It's just pointless wasting our remaining energy. I don't believe it's possible to get to the summit."

"Nor do I," said Hogan. "I don't think this has any purpose."

"Now I'll tell you," I said. "It *is* possible, because I made it to the top. Right? I've reached the surface, so it can be done. And now all of us can get there."

"Why didn't you tell us before?" asked Deslisle.

"Because I knew you would run out of spirit at some stage and I needed to keep this information in reserve, so I could give you the encouragement to take the final steps to the top."

"What did you see there?" he asked.

"Look, Dick," I said, "there's nothing exciting up there. I didn't meet any people; I didn't see a city. What do you expect?" I paused. "But this isn't the time to start describing the countryside. We have to finish this. You now know that it's possible, so let's just do it. What else? Do you want to spend the rest of your lives on the beach? Come on now."

I was glad that I had been able to tell the men a portion of the truth. Anyway, my encouragement led them to restart their climb.

We continued to wind our way upwards, pulling one another up where necessary, and stopping for air from time to time, until at last we reached the summit.

The men had been warned that there was not much to see at the top, but I had not described the hopeless sight they would encounter. I had feared that an accurate description would destroy any desire they had to finish the ascent.

As each man pulled himself up on the summit, he lay down for several seconds before viewing the scene. When they looked up, the barren landscape had such an effect on their senses that they remained lying on the ground speechless as they surveyed the dry and dreary waste stretched out before them. All hope vanished, and the little moisture left in their bodies flowed from their eyes as salt tears rolled down their haggard cheeks. I could see the men guiding their tears towards their mouths. Even in this utter despair, a few drops to soothe their cracked lips and parched tongues was a relief to be grasped. This proved to me that instinctively, if not realistically, they still hoped for survival.

"I know it's bad," I said, "but we must go on. There's always hope. Lying here and dying can't be better than going forward, even if that journey is likely to be unsuccessful."

The men responded with complete silence.

Hogan then got to his feet and assisted me in my efforts. He looked at the others and said rather grimly, "I can walk, and while I can walk, I will. When I can't walk any more, I'll just lie down and die. But until then, I'm going on with the Captain." Williams and Savage accepted this as a sensible compromise, and they too rose to their feet.

With the four most senior members of our group determined to leave, the others grudgingly followed. We moved off slowly, with a determination to make one last effort, though with scarcely any hope of obtaining the least relief.

There was no discussion about which direction we should take, probably because none of the men thought it made any difference. So, I just led them along the edge of the cliff in the direction we had been travelling for the last two days, keeping the sea in sight all the time, rather than walking into the barren waste.

The surface was baked hard as flint, and strewn across the top were small stones and gravel, while underneath from time to time we came across some reddish earth. We also found the remains of more locusts, although fortunately none of the men reminded me of my assumption that the presence of locusts must mean the presence of food.

I judged that Porter was one of the strongest, so I told him to walk at the back of our group. That way he could warn me if any of the weaker men collapsed. The last thing I needed was for us to wander on, unwittingly leaving someone behind, and then having to return to collect him.

So on we staggered. Not long before sunset, we discovered in a small area of the reddish earth what appeared to be the footprints of a camel, and possibly also those of a man. The tracks were old, but it was clear that other creatures had passed this way. Of course, it made little difference to us whether the tracks were made a week ago or a century ago, as we had only enough water to survive for another day or two. The gloom of despair that had settled in our hearts was now visible on every face.

Just as it was getting dark, we saw not far away another of the sandy beaches, but here the whole cliff had crumbled, leaving a slope all the way down to the sea. I told the men that we must gain the cliff above that beach before we stopped for the night.

So we trudged on in a silent column. We were about halfway to the slope when Clark, who was immediately behind me, shouted that we should look beyond the beach. Then he shouted again and again, "I see a light!" I looked. He was right; it was the light of a fire.

Joy coursed through my body. Hope revived within me. Looking at my crew, I could see that each of them was experiencing the same emotions. No words were needed. It looked as though our problems had been resolved; our prayers had been answered. And yet we had to be careful. Now it was necessary to be sensible, and being sensible meant being cautious.

I told the men that we must approach the natives, who had obviously encamped for the night, with the greatest of care. We must not alarm them, because if they felt challenged, we might fall victim to their fury. A sudden approach in the dark was the last thing we should do. It could easily be misunderstood and we would have no chance to explain our situation, nor would the natives be likely to realise our parlous condition and weakness.

Now I expected some resistance from the men, because I thought they might be impatient to rush to their presumed saviours. But they all agreed with me. Apparently, with new life and spirit suffused in them, the men had acquired a certain confidence and patience, and they realised that we must not abuse this chance of survival that Providence had set before us.

We made our way down the face of the cliff, and reached the sandy area at its base. The men wet their mouths with the few drops of water each had left, and this time several of them offered me a share. Of course it was no longer such a sacrifice; they all expected water in plenty in the morning.

As we knelt down, we could feel the heat throbbing within the sand, which had been warming throughout the day. We scraped away the surface to a depth of about fourteen inches so as to create sleeping spaces, and this left cooler sand below for us to lie on in our individual trenches.

The breeze of the night started to drift in from the sea. It soothed our bodies and minds, rewarding us for having survived another day of heat. The men quickly forgot their sufferings in the arms of sleep, no doubt dreaming of a return to food and comfort soon after they awoke. I was the exception, for my mind had become so excited by my hopes and fears for the next day that I was kept awake for much of this long and troublesome night.

Looking at the distant light of the fire, I had time to think. Probably the people by the fire would take us and hold us as slaves. Slavery was not a very inviting prospect, but it was better than remaining here and dying within days.

I tried so hard not to think about what the morning might bring, because this was not a preparation for our encounter; it was merely self-torture. What else could I think of? My home? My family? My distress had been so great, and my anxiety for my shipmates so extreme, that yet again all thoughts of my wife and children had been driven entirely from my mind. They were so far off now, part of another life. I felt guilty for not having thought of them, but I had to deal with reality, and my reality was limited to my present situation.

Still I could not sleep. Why was I denied what the crew were enjoying? I closed my eyes and prayed to be permitted to sleep, just for one hour; but it was in vain.

So the endless night passed with my mind full of confusion. I may have nodded off for a short time, but soon I was awake once more, impatient to learn my fate and urging the sun to show itself more quickly. But nothing could hurry it along.

My great anxiety and the lack of sleep had made my thirst doubly painful while my companions slept. The urine I had saved had all been used, and of course I did not have my bottle of water. I was so desperate for drink that in my madness I had recourse to theft. I actually stole a sip of water from the bottle belonging to our cook, Dick Deslisle. As I did so, I reasoned with myself that it did not really matter, for after he awoke he would soon either have as much water as he needed or else he would be dead. But at the back of my mind I knew that was no excuse, and I was disgusted with myself. Anyway, the few drops of water I took did little for my burning thirst. Within ten minutes I was just as thirsty as I had been before my momentary weakness.

At last, daylight arrived. It was 10th September - the day that would decide our future. I awakened my men and told them that we must now prepare to go forward and show ourselves.

"What nation do you think those people come from?" asked Barrett. "What country is this?"

"I think we're in the land ruled by the Sultan of Morocco," I said.

"What are they like?" Barrett continued. "Will they be friendly to Americans? Are we at war with them?"

"No," I said. "We're not at war with them. But I don't think that our futures will be decided by relations between our countries; it will be decided by the mood of the men by that fire."

"What do you think they'll do with us?" asked Hogan.

"I don't know," I replied. "I don't think they'll harm us. They must see straight away that we're defenceless and weak. We're no challenge to them and have no property to excite their jealousy or avarice."

"Does that make any difference?" said Clark. "They might kill us anyway, even if there's no advantage for them."

"Yes, James," I agreed, "that's a possibility. But I'm hoping they'll see that we're as miserable as human beings can be, and perhaps our condition will summon some pity. Anyhow, we must trust that fate will assist us. I can hardly believe that after all our providential escapes, everything will now come to an end as we're sacrificed to people to whom we pose no threat. Fate has been continually casting us down and picking us up; it's our turn to be picked up again."

"Captain," said Savage, "what do you consider 'picking up' means this time?"

"Well, Aaron," I said, "your guess is as good as mine. I expect that the best result is being looked after and taken to a large town bordering the sea; though that's probably asking for too much. But I also think that expecting to be killed instantly is fearing too much. Probably there will be a middle course, and we'll survive as slaves."

The men looked frightened. "Survival is our first aim, not our sole aim," I added. "Life as a slave may give each of us the opportunity to escape. If you do escape, try to get to a town and find the American or English Consul or failing that, the consul of another European country. You must tell him of the fate of our vessel and its crew. If that's not possible, contact any Christian trader in the hope that some effort will be made to rescue the rest of us. Is that understood?" The men nodded grimly.

"We're going forward now," I continued. "Submit to your destiny with courage. If you're taken as slaves, be obedient to your masters. Don't show any insubordination or anger; you must not argue, otherwise not just you but every one of your companions will suffer the consequences. Remember how you've been delivered from disaster after disaster. You must now prepare for some hard times before the Almighty comes to your rescue once more." I paused. "Shall we go?" They all agreed to advance.

We walked slowly, filled with apprehension. So much depended on the next few minutes. Reaching the end of the beach, we climbed over some sandhills. I led the way; I could feel the others falling behind, as no one wanted to be amongst the first to encounter the natives. If there was trouble, those at the back would have a better chance to escape.

Advancing carefully down the slope of the last sandhill, we saw a large drove of camels about half a mile away. Next to the camels, we could make out a group of people in a kind of small valley formed by a ridge of sandhills close to the sea on one side and by the high land on the other.

As we approached, I could see that the natives were busy giving water to their camels. We drew closer and closer; yet we still remained unnoticed by these people who were preoccupied with their tasks.

Then, all of a sudden, we were spotted. In an instant, one man and two women started running towards us as fast as they were able, their robes billowing about them. As they did so, many others turned to find out what had caused this commotion. On discovering us, they too ran in our direction.

What were we to do? I decided to continue with George and Aaron. As the three people neared us, we stopped and bowed to the ground, trying to show submission in the manner of cowed animals, yet also attempting to implore them to show compassion.

The man running at us was armed with a scimitar, which he waved threateningly above his head. But when he came within ten yards of me, he stopped, as if puzzled how to proceed. He stood directly in from of me. So I bowed again in token submission and said "*Salaam*", "Peace". Then he walked up to me and, without further ceremony, began to strip off my shirt. I did not resist, so the women ran to George and did the same to him.

By the time this performance had ended, I could see thirty or forty more of the natives coming close, some running with muskets or scimitars, others riding on camels. The three who had arrived first turned to the others and threw handfuls of sand into the air, yelling loudly. They did this in exactly the same way as the wives of the murderous old man on the first beach. Perhaps this was a way of telling the others to keep their distance, that the ground around them was theirs. Frightening though all this was, we were as yet unharmed.

The man who had taken my shirt now took off his robe, laid it on the sand and wrapped the two shirts in it. He then put the bundle on Dick's back, indicating that he must carry it. Next he pointed at Dick and me in turn and then to himself, making it clear that we now belonged to him.

As soon as those on the camels reached us, they made their beasts lie down. They jumped off the camels and ran towards us, their scimitars naked and ready for action. Those on foot soon joined them, and a great scuffling and noise ensued.

Several of them came up to me and grabbed hold of my arms, pulling me first one way and then the other. Deslisle suffered the same indignity, although he was treated more violently, each man trying to insist that Dick was his property. The man who had come first kept close to us, waving the others away, signifying that we belonged to him, but they could take our shipmates. I could only shout "Peace, peace!" in Arabic again and again; but they ignored me completely.

It was at least clear that we were of some worth to these people.

But there were not enough of us to satisfy all the claimants, so there was a real danger that the disappointed ones would be happy to see us dead, rather than watch us pass into the possession of their rivals. The dispute continued as they cut the air around us with their scimitars, which passed within inches of our heads. The swishing of the scimitars from every angle meant that we could not duck or dodge the blades, for we did not know which one would endanger us next.

Then, mercifully, they turned on each other - not trying to kill one another, but letting their blades come close enough to put each man in fear of injury. On several occasions their poor aim caused gashes on their rivals' faces and bodies. I expected the violence to increase as blood streamed from these cuts, colouring their clothes. But not a bit of it; none of them, not even those who had been cut, attempted to wound the others.

The skirmish carried on for some time, although never for any apparent purpose, until the tribesmen grew exhausted and the contest ground to a halt. Fortunately for them, those who had been cut were not badly hurt, and they paid little attention to their wounds.

It was impossible to discern who were the winners and who were the losers of the conflict. I looked about me and saw that Dick was still close by, but my other men were in a group some yards away. The tribesmen were standing around, panting and trying to recover their strength. Then, as if by prior arrangement, my distressed companions were divided amongst several groups of men, and were marched off towards the drove of camels some distance from Deslisle and me.

The two of us were handed over into the charge of the two women, who urged us on with sticks towards the camels. Worn out and barefoot, we could not go very fast. I turned to the women and opened my mouth, pointing at my tongue, which was parched white as frost. "Water," I said in Arabic. The women nodded, indicating that they understood, and they directed us towards the camels.

When we came near the camels, I saw that there was a well. We were ordered to stop. Then one of the women called to another, who came to us with a large wooden bowl containing about a gallon of water. She set it down and forced us to the ground. Then she put our heads towards the bowl so that we should drink like animals.

We must each have gulped down about three pints. I had been very particular about cautioning the men against drinking too much at one time, should they ever find water. What a waste of time that had been! None of us could have resisted the opportunity to drink whatever was available.

The women then made us get to our feet, and they led us to the well. I could see that the water being taken from it was dark and disgusting. We were made to sit down next to our shipmates, who had also been given water to drink. There was not much joy at this reunion. We sat in silence, awaiting our next instructions.

Now the women brought forward several bowls containing filthy water from the well. They poured into each of the bowls a little sour camel's milk from a goatskin. We were then told to drink this ugly-looking mixture. To my surprise, it tasted fine, and we drank until we were full. All of us suffered immediately from sharp pains in our stomachs, for we had taken too much too quickly. But we were beasts crouching semi-naked under the sun, and our only interest was slaking our thirst and replenishing our stomachs by taking repeated drafts of this unwholesome swill. I begged for something to eat, but the women told me that they had no food, and they seemed truly sorry that they could give us none.

We sat on the ground together, not knowing what we should do. At least we were no longer thirsty, but I could not accept that just because we had been given water, we had nothing to fear. I looked over towards the well; there must have been about a hundred men, women and children there, as well as four or five hundred camels. What a feast one of those camels would have made. How could they say they had no food?

It was now midway through the morning, and the sun was high and beating down on us so that our skins seemed to fry.

I was surprised that these people were not inquisitive about us. However, they now appeared completely calm; it was as if the mock battle and the outpouring of rage had never happened. Anyway, they were too busy to care about us, most being engaged in drawing water for their camels, which drank enormous quantities.

When all the camels had been watered, I saw about twenty of the tribesmen separate a group of camels from the rest. Four of them then came over to us and took Williams, Robbins, Porter, Hogan, Barrett and Burns, and mounted them on the backs of the camels.

I stood up to say goodbye, not knowing if I would ever see them again. Their new masters understood what I was doing, and permitted me to speak without interruption. "Remember what I told you," I said. "I'm convinced that some of us will return home. So keep fighting on and endure whatever you have to endure to get to the next day. May God preserve and protect you."

Each man said farewell to me, and then they left, climbing to the desert surface, and soon they were out of sight. It was a numbing and troubling moment. I could do nothing more to help those men. But now I had to show resolve and give all my attention to the four who were left behind, and to myself.

We were a five-man group: Aaron Savage, Horace Savage, James Clark, Dick Deslisle and me. What a sad little band, sitting there ignored on the sand whilst those about us were scurrying around seeing to their business. For some reason, Clark had been allowed to keep his shirt, but the rest of us were wearing only our ragged trousers.

Dick and I were told to stay where we were, while the others were compelled to assist in drawing water for the camels. Then our captors brought a considerable number of goatskins forward and threw them in a heap on the ground. The skins had been cut around the neck and stripped off the animals over the tail. Then they filled the skins with water so that, except for the missing heads, they looked like the animals they had once been. These were then tied at the neck and slung over the camels. Next they placed basket-like contraptions on to the beasts, which I later discovered would serve as seats for the women and children.

We were now called forward and required to assist in securing the baskets to the camels. It was evident that we would soon be leaving. A number of the men fixed saddles to some of the camels. These were made of skin stretched over a wooden rim, and they were placed on the animals' backs in front of the hump. The saddle was then fastened with a rope under the camel's belly.

I hoped that we would be allowed to ride, but I was forgetting that we were now slaves. The tribesmen mounted the camels, which got to their feet in a most ungainly series of movements, and then they started to climb the sandhills towards the desert. We were forced to walk alongside the animals and to drive and keep together those that carried no one. The sand was so soft and yielding that we sank in at every step, so it required a great effort just to match the slow progress of the camels, which negotiated the sand easily with their broad feet.

The blazing heat of the sun's rays seared our bodies and burned us as they reflected from the sand. For my own part, I had difficulty in keeping up, but I was hurried on by the application of a stick to my sore back. So much for my hopes for compassion.

At last we reached the summit of the sands, and were on the hard desert level. After travelling on for some time, the men stopped the camels, and the beasts were made to lie down and rest. We were allowed to rest as well, but we were bewildered. We were alive, we had taken water, but in every other respect it seemed that things were getting worse.

... and the beasts were made to lie down and rest

CHAPTER EIGHT

A council and sale

It is such a relief to rest after toil. I just lay on the ground, viewing the vastness of the desert. The surface consisted partly of solid rock, of gravel, of sand and stones mixed, and in some places soil. This mass was baked down together in most places by the extreme heat of the sun, nearly as hard as marble, so that no tracks of man or beast were discoverable, for footsteps left no impression.

What a place! What were we to do? Our past was filled with disaster and our future was filled with the possibility of disaster; but now I thought nothing of the past and nothing of the future, I was resting and I just wanted to continue to rest forever. Sadly, about two hours later I saw the tribesmen preparing to leave. The camels were made to rise to their feet; we would be next.

Five camels were brought forward, and each of us was put on a separate mount. We had to cling on by grasping the beast's long hair tightly with our hands. My growling animal was forced to its knees, and then rose abruptly, first on its hind legs and then on its front legs. Its backbone was covered only with skin, and it seemed as sharp as the edge of an oar's blade. Below me, the beast's belly, distended with water, made it perfectly smooth, leaving no projection of the hips to prevent me from sliding off. Its back was so broad that I had to extend my legs sideways to the limit. Riding in this way, I was constantly slipping down the camel's back towards its tail. I knew that I must not fall off, so I clutched at the beast wherever I could, alternately slipping down a little and then pulling myself back up the hump.

My camel was obviously not very happy with its rider. It would not follow the steady pace of its brethren, but kept running about amongst the drove, making the most woeful bellowing. Without any bridle or halter with which to control the animal, my only concern was to hang on as well as I could, regardless of the direction the beast decided to take.

We continued until midday, and then we stopped. Everyone dismounted, and the five of us sat together once more. We were each given about a pint of water, and allowed to rest.

Then some of the tribesmen came over and started to ask me questions in Arabic. Obviously they had realised that I could understand that language. They were anxious to know where we had first reached the shore. I satisfied them on this point, and they talked excitedly to each other in a strange language. After that, we all mounted our camels once more and set off at a great trot.

Sitting on the camel and struggling to hold on, I tried to think of nothing but that extraordinary animal. Its heavy motions seemed not unlike those of a small vessel on a heavy sea as it sailed up and down over the waves, steadily making its way forward, which seemed appropriate for 'ships of the desert'. These movements were not at all smooth; in fact they were quite violent, so that, aided by its sharp backbone, the animal began to cause horrible damage to the insides of my legs. My trousers were so torn and ragged that they offered me little protection, and my thighs became dreadfully chafed. As a result, trickles of blood began to run down my legs and drip from my heels. I could not administer any healing or even touch my legs; my hands were fully occupied in hanging on to the beast.

So, bleeding and burning, we continued our advance on the flat, hard surface of the desert. I was only waiting for our bodies to cry out for an end to this torment, where fate was constantly discovering more and more ways to cause us grief, with each new method supplementing, rather than replacing, the previous methods.

The sun, whose beams had shone upon such a momentous day, now sank in glory behind us. It was night, and I had expected that we would stop; but no, our troop continued on and on. A cold wind started to blow, chilling our blood so that it ceased to trickle down our lacerated legs. But although there was relief for our blood, the force of the wind on our blistered skin increased the discomfort beyond description. In the name of God, why did we not stop?

We cried out for the troop to halt. I shouted in Arabic, asking for rest, but our captors paid no attention to my pleas. They seemed intent on getting as far forward as possible before the stop for the night. But why? What difference did a few miles make?

Yet on we went, until we could stand it no longer. We intentionally fell off our mounts, risking broken bones in the fall, in an attempt to arouse the compassion of our masters and obtain a drink and some rest. But they kept the camels going even faster.

The next problem was that we could not get back on to our beasts, and we had to run alongside them over ground covered with stones, which were nearly as sharp as gun flints and which cut our feet at every step.

We all shouted with pain and begged for mercy. Then, realising that our efforts were wasted, we continued in silence. When we ceased to make a noise, our masters immediately stopped. So, they were afraid of losing us in the dark. We were granted a few moments of rest, and I was encouraged to believe that our lives might not be at risk. If they wanted to kill us, they might just as well have ridden on and left us to perish in the desert.

Our rest did not last long. These people were determined to

ride on as if an army was chasing them from behind. So they placed us once more on our camels and continued at full speed until about midnight, when we entered a small dell or valley excavated by the hand of nature, which was about fifteen feet below the surface level on which we had been travelling.

At last we all stopped. The tribesmen made the camels lie down and then ordered us to do the same. Had all that effort been made just to reach this little sunken area? We had probably travelled no more than forty miles during the day. It seemed no distance at all in the vastness of the desert, but clearly our leaders knew where they were and where they were going, and they were determined to keep to some sort of itinerary. I was aware that for centuries traders had been able to find their way across the Sahara. The routes are well known to them, and I guessed that we must be near the western trail linking Morocco in the north to the lands in the south. I had no argument with the trail; it was just that I would have preferred to be travelling in the opposite direction, towards the north.

But now I wished to think not of travel, but of rest. Our stopping-place was hard and rocky. There was no sand to lie on, nor any covering to shelter us from the cold night wind that sweeps the surface of the desert. As we lay on the ground, the women set about milking the camels, and then gave each of us a pint of pure camel's milk. It was of a bluish hue and rather glutinous. It warmed our stomachs, quenched our thirst and allayed to some degree the cravings of hunger.

Savage was ordered away from us, and the other three - Clark, Horace and Deslisle - lay down with me to sleep. With our blistered bodies tender all over, the stones attacked our naked flesh. These agonies and our sad reflections rendered this one of the longest and most dismal nights ever passed by any human beings. But at least we were still alive.

When I awoke the next morning, the sun was blazing into my eyes. My men were already awake. Horace pointed to the left, and I saw one of the women approaching. She brought half a pint of milk to be shared amongst the four of us. It was little more than enough to wet our mouths.

Then some of the men came over, and they made us go forward on foot to drive the camels. The condition of our feet was horrible beyond description, and we moved on very slowly. We proceeded over the desert for a considerable time, and then we entered another small valley, where I saw many tents made of coarse cloth. Near these tents we were met by a number of men, all well armed, carrying double-barrelled muskets, scimitars and daggers. These men were presumably from the same tribe as our masters, for they were very well disposed to one another.

But now that they saw us, things changed. Arguments started and their faces became far less friendly. There was apparently some difficulty in deciding to whom each of us belonged. Some came and seized hold of us, disputing very loudly, many drawing their weapons. In the end, and I don't know how, it was decided that Dick and I should remain in the hands of our first master. They gave Clark to another and Horace to a third.

Although it had been made clear to whom each of us belonged, we were still allowed to remain together. We sat close to two of the tents and we were certainly disgusting objects, being virtually naked and almost skinless. Three women came out of one of the tents. Having satisfied their curiosity by gazing at us, they expressed their contempt by spitting at us. Frankly, they also looked rather awful, and their faces were made more horrible by every contortion of their frightful features as they sneered in disgust. Some of the men came out and rescued us; but it was only to announce our departure.

We were told to mount the camels, and again we proceeded on our painful path across the wilderness. It was like a never-ending journey through hell. Then I thought that perhaps we were already dead, and were now in hell itself. But no, I had to resist such delusions. I had to concentrate on keeping going until the next stop and think of nothing else.

Towards evening, we halted in a small valley and dismounted.

Now something was up. We could see the natives gathering together in a sort of council. There must have been about a hundred and fifty of them, all sitting in a large circle with their legs crossed. Although of varying ages, they had certain common characteristics. They were tolerably well set in their frames, though lean, with complexions best described as dark olive, and all had high cheekbones and aquiline noses, with eyes that were black and sparkling.

"What's happening?" asked Horace.

"I'll try to listen," I said. "Maybe they're discussing us, maybe they're debating which way to go."

The men started their discussion. There was a lot of talking and a lot of shouting. Then there was a lot of pointing towards us, so no doubt our fate was in the balance.

"What are they saying?" asked Clark.

"I don't know," I replied.

"But you said you could understand Arabic, or aren't they Arabs?"

"I do understand quite a bit of Arabic," I said. "But they're not speaking Arabic. It's some other language."

"Are you saying these people aren't Arabs?" asked Dick.

"Well," I said. "I think they must be. They're using names like Seid, Sideullah and Abdallah, so they must be Arabs or Moors."

"What do you mean Arabs or Moors?" said Dick. "What's the difference?"

"The Moors are Moroccans or North Africans and also descendants of the Muslims who conquered southern Spain but were later expelled. They're a mixture of Arabs, Spanish and Berbers. That's it, they must be Berbers; that's the language they're speaking. The problem is that I don't understand anything of the Berber language, but I guess that most of them speak Arabic as well. We'll see." I knew that 'Berber' derived from the Greek word for 'barbarian', but I spared my shipmates that piece of information.

In the end, the tribesmen finished their debate, and they arose and walked over to us. One of the old men then addressed me. He spoke in Arabic and then repeated to the others what he had said in, I presumed, Berber. He wanted to know to what country we belonged. I decided to tell him we were English. England was the major power in the world and we might get more respect. Also, there was more likely to be an English consul in the towns nearby than an American one.

"*Inglesis,*" I said.

This seemed to please them, and the old man replied, "*Oh Fransah, Oh Spaniah.*"

I assumed he meant Frenchmen or Spaniards, so I repeated that we were English.

He told me that some of them had found the remains of our small boat, and he asked if we had come all the way from England in it. I told him that we had travelled in a very much larger boat. Then I knelt down and drew an outline of the Commerce, using small stones and sand. I explained that our ship had been totally lost, and we had reached these shores in the small boat that had been kept on board.

I was now sitting on the ground with the old man in front of me. The others were seated in a circle around us. They were paying keen attention to everything that was said, and some now prompted the old man with further questions.

This was quite a civilised interview. They were treating me almost like a human being, rather than a beast. But how long would that last?

Now they asked me to tell them what cargo we had been carrying. I said that we had sold our cargo in Spain, and as a result, when we were wrecked we had been carrying only money.

Not surprisingly, their next question was: how much money? They gave me a small bowl so that I could indicate the quantity. I did this by filling the bowl with stones, saying '*mia*', the Arabic for 'a hundred', each time I dropped a stone into the bowl. They were surprised at the quantity and became very excited. There was a good deal of chatting to each other. I was pleased at the reaction, because I wanted them to think that we were substantial and wealthy traders, so that we would have a value for ransom.

Next they asked in what direction the wreck lay, and whether we had come across any natives when we first landed. They referred to the natives in a contemptuous manner, so probably these people were not of the same race as the wicked old man and his family.

I described our encounters with the natives, saying that they had taken our spare clothing, our money and provisions, had killed one of our number and driven the rest of us out to sea.

A younger man now spoke, telling me that they had heard of our shipwreck, but had been told that all the crew had perished. However, he seemed satisfied that I had been telling the truth, so he began to enquire further.

They wanted to know more about us, though it was obviously for general interest, now that they had discovered our money was gone.

I was next asked if I knew anything about Marocksh. This sounded something like Morocco, so I said that I knew it well. They were pleased when I referred to the *maghreb el aksa*, 'the land of the farthest west', as I had been taught in my French prison. Then the old man mentioned the *Sooltaam*, which I took to be their word for the Sultan, so I nodded. I heard one of them say 'Mulay Solimaan'. I knew this meant 'Prince Solomon', and was the name of the present Emperor or Sultan of Morocco. So I gave them to understand that I knew him, that I had met him several times, and that he was a friend to me and to my nation. They were very pleased with my answer, and jabbered amongst themselves.

Then they turned to me again and asked me to point to the Sultan's dominions, so I waved in an arc towards the north, and they nodded excitedly. I did not know whether these questions were a test for me or a quest for knowledge. However, I believed I had satisfied them that I knew something of Morocco and the Sultan. Finally, I decided to play my only card. I told them that if they would carry us to the Sultan, I would be able to provide them with a substantial ransom. They shouted '*Oho, oho!*' several times, which I soon learned was the Berber for 'no'. They said that the Sultan lived in Fez, which was far off, and there was insufficient for the camels to eat and drink on the way. I did not believe that such a journey was impossible, but I was satisfied that at least I had planted the thought of reward in their minds, and I might be able to play that card again in the future.

Of course, my shipmates could not understand one word of what had been said. Goodness knows what they made of '*oho*'. I explained to them that I thought that in time we might get ransomed, but they were dismissive of my suggestion and seemed to think I was trying to delude them with false expectations. So be it; they could believe what they wanted. I had some hope, and I was not fighting just for their lives, I was fighting for my life as well.

Having finished the questioning, the tribesmen arose, and we were each taken away by our masters. I had been so fully occupied since noon that no thoughts of food or drink had entered my mind. None of us ate anything that day except for a few sips of milk at dawn and about half a pint of filthy water in the middle of the afternoon.

Next I was delivered to a man named Bickri, who took me to his tent, where he made me lie down like a camel. I had been so proud of my captain's command. Now I was a slave and a starving beast. What a fall! How could I be treated this way? But for these people we were just slaves. They considered themselves as much above me and my companions, both in intellect and acquired knowledge, as the proud and pampered West Indian planter fancies himself above the meanest negro newly brought in chains from the coast of Africa.

But even a slave has to be fed if he is to be of use. Near midnight Bickri brought me a bowl containing about two pints of a mixture of milk and water. It tasted so good, and as my stomach had contracted, it was a plentiful portion.

What an exhausting day. I sank into a deep sleep and was overwhelmed with the most frightful dream.

In the morning I awoke to be confronted by about ten smallish men wielding pointed sticks, which they poked at my body. As I got up, they jabbed at me furiously, and I began to run away. I ran and ran and came to a part of the desert where there were many thorn bushes. Some of the branches had become detached and been rolled by the wind into large balls.

One of them caught fire in the heat of the day, and as they rolled along, one ignited the other until they were all on fire and rolling after me.

Naked and barefoot, I ran for miles, the flames scorching every part of my body as my skin was burned off and my flesh roasted. I looked towards heaven and prayed that the Almighty would receive my spirit and end my suffering.

Then I climbed a rocky hill, and below me I saw a deep valley where there were green trees, shrubs in blossom, cows feeding on grass, and horses wandering about. As I hurried down into the valley, I discovered a brook of clear running water. I could not resist; I threw myself down and drank my fill of this freshest of liquids. When my thirst was quenched, I rolled into the brook to cool my body, thanking God for his mercies.

I stood up to take in the sight, and a tall young man dressed in the European manner rode up to me on a white horse. He dismounted, rushed towards me and took me in his arms. I fainted in his grasp from an excess of joy and relief.

When I came round, I found myself in a large room with a table next to me covered with the choicest meats, fruits and wines. My deliverer invited me to eat and drink, and told me not to worry; I would once more see my family.

At that instant, I was called by my master. I awoke; the dream was over.

It was early morning on 12th September, and Bickri ordered me to gather some of his camels. They were near to us, and all I had to do was take hold of the ropes hanging from their necks, lead them to the tent and hold them together. But this task took me almost an hour, as I was slowed by the dreadful condition of my feet, which were so swollen and lacerated that I had to move carefully, stooping and crouching almost to the ground.

Why didn't these people either treat us fairly or else kill us? Why did we have to be kept in a near death state, so that we were of little use to them? The only rational reason I could think of was that they wanted to keep us alive, but they needed us to be weak so that we would be no threat to them and could not escape. Hunger and thirst were our shackles.

When I had finished my task, I saw my first master, Hamet, ride up to Bickri's tent on his camel. He dismounted and spoke with Bickri and gave him a blanket. Then Hamet ordered me to mount his camel. He got on behind me and steadied me with his hand as he made the animal rise. We then moved off, accompanied by four mounted men.

So that was it; I had been bought for the price of a blanket. Perhaps in these parts it was a good price; who knows? I could not judge whether or not this was an improvement in my condition. It was just another episode, and I had to accept it. I could not influence my fate.

As we rode along, the sun beat down dreadfully, until my head felt that it must soon split open and fall to the ground in pieces. I was frightened that these ridiculous thoughts were a sign of oncoming madness. But then I reasoned that if I could rationalise about the possibility of madness, I could not yet be mad; I must still be sane. I needed to make some sort of effort to maintain my sanity. But how?

In this wretched distress my thoughts drifted to my recent dream. It gave me a gleam of hope, sufficient to keep alive the declining spirit of a man in deep misery. I also remembered how narrowly I had cheated death in recent days. Perhaps my dream was a message to me that all these events would lead to my rescue. Such a rescue was possible only if I could stay alive. I was sure that if we reached a town, I would come across someone who would redeem me and my companions, a person whose heart was already prepared for such an event by fate itself.

Eventually I noticed that we were in another small valley, in which a cluster of tents had been pitched. As soon as we came to the tents, Hamet made his camel kneel down, and we both dismounted. Hamet was greeted by several women and children, who all seemed very glad to see him. As I walked slowly towards the tent, the women and children ran to stand between me and the entrance. They would not allow me to enter, driving me back with sticks; and then when I stood several yards away, they threw stones at me. I retreated out of their range, and sat on the ground awaiting new orders.

Not long afterwards, Hamet came out of the tent and gave me a little sour milk and water in a bowl, which refreshed me considerably. It was now early afternoon, and I was forced to remain outside until dusk, without any shade to shield me from the scorching sun. Then, as night began to fall, I saw our cook, Dick Deslisle, approach. He was leading three camels. Dick came up to me, and we shook hands warmly.

The tribesmen, noticing the way we greeted each other, laughed and sneered at us. Their own method is to place the insides of the open hands together as if praying, bring them to their lips, touch them and then drop their hands.

"Dick," I said. "What's been happening to you?"

"Captain, I'm so relieved to see you," he said. "I'm Hamet's slave; it's my job to drive his camels."

"Hamet owns me as well," I said. "He bought me for the price of a blanket. What do you think of that?"

"It's meaningless Captain," said Dick. "We must accept everything that happens if we're to stay alive. I'm at least permitted to sleep in a corner of Hamet's tent, and he gives me as much milk as I want. Of course, as I'm allowed in the tent, when no one's watching I take water and more milk."

"You're fortunate," I said. "They won't let me into the tent." That was how low our values had fallen. The theft of a little water was a luxury and the right to lie on the ground in Hamet's miserable tent was a privilege to be envied.

"Captain," said Dick, "you know, we might be the lucky ones. I fear for the others and whether we will ever – look, Captain, it's Hogan."

As I turned round, I saw John Hogan walk up to us and fall to the ground. He didn't look fearsome any more. In fact he was almost unrecognisable, apart from his ponytail. The tall thickset man was now a thin stooping creature.

"John," I said, "whose slave are you?"

"I belong to Hamet," he replied. "He bought me this morning."

"That's good, John," I said. "I was also bought this morning. Perhaps Hamet has a plan to get us all together again. At least we're three now; you, me and Dick."

"Horace isn't far off," said Dick. "He's been bought by the man who lives in that tent behind you. There he is. Horace's master is coming over to us."

An ill-looking elderly man came up to us. He addressed me, using the name '*Rais*', meaning 'captain' or 'chief', and asked me the name of his slave. I told him that his name was Horace. I had to repeat this to him several times so that he could pronounce it and remember it. He then returned to his tent, and could be heard summoning Horace periodically by shouting '*Hoh Ras!*'.

Hamet came out of his tent once more and ordered Dick to go inside. I looked at my master. He was of a lighter colour than most of the other tribesmen, and I thought he might be less cruel. But I was much mistaken, for he now made Hogan and me lie on the ground in the place he chose, where the stones were very numerous and baked into the ground so tightly that we could not pull them out with our fingers. We had to lie on their sharp points, even though not thirty yards away there was an area of sand. I made Hamet understand this, and I pointed to that area; but he would not let us move. He told me that if we did not remain where we were, there would be nothing for us when he milked the camels.

Fine; so there was no choice. Here we stayed. We could not sleep, but we were too tired to talk, so Hogan and I just rested with our thoughts. I contented myself with the more pleasurable parts of my recent dream.

When it was about midnight, Hamet came to us with our milk, about a pint each. Here was our reward for not resting on a soft surface. Having had our milk, we waited until Hamet retired to his tent for the night. Then, without a word between us, Hogan and I crawled slowly and quietly to the sandy area, and we slept soundly for what was left of the night.

As it began to dawn on the thirteenth, we were awakened. The first thing that each family does upon rising, which is invariably at daybreak, is to go to *sulle*, or prayer. They begin by taking off their camel-skin slippers, then they kneel down on the ground facing the east and rub sand on their hands, arms and faces. This is a symbol of ablution or cleansing, as they do not have enough water to wash in the normal manner.

After this has been done, they stand up, still facing the east, and exclaim, '*Sheda el la lah, hi, Allah, sheda Mahommed rah sool Allah!*' Then they throw their outspread arms forward, exclaiming, '*Allah hooakbar!*' – 'God is great!'; after which they kneel down again and kiss the ground, saying again '*Allah hooakbar*'. Next, they stand up, and repeat the same expression. There follows a prayer in which they thank God for the favours they have received, for the food they eat and the clothes they wear. They pray for rain when the earth is dry and food for their camels, for an abundance of plunder and that they may take numerous slaves, that God should destroy their enemies, protect them and their children and bless all their possessions.

Then they mention Mulay Solimaan several times, and again say, '*Allah hooakbar*'. Next they kiss the earth three times, repeating '*Allah hooakbar*', after which they sit down and recite some parts of the Koran. During this recitation, they hold a string of beads upon which they cast their eyes in the most profound adoration, counting the beads and stopping as they come to a particular one.

They complete the ceremony by saying '*sulle mulla*'.

The ceremony having ended, we were summoned to proceed. Nothing was said about our softer resting-place; there was too much to be done. The families struck their tents, packed them on the camels and began their journey, leaving no trace of their visit but the marks of tent poles and the ashes of their hearths.

This time we were not to ride. They made us walk, and we had to keep up with the camels. We were so stiff and sore that we could scarcely refrain from crying out at every step, such was our agony; but fortunately the pace was slow.

As I struggled on, half-dreaming in the oppressive heat of noon, I chanced to see George Williams. He was riding on a camel behind his master. I hobbled along towards him, and walked next to his camel for a while. He was an appalling sight; his skin burned off, and his whole body so excessively inflamed and swollen that I feared for his life. What a difference from the upright proud man I had met at the Liberty Inn a few months ago.

In a feeble voice, George told me that he had been obliged to sleep almost naked in the open air, that his life was fast wasting away in dreadful torment, and that he could not live one more day in such misery. He also told me that his master's wife had taken pity on him and had soothed his body with some form of grease; but it had been too late for medication.

Williams whispered to me, "I cannot live any longer. Should you ever get away from this evil place and return to our country, tell my dear wife that my last moments were spent in prayers for her well-being." He could say no more; the breath of life was disappearing. Tears and sobs were all he could manage.

This was a man stripped of all his strength, pride and hope. But I could do nothing for him. His master then arrived and drove him forward and away from me. I called to him as he left, "God bless you and care for you". Worthless I know, but it was all I could do. As George went from me, I could see blood from the insides of his legs and thighs trickling down the sides of the camel. "Dear God!" I cried. "Why are we made to suffer such tortures?"

Whilst I had been talking to Williams, my master's camels had gained some distance from me. I saw my master, not far off. He stopped so that I might catch up with him. For a moment, I thought this was a small act of kindness, but I was quickly disabused. As soon as I came near Hamet, he threatened me, shaking his stick over my head to let me know what I might expect if I dared to misbehave again. He then rode off, having ordered us to drive the camels forward as fast as possible.

We carried on for about an hour, and then we all stopped. Hamet came over and beckoned me to follow him. I walked after him for a few minutes, passing the other groups who were resting. Finally he halted, and showed me to three men. One was an old man, and he was accompanied by two younger men, whom I later discovered were his sons.

I was given to the old man, whose features showed every sign of the deepest-rooted unpleasantness in his disposition. So, I thought, I have been sold yet again. This was my new master. Defend me from such cruelty! But my main concern was that I had once more been separated from my shipmates. Somehow, I felt that could not be for the better.

My new master told me to follow him, and we walked on with his two sons, the old man snarling at me in the most surly manner to make me keep up with them. I tried my best, as I was anxious to please him, if such a thing were possible. But I could not go fast enough for him, so after he had growled at me for a considerable time, and finding that I still could not keep pace, he walked behind me and thrust me forward by applying heavy blows to my exposed back with a stout stick.

Staggering on under my wounds, I made the greatest efforts to go faster, but one of my master's sons gave me a double-barrelled gun and a powder horn to carry. They were very heavy and slowed me even more, but the old man did not strike me again. He just went forward to the place where he had pitched his tent, leaving me to follow as well as I could.

When I reached the tent, I lay down on the ground. Looking

about me, I saw camels in every direction. Where were they going? If only we could get near a city. There must be some Europeans there.

I crawled to the entrance of my master's tent and asked him for some water, but he would not give me any. The three men were too busy preparing themselves for their prayers. They walked away to join the others, leaving me lying in the shade. I tried to soften the hearts of the women, begging them to give me some water, but they only laughed and spat at me. One day, if my luck changed, I would dearly love to give some of these people a good beating. While I was thinking these dark thoughts, in order to increase my distress as much as they could, the women came over and drove me away from the shade of the tent.

A little later, I was pleased to discover that Clark had the same master. He came over and sat down beside me. It ought to have been pleasant to be together, but his situation was such that it made my heart ache. He was nearly without skin, every part of his body was exposed, and his flesh was mangled and inflamed. His young face was so drawn; the only sign of youth was his spiky hair. I had to admire his fortitude in carrying on in such circumstances.

But although he had not given up trying to continue, he was nevertheless resigned to what he considered to be his unavoidable fate.

"I'm glad to see you once more, Sir," he whispered, "for I will not live through this night. I beg of you, if you ever return home, please tell my brothers and sisters that I tried to survive, but explain to them that my suffering was endless and it was just too much for me."

Comforting him as well as I could, I assured him that he would not die that night. I told him that the nourishment we were now getting, though very little, was sufficient to keep us alive for a considerable time, and that although our skin was roasted off, we were still alive and there were no signs of our bodies surrendering.

"Look, Clark," I said, "why should these people let us die? We're worth something to them, either for ransom or for work or for sale. Why should they give us some of their precious milk if we're not to live? It doesn't make sense. They're going to keep us alive, but only just. We must maintain our spirit and hope. If we can get near a town, however long it takes, that will be our chance to be sold or to escape."

"Very well," Clark said. "I'll try, but I doubt I can last long enough."

"Think only of keeping yourself as strong as possible in mind and body for that moment," I said. "I have great hopes that we'll be taken beyond this accursed desert to some place where food will be available. And don't forget, I can converse with most of these people in Arabic. I'll keep trying to persuade them that if they take us to a large town, someone there will pay them a great ransom for every member of the crew."

Clark stared at me with such a sad look. He could not say anything to signify his agreement to my self-indulgent thoughts; but his face told me that he would accept whatever I said, however ridiculous he believed it to be.

We rested for a while as night came on and cold damp winds replaced the heat of the day. My master walked up to his tent, and I begged him to let us go inside. He seemed willing to allow this, pointing to a place where we might lie down, but the women saw him and they screamed to signify their displeasure. So we remained outside and waited for the men to milk the camels. The milking started about an hour later, and they gave us a good drink, nearly two pints each. Perhaps the extra ration was compensation for not being allowed to enter the tent.

Having had our milk, Clark and I lay down to sleep. A little later I was awoken by a hand shaking my shoulder. It was Omar, one of my master's sons. He whispered to me to awaken Clark and follow him to the tent. Omar had taken pity on us and had lain awake until the women were asleep. Then he had come out to bring us into the tent. He showed me where we might lie down;

some soft sand served as a bed, and the tent kept the cold air away for the whole of the night.

This was the first act of kindness we had come across since we left Gibraltar. But no - maybe it was the second such act. It was Omar who had given me the gun and powder horn to carry. At the time I had thought him cruel to give me such a burden; but perhaps he had had another motive, for after I was carrying a weapon, his father had stopped beating me.

When morning came, the women awoke before us. As soon as they discovered that Clark and I were in the tent, they ran over and started to kick us to make us leave. The old man was somewhat concerned, no doubt fearing damage to his property, and he told the women to let us be. They walked away, cursing and muttering as we left the tent.

We sat down under the sun and awaited events. The men went to the camels and milked them. When they had finished their breakfast, we were given what was left, which was almost a pint each. Omar told me that there would be no travel that day. He arranged for the two of us to remain in the tent, and he brought our warm camel's milk, frothy, heavy and sweet, at noon and in the evening. We were allowed to stay in our little corner, and Omar even supplied some pieces of goatskin, which would partly cover us during the night.

In the evening, Omar came over, and he appeared to show genuine concern for our condition. Clark pointed to his mouth, begging for water.

"*Amen*," said Omar. Clark and I looked at each other.

"He's a Christian," said Clark. "We're saved."

"Yes," I said, "that's why he's been so kind."

"*Amen, amen*," Omar repeated, smiling. He then went to the other side of the tent and came back with a bowl of water, which he gave to us.

"*Amen*," he said. Then he turned to me and added "*el-maa*", which I knew was the Arabic for 'water'. It did not take me long to work out that '*amen*' was the Berber word for 'water'. He was not a Christian after all. Nevertheless, Christian or not, he was compassionate and we were grateful.

Two nights and a day of rest with periodic pints of milk revived us considerably. The next afternoon, Clark was ordered to go out to the edge of the encampment to search for shrubs for the camels to eat. He brought some back, and the shrubs were given to the camels by my master's black slave, who was a stout fellow called Boirek. This man then tried to drive us out of the tent, but my master would not allow it. So Boirek had to content himself with pointing at us and making disparaging remarks. He then sneeringly addressed me as '*Rais*', which made our captors laugh. His continued mocking kept the whole family in a constant roar of laughter until midnight came and it was time to milk the camels once more.

We had our milk together, and Boirek then poked at our sore flesh with a sharp stick to make sport and to show his masters what miserable beings we were. Clark could scarcely contain himself. "It's bad enough to be a slave and to be skinned alive without having to listen to that swine! I don't need the derision of a damned slave!" he whispered fiercely.

"I'm glad you've recovered your spirits and have the energy to be angry," I said. "Let the slave laugh if it gives him pleasure. Remember, we're going to escape; he's going to be a slave for ever."

"Captain," said Clark. "If I get him alone, for ever won't be very long."

"Calm down," I said. "This man is a slave who accepts his condition and is trying to impress his masters and mistresses. He considers that we're inferior to him, just as he's inferior to them. We are indeed inferior, but not for long."

But Clark would not be reconciled to this mockery. However, he kept his temper and did nothing to cause any beatings, which is what I had feared.

We were allowed another night of rest. By the morning we were both considerably recovered, and we were able to cope with our routine of camel riding, drinking milk and sleep. From 16th to 18th September, the troop journeyed each day to the south-east for about thirty miles. There was nothing much to be seen, except for the occasional shrubs that we collected and fed to the camels. However, I noticed that the further we went, the plainer the desert became, with fewer and fewer valleys; and those that we came to were very shallow.

But now we ran out of shrubs, and as there was nothing to feed to the camels, their output of milk decreased. Our ration was reduced to half a pint a day. Who would believe that humans could exist on such a paltry allowance? But when you are used to little, slightly less is always manageable.

I guessed that we were now over two hundred miles from the sea. But where were we heading? I no longer had any confidence that the tribe knew where they were going. That lack of confidence was confirmed by the sight of the tribesmen offering up prayers to the Almighty every day, and most fervently imploring Him to send them refreshing rains. There seemed to be no purpose in our journeying, and the periods of rest were longer and longer. I was fearful that we were unlikely to find water for some time. The sustenance we received was just sufficient to keep the breath of life in us; but at least our flesh was much less inflamed than in the first days, for we had continued to lie in the tent at night and also during the day when the tents had been pitched, which was generally in the early afternoon.

On the morning of 19th September, the tribe held a long council. I could not hear what was being said, but there was certainly a great deal of arguing and shouting. My master was looked up to as a man of seniority, and when the arguing had finished, he stood up and made a short speech, which I took to be a declaration of the decision that had been made.

Everything was packed on to the camels, and we started off back in the direction from which we had come. I was relieved that we were ending our march into the desert. But the question now was whether we had any chance of getting back to the shore on our reduced milk allowance. I had been in the habit every day since I was in the desert of relieving my excessive thirst by the disagreeable expedient we had used in the boat; however, now even this resource failed for want of sufficient moisture in my body.

We had travelled for a week to the south-east, and I assumed that it would take the same time to get back to the shore. But we launched out upon the scorching track in a due westerly direction, so perhaps our return would be quicker. It would have to be if we were to survive.

Later in the day, we entered a small valley, where we found a few dwarf thorn bushes not more than two feet high. On these bushes we found some snails. Amazing; how had they got there? Most of them were dead and dry, but I got a handful that were still alive. Clark also grabbed a few. What a prize! All this time in the desert, and finally a few snails. Our masters made a fire, and the two of us roasted our snails and ate them. The tribesmen were greatly amused at our excitement and the relish with which we ate the snails; but as our allowance was now no more than a cup of milk a day, our new nourishment was very welcome.

On the twentieth we started as soon as it was light, and we drove fast all day. The sun rose higher and higher into the cloudless sky, and the bleached surface of the desert glared under its fiery beams. We had no drink other than the camels' urine, which we caught in our hands as they produced it. It was thick and salty, as the animal retains as much water as possible. Drinking it was easy; all we had to do was not think what it was. Dreadful? Yes, but to die of thirst was more dreadful.

In the course of the day, Clark and I each found another handful of snails, which we again roasted at night and ate as our feast. These snails filled our stomachs to a degree, but the other parts of our bodies were in a sorry state. Our limbs were nearly deprived of flesh, for we were continually wasting away, and what little flesh we had left was dried hard and stuck fast to our bones.

Although we had proceeded with much speed on the twentieth,

on the twenty-first we did not travel at all. On that day, the masters of Savage, Horace, Hogan and Deslisle pitched their tents near to ours. My men were all so weak, withered and sore that they could scarcely stand. I was surprised that their condition was so much worse than mine.

Hunger is a terrible thing. It had preyed on my companions to such a degree that they had sucked at their own limbs. Thankfully, it had not yet had such an effect on me. Perhaps the snails had been my salvation. But, apart from Clark, my men had not had such luck.

Some hours later, when the tribesmen were resting, I caught two of my men (whom I will not name) holding a young child. The boy was about four years of age and had strayed to the edge of the encampment, not fearing any danger. There were no enemies and no wild animals about. But a starving man is both of those things, and the child had come upon two of them. Out of sight of the tribesmen, they were about to dash the boy's brains out with a stone so that they might eat him. Luckily I chanced upon them, and I determined to rescue the child from their voracity.

"My God, what are you doing?" I said.

"We're trying to stay alive," one replied. "Do you have any better ideas, or do you want us just to lie down and die?"

"But you can't kill a child, let alone eat him," I said.

"Why not?"

I had no answer. Morals and decency and the fear of God had long since passed behind us. The men were so inflamed with hunger that it was clear they would be willing to die if only they could have one last meal of the child's flesh.

"I won't let you do it," I said. "Listen, these people are not going to let us die. You're not nearly dead yet. If you have the energy to murder, you still have some way to go. Let the boy alone. Remember, not only you, but the entire crew will be massacred instantly as soon as the murder is discovered."

Reluctantly, they let the child return to his tent, and the men slunk back to their colleagues without another word. I followed them, and we sat together once more.

Despite my sadness at their appearance, I was extremely glad to be with half my crew. If only I could have seen George amongst them; but that was asking for too much.

The men expressed the view that they could not live another day. We had all been thinking that for some time. It had not been true so far, so there was no reason why it should be true now. We had to keep going, and I told the men that there was no other choice. They must not give up and die when salvation might come at any moment.

Horace, Hogan and Dick were now called away, and were employed in attending their masters' camels in company with some of the tribesmen, who kept flogging them. I was sorry for my men, but my main concern was that one of them would fly into a rage and kill one of these cruel people. That would be likely to spell the end for all of us.

Fortunately, my master did not employ Clark or me in this way. He was a rich man amongst the others, and he owned more than sixty of the camels, and had two black slaves to tend them. It would be nice to believe that our master valued us above the black slaves, but the reality was probably that he appreciated that they were stronger than us and could do the job better and quicker. Nevertheless, his ownership of those slaves was certainly a benefit for us.

So Clark and I could rest and await our milk. Another night passed. In the mid-afternoon the next day, we saw two strangers approach our encampment on camels loaded with goods. They came right up to my master's tent, made the camels lie down and then dismounted. Without a word, they seated themselves on the ground, facing the other tents of the tribe.

What did this mean? Would the arrival of the strangers signal a turn for the better or for the worse?

CHAPTER NINE

A plan and a deal

The newcomers sat waiting for the tribesmen to return. Most of the tribesmen had gone out on their camels several hours earlier, carrying their weapons. I assumed that they were hunting for some beasts to kill or else looking for plunder, though goodness knows what they expected to find in this wilderness.

Waiting there, I watched the women as they went about their tasks. They are somewhat taller than American women, and, like the men, are remarkably straight when young. Their cheekbones are high and prominent; their lips are thin, the top lip being kept up by means of the two eye-teeth. The eyes of the young women are round, black and sparkling, very expressive and extremely beautiful. They generally have long hair, which they braid behind, and coil up to the back part of the head. Upon the forehead and temples are a number of small plaits of hair, to which are fastened a variety of shells and rings made of white stone.

Most of the women I saw had strings of black beads round their necks, and some wore bands of shells and other ornaments around their wrists and ankles. A few had necklaces of amber and coral, with coins and triangular pieces of silver prominent. As I later learned, the triangle derives from the eye of the partridge, a bird of grace and beauty and therefore associated with a good wife. The bird's sharp eye is a vigilant watcher against dangers, so the triangle is also a guardian against evil.

All the women wear dresses made of coarse camel's hair cloth, similar to their tent cloth, or a blue cotton cloth. It is sewn up on each side, and falls down to the knees. They have a fold in this, like a sack, next to the skin on their shoulders, in which they carry their infant children.

As infants are generally suckled for two years, the breasts of the middle-aged women become so extremely long and pendulous, that they have no trouble in nursing the child on their backs when walking about, by throwing their breasts over the top of their shoulders so that the child may apply its lips.

Now I looked towards the two men sitting imperiously in the sunlight, as if they were monarchs waiting to survey their army as it marched past. But all they had to review was the women coming out with a large roll of tent cloth. The strangers greeted the women as they approached, saluting them with the words '*Salam, salam alaykum; labaz?*' - 'Peace, peace be with you; how are you?' - and the salutations were returned. Then the women unrolled the cloth on the ground and went back to the tent. They soon came out again carrying some sticks, and with the sticks and the cloth they made an awning to shelter the strangers from the sun.

This done, the women went to the camels and unloaded them. They took the saddles and the bundles and other things, and carried them into the tent. The strangers had also brought three large skins that contained water, and the women hung the skins on a frame.

During the whole time that these tasks were being performed, the two men remained motionless, with their guns and scimitars on the ground by their sides. The barrels of their rifles were covered with several bands of silver, and the butts were inlaid with camel bone. Neither of the men paid any attention to me or, indeed, to anything. They just sat there, staring ahead.

The women now bowed submissively and sat down in front of

the two men. I saw the women pointing at me, obviously explaining who I was. Then they started to ask questions, but I could not hear what was being said.

Anyway, having satisfied their curiosity, the women stood up and walked over to us. The oldest woman, in whom I had discovered not one spark of sympathy or humanity, told me that Sidi Hamet and his brother had brought blankets and blue cloth to sell. She said they had come from the Sultan's dominions, and they could buy me and take me to one of the Sultan's cities if they so chose. Then, she continued, I might be reunited with my friends, and we could return to our country. We were very lucky, she claimed, that they would need to use us for barter. This all sounded very grand, but it did not seem to be the natural consequence of the strangers' arrival. Nothing in this land had been quite so simple for us.

With the women now back in the tent, I had the opportunity to approach Sidi Hamet. I walked slowly over to him and begged for water, showing him my mouth, which was extremely parched and stiff. He stared at me, showing no emotion or interest. Then, breaking his silence, he asked me if I was *El Rais*. I nodded in confirmation.

Sidi Hamet turned to his brother and told him to give me some water. His brother looked sideways at him for some moments, and then resumed his position, staring straight ahead.

So, Sidi Hamet stood up and walked to my master's tent. He took a large wooden bowl and filled it with about two pints of water from one of the skins he had brought. Coming out of the tent, he gave me the bowl saying, '*Sherub Rais*' – 'Drink Captain'. I said nothing; he must have seen the gratitude in my eyes. This man was different from the others. Perhaps his name of *Sidi*, or 'Saint', was a good omen.

I drank half the contents of the bowl. Then I thanked Sidi Hamet, and invoked the blessing of Heaven on him for his humanity. Having done so, I turned to take the rest of the water to the tent where Clark lay stretched out on his back, no more than a bundle of bones, breathing like a person in the last agonies of death.

Sidi Hamet stopped me and told me angrily that I was *El Rais* and I must drink all the water; it was not for others. I pointed to my distressed companion and implored Sidi Hamet to allow me to give Clark the rest of the water; I had had enough to drink. It seemed that the sight of Clark excited Sidi Hamet's pity and, rather grudgingly, he waved me on to give Clark the bowl.

The water was perfectly fresh, and Clark was visibly revived. It was a cordial to his despondent soul. His eyes, sunk so deep in their sockets, brightened, and he even found the energy to speak. He told me that if only he could have one more such drink, he thought that he might survive.

As Clark spoke to me, I heard the sound of the tribesmen returning. I looked out of the tent. Sidi Hamet and his brother were once more seated together in silence. The tribesmen dismounted and walked over to the new arrivals. All sat before them in a semi-circle, and I could hear them speaking animatedly, asking Sidi Hamet questions and listening earnestly to his replies.

After a time, I dared to crawl nearer and I heard Sidi Hamet saying, "... and then when he had news of my arrival, Sheikh Ali came to me. After staying with me for one moon, he invited me and Seid to go to his place, which invitations we accepted. He furnished us with two camels and some *haicks* and blue cloth. Sheikh Ali advised us to go to the desert and trade these items for ostrich feathers to sell in Essaouira. As our fortunes were low, we accepted his offer, bought his goods and his camels and promised to pay him on our return. We set off for the desert, hoping to join one of the caravans, for the desert is the greatest ostrich-hunting territory. Having passed many tribes without finding any feathers of consequence, God directed our steps to this place..."

There must have been over a hundred men present, and not one left while Sidi Hamet spoke. But now it was nightfall, and Sidi Hamet stood up to indicate the end of the audience, and his listeners drifted back to their tents for the night's sleep.

However, Clark and I could not share in such luxury. This time we were turned out into the open air, and were obliged to lie down without any shelter. But it was not a miserable night; Sidi Hamet's arrival had given me hope, even if I could not be sure that the hope would be turned to my advantage. If only he would buy us as the old woman had suggested.

First, I had to convince Sidi Hamet that there was money in it for him.

Later on the men milked the camels, and our master came over and gave each of us a pint of milk to drink. This milk tasted better than any I had yet drunk; it was sweet and warm, and it gave Clark the extra portion for which he had yearned. Such generosity. No doubt our master wished to improve our condition so that we might be more saleable to Sidi Hamet in the morning. Good; exactly what I wanted.

Clark and I slept soundly for the rest of the night. When we awoke, we crawled to our master's tent to get some shade, and just lay there waiting for events to develop.

About half an hour later, Sidi Hamet walked over and told me to follow him back to his tent. When we reached the tent, he sat down outside it and told me to sit facing him.

He began to question me about my country and how I had come to be a slave in the desert. I explained to him that I was an Englishman and that my vessel and crew were from the same nation. He said that he had heard of my country and that he knew that Englishmen had visited some of the coastal towns he had passed through on his travels.

Then I recounted as well as I could the manner of our shipwreck and our desperate times once we had reached the shore. I also said that we had been reduced to the lowest depth of misery, and that I had a wife and children in my own country besides Horace, whom I described as my oldest child. I told Sidi Hamet everything that had happened up to that day, mingling the story with sighs and all the other signs of despair that my words naturally produced.

Sidi Hamet seemed to be an intelligent and feeling man. He

actually looked tearful as he listened to my tale, despite the fact that these people regarded weeping as a womanish weakness. He appeared to be ashamed of his own feelings, saying that men who had beards ought not to shed tears, and he walked away, wiping his eyes.

I returned to join Clark outside our master's tent. To my surprise, Clark did not question me about my meeting with Sidi Hamet. He merely greeted me and then we lay together on the ground, each thinking his own thoughts.

My thoughts related entirely to Sidi Hamet. I had aroused his sympathy, and I felt that I must use this success as a stepping-stone. Soon I would have to make my next move.

A little later, I saw Sidi Hamet outside his tent. I went over to him. He was surprised to see me; a slave comes when he is summoned, not when he wishes to have a discussion. Never mind, this was my opportunity; I could feel that the moment had arrived.

"You should buy us," I said. "It will bring you much money."

"What do you mean? What are you talking about?" Sidi Hamet responded.

"I will tell you," I replied. "Before we were wrecked, we were prosperous traders. We are known to all the European merchants in your country. Buy us and take us to any of the great cities of Morocco and one of my friends there will pay you a good sum of money to redeem us. You will be a rich man with more money than you can ever earn by selling blankets and the feathers of the camel bird" - which is what they call the ostrich.

Sidi Hamet studied me carefully. He stroked his beard slowly and then looked from side to side. "No," he said. "I will not take you to one of the great cities, but I will take you to Essaouira. It is a large town on the coast. It is a seaport and there must be some English there."

"Yes," I said. "Essaouira. I have been there and I have a friend there." I hoped that my instant response was convincing. In all truth, until Sidi Hamet mentioned that town to the tribesmen, I had never heard of Essaouira, and there was no chance that anyone in that town had ever heard of me. "My friend there will pay you well," I continued for good measure.

"What is well?" Sidi Hamet challenged me. "How much will I be paid for you?"

"Many dollars," I said, forgetting that I was meant to be English. But Sidi Hamet did not notice my mistake.

"Dollars, pah!" he said. "*Benduqis.* How many gold *benduqis*?"

I had no idea whether a *benduqi* was more or less than a dollar; but if they were gold, they must be quite valuable. "Five *benduqis*," I said. "And five *benduqis* for each of my men."

Sidi Hamet's face contorted with the effort of calculation. After a few moments the contortion dissolved into satisfaction. "Very well," he said. "But do you have money in Essaouira, or must I wait until you get money from your country?"

I replied that my friend in Essaouira would give him the money as soon as we were brought there.

"You are deceiving me," he said. "You know no one in Essaouira."

"Of course I do," I replied. "I am a frequent visitor to this land. That is why my ship was near the coast. I am known in all the cities and seaports." I then continued with the most solemn protestations of my sincerity, and step by step it worked.

"I will buy you then," he responded at last. "But if you deceive me, I will cut your throat." He raised his right hand and moved his index finger from his left ear to his right ear via his neck, to show me exactly what would happen.

Having agreed to the arrangement, I begged him to buy my son, Horace, as well; but Sidi Hamet would not hear a word about Horace or any of my companions. He told me that he could not take so many men over such a long distance.

"But you must at least take my son."

"No!" he barked. "I will buy you and that is it. Say nothing to your master, nor to my brother, nor to any of your countrymen."

With that he went into the tent, and I returned to sit with Clark. I saw Savage and Hogan several yards away, and beckoned them to join us.

A few minutes later, Sidi Hamet walked past. He looked at my three companions, and was clearly shocked at the sight. Hogan asked me who this man was, and I told him that Sidi Hamet had promised he would buy me, and that I had great hopes that he would also buy the three of them and then take us to one of the towns on the coast. But my men feared that they would be left behind. I told them not to worry, but I did not argue the point, as I knew this was Sidi Hamet's intention.

That night my mind was troubled. Sidi Hamet was going to buy me and take me on the road to freedom, but he had no intention of taking any of my crew. How could I, their leader, abandon them to the desert and accept salvation for myself? On the other hand, what good could I do by remaining here? At least if I was once more free, I might be able to organise a search party to recover my men. But no doubt they would be dead by then; or would they? Whatever I did would be wrong. Anyway, I had aroused Sidi Hamet's hopes of wealth; it would not be a good idea to let him down. I decided not to worry about what I should do, because it was more than likely that everything would be decided for me.

On the twenty-fourth, we journeyed to the north-west all day, along with Sidi Hamet and his brother. Near nightfall we stopped and the women set about erecting the tents. The women had the entire control of the tents. They made the cloth for them, put them together, and they pitched, struck and repaired them.

My mistress arranged for a tent to be set up near us for Sidi Hamet and his brother. This gave me the opportunity to approach him once more and beg him to buy my companions. I explained that this was a chance he might never find again; he owed it to himself to buy all of us. He said nothing, he just turned and walked away. Well, at least I had given him something to think about.

When I awoke the next morning, I saw my master and Sidi Hamet sitting outside my master's tent arguing with one another, while Omar sat and listened. I could not hear what they were saying. Were they arguing about me, would my master agree to sell, could they agree terms? These thoughts raced around my mind. Then I saw them gesticulating wildly, pointing at blankets and ostrich feathers that Sidi Hamet had obviously brought for the purpose of payment. What a relief; it was down to price.

Finally, I had the joy of seeing Sidi Hamet pay the agreed amount. Two blankets or coarse *haicks*, one blue covering and a bundle of ostrich feathers. Quite a profit for my master - or rather, my ex-master. He looked very pleased.

Sidi Hamet waved to me to go to his tent. I went, having told Clark not to worry; this was just the start. He nodded, but I could see that he had no expectations at all.

A little later in the day, Horace's master came to Sidi Hamet's tent to negotiate some business, and he brought Horace with him. As soon as I saw Horace approaching, I went forward to meet him. I embraced him with tears and held him close to my chest, saying, "My son, my son", which I repeated in Arabic. Fortunately, Horace was so debilitated that he showed no surprise at his summary adoption. I was relieved, as I hoped that this show of love would convince Sidi Hamet that Horace was indeed my child.

When Horace left with his master, I gave him some of the snails that I had found earlier that morning. Probably this weighed more heavily with Sidi Hamet as a sign of parenthood, for he came up to me and said that he had tried to buy my son, but had failed. My heart sank. I had to take at least one of my men with me; it was impossible to leave on my own.

Now Sidi Hamet informed me that we would set out for Essaouira in two days' time. So I had two days to arrange the purchase of some of my crew. But how? My first step was to tell Sidi Hamet that I did not wish to go with him. He should exchange me for Horace and take him in my place; my friend in Essaouira would give him the same amount of money as he would have given for me.

"I cannot return to my wife and tell her that I have left her son behind as a slave. It will bring great shame on me and dishonour on my family."

"You will have him," Sidi Hamet replied. Well, I thought, not so bad. I have a promise for one of my men after only a few minutes of my two days. Now I felt that I was entitled to rest for a while before I took my next step. I needed to await an opportunity to encourage another purchase.

As I was resting, I noticed quite a commotion starting. Men of all ages were walking towards the area behind Sidi Hamet's tent. As each man arrived, he sat down. This process continued for some time, until everyone was seated in a large circle. I realised that the men of the tribe were once more in council. A debate started, with many of the tribesmen speaking. They seemed to be talking about us, and within minutes the conversation had grown animated. The temperature rose, and I could see that the use of fists had become necessary to support some of the men's views.

The meeting eventually broke up, and Sidi Hamet came over and told me that Horace had been purchased. The tribe had forced his master to sell Horace to Sidi Hamet, though at a great price. Good, so we were two.

I now redoubled my entreaties to Sidi Hamet to buy Savage and Clark, promising that I would give him a large sum of money if we were all returned to our nation. I would send money from England on top of what my friend in Essaouira gave him. But Sidi Hamet told me that it would be impossible to take more men. He would have to lead us through country where bands of robbers operated, and four slaves would be too much of a temptation.

So be it - for the time being anyway. I would have to hold back on my mission for a while. What else? Actually, my mind had been so occupied in thoughts of escape from slavery that I had almost forgotten my sufferings. But this was no time for misery. I must plot escape for more of us, and then I must execute my plan.

On the morning of the twenty-sixth, when Sidi Hamet brought me some milk, I renewed my entreaties for him to purchase more of my men. I asked him if he had seen any of them in the encampment, and he told me that apart from Horace and me, he had seen five others. He added that he was sure that the seven of us were all that remained here.

I described each of my men as well as I could, making allowance for the effects of our starvation and ill-treatment.

"A very tall man," I said. "He has light brown hair and a curved nose." It would have been pointless to mention that George was slim, for all of us were now extremely slim. Sidi Hamet shook his head.

"No, no such man." So much for George Williams. He was beyond my help, if indeed he was still alive.

"A man of medium height, with thinning hair and sunken eyes."

"Yes," said Sidi Hamet. "I think I know him." Good, Savage was still here.

"One with dark curly hair and staring eyes."

"I know of such a man," he replied. "But not with staring eyes." To me that meant Burns, but no Porter.

"What about Robbins; a man with blond hair and small eyes?"

"Yes," he said. So Robbins was somewhere near.

"The man with spiky, reddish hair; quite short, whom you saw when you first met me?"

"Yes." James Clark still had hope.

"Who is the other?" I asked.

"A tall man with hair tied together behind his neck." So Hogan had drawn the last long straw and Barrett had lost.

"What about a tall black man?" I asked.

"There are many black slaves here," said Sidi Hamet, "but your man is not one of them. I saw your man, but I also saw him sold. He has been taken away." Poor Dick. Poor all of them. None of them deserved this.

But now I must fight for the five to join Horace and me. The lost four would have to rely on my prayers.

I started with Clark, for he was the nearest. But Sidi Hamet told me that Clark had no more than a few days to live, so it made no sense to buy him.

"No," I said, "it makes no difference. I will pay you whether he lives or dies." Then I had a thought. "I will pay you more for each extra man. For the first, five *benduqis*; for the second, six *benduqis*; for the third, seven, and so on."

Now Sidi Hamet really had something to think about. He moved his jaw around as if chewing something, and then he smiled broadly.

"We shall see, we shall see," he said, and he walked away.

And indeed, we did see. Later on in the day, Sidi Hamet came to me and announced that he had bought Clark and had made an offer for Hogan. Good; real progress. Now we were three, with one possibility and three to deal with the next day.

"I shall buy and kill a camel," Sidi Hamet continued. "It will give us provisions for our journey. You will help."

Good news following good news. I awaited the killing of the camel with the greatest impatience, hoping that we would have a meal of it before we left.

Clark's purchase having been completed, he now joined me outside Sidi Hamet's tent, and I told him that we might soon eat some meat. The thought of food made the hours pass slowly.

It was after midnight when Sidi Hamet came and told us to follow him to a little gully about five hundred yards from the encampment. We waited there for a short time, and then his brother arrived, leading a large, slow-moving camel. Sidi Hamet told me that he had bought the camel for one blanket - it had been cheap because it was old and could no longer keep up with the drove.

Clark and I watched as they made the camel lie down. Then they brought a large copper kettle. Sidi Hamet took out his knife and cut a vein on the right side of the camel's neck, close to its breast. His brother held the kettle near to the beast, and the blood streamed out, quickly filling it.

Now they made a fire. They dug a hole in the ground and filled it with dry weed that served as tinder. They struck the fire with a flint and a piece of metal, and when the weed was aflame, they added camel dung and a few sticks as fuel. The camel's dung is always dry and can be used as fuel immediately, because the camel is jealous of its liquid and parts with the minimum amount of moisture, just as it declines to pant and perspire, and gives out little water with its urine. Next they added some stones to the fire, then they put the kettle over the flame and slowly stirred the liquid with a stick as it heated, until it became very thick. Finally, they took the heated stones from the fire and put them inside the kettle to keep the contents warm.

Taking the kettle, they passed it to me, telling me to eat the foul-looking stew. I did not hesitate for a second, and I shared this devil's brew with Clark. Our appetites were voracious, and we soon filled our stomachs. We did not need so-called civilised food; we did not need tasty food. We just needed food.

Although it was now very late, and we had hidden ourselves in the gully, many of our hungry neighbours discovered the feast, and in dribs and drabs these uninvited guests arrived. They crept down into the gully and began to assist in the dressing and eating of the animal. Several of them insisted on having some of the blood, and snatched the kettle to drink what was left, despite our masters doing everything they could to prevent them, short of drawing their swords.

These people then helped in stripping the hide off the creature. As soon as this was completed, the entrails were rolled out and put into the kettle together with the beast's liver. But now I could see that there was a problem; there was no water in which to boil this offal. Then a young man pushed his way forward and knelt down beside the carcass, thrust a knife deep into the camel's paunch and slit it open in one brutal movement. He then poured some of the filthy water out of the animal and into a bowl. Next, he took the bowl to the kettle and emptied the contents on to the entrails. Now they could boil the meat over the fire.

During this operation, half a dozen scoundrels were at work on the camel, pretending to cut it up for my masters. Every now and then they turned to face Sidi Hamet and smiled and nodded, as if they were doing him a service. All the while, they only kept repeating '*barakalautik*', which means both 'please' and 'thank you'. Of course, they were mainly occupied in stealing pieces of meat for themselves, and by the time they had finished, more than half of the camel's meat, bones and skin had disappeared.

Our masters were as hungry as any of the tribesmen; yet though they had bought the camel, they had to fight for a share of the intestines. But in the end they had a decent meal, and they gave us some scraps when they had finished eating. The meat was tough, rather like beef, but it was very nourishing.

Although the boiled blood that we had eaten was perfectly fresh, it made us very thirsty. There was little we could do about that until a young boy showed us how to deal with the problem. As soon as daylight came, this child ran down into the gully and came right up to the camel's paunch. He put his head straight into it and began to drink the contents. My master saw this and he also saw that my mouth was very dry. He told me to pull the boy away and drink the liquid myself. I did not need to be told twice. This was not a time for discussion; I took hold of the boy's arm and threw him to the side. The liquid was very thick, but although its taste was strong, it was not at all salty, and it allayed my thirst. When I had had my fill, I called Clark over, and he took his turn.

What we had had to drink in recent days was the most disgusting and abominable collection of liquids; but now we were not thirsty for the first time since we had reached the shore, and we were grateful for this improvement in our condition and our luck. Although it was already daylight, now we could sleep.

In the morning we cut off the little flesh that remained on the carcass of the camel. We laid the pieces out to dry and roasted the bones on the fire for our masters. When the bones were ready, Sidi Hamet and his brother cracked them between stones and then sucked out the marrow and the juices.

We took what remained of the food and returned to Sidi Hamet's tent. He told the two of us to stay inside, as he had business to attend to elsewhere in the camp. Sidi Hamet left, and returned at about noon with Horace. What a sad sight he was.

His blond curly hair was matted with sweat and dirt, and each of his ribs stuck out from his chest. He was very hungry and thirsty; he told me that he had not eaten for three days. Sidi Hamet smiled broadly. "This is your son, *Rais*," he said. "I have bought him for you."

Sidi Hamet was obviously very proud of what he had achieved for me. He gave Horace some of the camel's entrails and meat that he had saved for him, as well as a drink of the camel's thick water. I was already well aware that hunger and thirst give flavour to anything and everything.

Now the three of us lay down to rest. About an hour later, Sidi Hamet came to me with Burns. He asked me to confirm that this was one of my men. I told him that he was.

"His master wants to sell him, but he is weak and useless and there is no reason for me to buy him, even for the price of one *haick*," said Sidi Hamet, showing me an old blanket.

"Buy him," I said. "Everyone is weak and useless if he is not fed. This is one of the strongest of my men. Just feed him and you will see his worth." Without another word, Sidi Hamet went away and bought Burns for the lousy blanket.

Sidi Hamet brought Burns back and pushed him down to the ground in disgust, as if he had been forced to buy a piece of rubbish. Burns was in a pitiful state, yet overjoyed to see me again and to discover that he now had a hope of regaining his freedom, or at least of having something to eat and drink. He was in luck. Food and drink were given to him immediately. It gave me great pleasure to see three of my men fed. Clark, Horace and Burns were very grateful. But I was aware that I had only saved them for the time being. Who knew what lay in store for us?

My concern was not just fatalistic. I was worried about the availability of food on our journey to Essaouira, for during the day many members of the tribe had come to visit us, and as a result of their constant begging and thieving, our stock of camel meat was severely reduced.

However, my spirits were lifted when my master came over to me a little later and told me that he had bought another of my men.

"Who is it?" I asked. "What does he look like?"

"He is a tall man with dark eyes; the one with long hair, who ties it behind his neck," said Sidi Hamet.

So, it was Hogan. He was still alive, and he now had a chance of rescue with us. Marvellous. I was making progress almost every hour. Perhaps I could rescue all my men.

"Your man will come soon," said Sidi Hamet.

Yes, I thought, Hogan deserves to survive. But then all of them deserved to survive, not least Antonio, and he was already dead.

Within a few minutes, Hogan came with his master, who was one of my former owners. But Hamet had not come to keep his bargain, he had come to improve it, and he demanded that the price be increased by an extra blanket. Sidi Hamet rejected the proposal with indignation; anyway, he had no more blankets left.

I begged very hard for Hogan, but it was hopeless. His master threw back the one blanket he had already been given and drove Hogan away from us, laying his stick repeatedly on Hogan's back. My heart bled when I saw the blows fall on his emaciated frame, but I could do nothing for him.

My God, it was awful to be so helpless. To see one of your compatriots beaten and to have to just sit and watch. No justice; no justice at all. I turned round and hid my face so as not to witness his further tortures.

But I knew that my job was to look after those who had hope, even if it was only me. Care for the lucky few and just pray for the others. What an evil arrangement; yet I must accept it.

We spent the rest of the day preparing for our departure. Our master made me a pair of sandals with two layers of the camel's skin. Horace was similarly supplied. Clark and Burns had to make do with a single layer, but were well pleased with this kindness. Were we at last to be treated as human beings, or was

135

this just a veneer of friendliness?

Sidi Hamet then gave me a small knife, which he put in a leather wallet and hung around my neck. I took this as a sign of his confidence in me and also recognition of my position. However, a little knife and makeshift sandals did not exactly give my pathetic body the aura of high rank.

Having supplied me with a uniform, Sidi Hamet now gave me details of my authority. I was told that I was in charge of the goods and camels and slaves. Quite a position of trust, for this was just about everything they possessed. Naturally, this high command meant that I was responsible for the related tasks. My men were so weary that even the hope of liberty could not prompt them to the least exertion. As a result, my new rank meant that I had to do all the work.

Early in the evening, Sidi Hamet came over and told me that he had used the blanket that had been returned by Hogan's master to make another purchase, and the one with the sunken eyes would soon be joining us. I was pleased that Savage was coming at this late stage, as he had watched and waited as the opportunity for escape had come to me and not to him. But Sidi Hamet had yet more news for me.

"In the morning we will start out on our journey to Essaouira. With the blessing of God, you will soon return to your country and your family."

Of course, such a blessing would bring not only our liberty, but also the reward of a considerable amount of money for Sidi Hamet, so his sincerity in hoping for the Almighty's assistance was beyond doubt. That was good, for I needed him to have a financial motive that would make him eager for our redemption.

He then told me, with signs of great pain, how much he had paid for each of us and that the total meant he had expended all his property; adding that if I was not telling him the truth, he was a ruined man. Sidi Hamet also told me that his brother was a bad man and had tried to prevent him from buying us.

"But he has now agreed," said Sidi Hamet, "for I have promised him a share of the money. You must repeat your promise in front of me and my brother."

"I made the promise. There is no problem in repeating it," I said as firmly as possible.

"Not just the money," he replied, "also that you agree that your throat will be cut if your words are not true." Although I had faced death every day for some time now, this further prospect of dying made me feel uneasy. But what matter if I agreed or not? They would kill me anyway if they did not get their money. So I made the promise and confirmed my agreement.

Later in the evening, Savage was brought to us. He was so pleased, because he had known we would soon be leaving, and had resigned himself to being left behind. Savage was very thankful, even more so when Sidi Hamet brought us some of the camel's intestines to eat.

But Savage's gratitude soon gave way to pessimism. After satisfying his hunger in some measure, he began to express his doubts as to where we would be taken, declaring that he did not believe a word these wretches said. I explained to him the deal I had made with Sidi Hamet, but Savage's response was that I had offered too much and nobody would advance the money to us in Essaouira - looking at us, who would believe that we could repay them? I must confess that for a moment I thought it would be preferable if Sidi Hamet sold Savage back to his old master; but in our circumstances I had to make allowances for scepticism.

"My deal is going to get us away from the people who enslaved and starved us. That's an advantage, isn't it? Let's just get on the road to a town. Then we can worry about what happens next."

"Those two men are just wandering about the desert," answered Savage. "They couldn't lead us to a town if they wanted to."

"All these nomad travellers and traders know their way about the Sahara. You can come with us and find out, or if you want, I'll try to arrange for you to be sold and you can stay here. Make your own choice." With that I walked several yards away from my men and lay down to sleep.

Lying there in the open air, I could reassess our position. We were now five together and six missing; the figures had shifted to our advantage. If only we could collect a few more. I realised that my joy at leaving the next day meant that I had accepted the abandonment of the other six. If we stayed longer, I might be able to negotiate the purchase of more of them. But, on the other hand, any delay might lead to a change in Sidi Hamet's intentions. These thoughts troubled my mind for hours. In the end, I knew that we must leave as soon as our masters would allow. It was too great a risk to stay.

At daylight on the twenty-eighth, soon after sunrise, Archibald Robbins arrived with his master. I asked Robbins what had happened to him after we were separated.

"I was taken by a man called Ganus, who speaks a little Spanish as I do," he said. "We travelled on camels together with Williams and Barrett and their master. But when we were resting the next night, Williams and Barrett were stolen."

"Have you been given food and water?" I asked.

"I have," replied Robbins, "but not much." However, he had managed to keep his piece of salted pork, and had been allowed to cook it and eat it, because these people would not eat meat from a pig. "They seem to live mainly on camel's milk, which they drink at midnight," said Robbins.

"It's the same with us," I replied.

"They milk the animals at midnight because that's when the milk is coolest," explained Robbins. "My master told me that during the day the milk is heated because the camels raise the temperature of their bodies and that way they don't sweat and lose liquid. But by midnight, the camels and their milk are cool again."

"Have you seen any of the others?"

"Yes," said Robbins, "I saw Porter. He went with his master and Ganus to the Commerce. They brought back some rotting rice, ropes, part of a sail and even our flag. Then we travelled inland with many other tribesmen. The next day I saw Williams and Barrett again. Their master had recovered them from the thieves. They're both in a very sad state."

"Anyone else?" I asked in hope.

"Only Aaron," replied Robbins, "but I see that he's now with you. How are all of you? I hear you've been given camel meat to eat. That's why we came here. My master saw the smoke of your fire and said he would get some of the food and that I would see the other *kellup en-sahrau*. That's what they call us, 'the Christian dogs'."

I explained to Robbins my deal with Sidi Hamet, and promised that I would try to have him purchased as well. But despite all my efforts, Sidi Hamet said that he could not buy Robbins, and he went away to speak to Robbins' master. I told Robbins that he must try to do a similar deal for himself and the others, either with his own master or the master of one of the other men. But I was completely forgetting the problem Robbins would have with communication if they spoke no Spanish.

Horace gave Robbins a piece of the camel meat that he had saved. Then the five of us said farewell to Robbins as he left. Our hearts were heavy at the thought of leaving the other six behind. I explained to my men that I had done all I could, but we must accept that the five of us would be leaving, and without our shipmates.

Although we were filled with sadness and guilt at the thought of deserting them, it was by no means certain that our path would be a better one than that followed by those we were leaving behind.

CHAPTER TEN

Departure and a miracle

We were eager to set out, but then I looked at that desiccated furnace. Was this really the way to freedom? No matter; my masters were preparing to leave and so must I. Sidi Hamet and Seid, his brother, had two fully-grown camels, as well as a young one. Sidi Hamet placed Savage, Burns and Horace on one of the large camels and then placed Clark and me on another. A young man named Abdallah, who had been Savage's master at one stage, came to join us on his camel. Seid climbed up behind Abdallah, and Sidi Hamet rode the young animal to break it in. With one shout of Berber farewell, '*Akayoon arbey*', from Sidi Hamet, we set off at a full trot.

We soon slowed down to the camels' leisurely walk, and continued for about three hours. But although the camels appeared to amble slowly, their legs were so long that they covered the ground deceptively quickly. What a strange animal. Quite a different order of leg movements compared with other animals: one side moving forward at a time - right back leg forward, right front leg forward, then the left back and then left front. The order never altered, and we travelled without rest until we stopped in a small valley to adjust our saddles. Here Sidi Hamet pulled a shirt from one of his bags and gave it to me, declaring that he had stolen it and had tried to get another for Horace, but had failed.

"Put it on," he said, "your poor back needs a covering." I kissed his hand in gratitude and thanked him for his mercy. Clark, who was still wearing the tatters of his shirt, was given a piece of cloth that partly covered him, Burns a sort of old jacket, and Horace and Savage were handed large pieces of goatskin. Now partly clothed, we moved off from the valley and travelled east until the last rays of the desert sun slipped over the horizon.

We stopped and dismounted near some thorn bushes. Our masters kindled a fire and gave us a few morsels of camel meat, which we roasted and ate. The goatskins still contained about eight pints of the liquid from the dead camel's paunch, and this was divided amongst the eight of us. Each quickly drank his portion.

Apart from their riders, the camels were not too heavily loaded, so we must have been proceeding at about seven or eight miles to the hour, and had probably advanced over sixty miles into the desert. Sidi Hamet had told me that Essaouira was on the coast, so I was concerned that we were heading further inland. I walked over and sat down beside him.

"This is not the way to Essaouira," I said. "Where exactly are we going?"

"I wish to join one of the caravans on its way back from the trading post at Timbuktu," he replied. "Travelling with them will be safer and will give me the opportunity to buy and sell goods."

Hopefully we were not going to be part of that trade; but for the moment I would say no more. We all found shelter under the thorn bushes and had a good night's sleep.

When I woke up early the next morning, my mind was occupied with the thought that perhaps we were being taken to be sold somewhere deep in the desert. I would have to keep my eyes and ears open. There were five of us and three of them. If danger lay ahead and we wanted to escape, we would have to take up the challenge while the numbers were favourable. Once we had joined the caravan and there were more of them, our inferior numbers would make escape impossible. From now on Sidi Hamet was not only our rescuer, he was also our main threat, and I would have to view him as both at all times.

Before daylight we were already on our camels, and although the sun was not yet up, there was a glorious radiance across the vast concave of the sky. The camels growled, struggled and showed their teeth as they were forced to kneel and receive their loads. Then they resumed their placid expressions, which never varied through the long and weary day.

We were still advancing eastwards towards the centre of the continent, rather than towards the sea, which must be our route to safety. I would have loved to believe that what Sidi Hamet had said was true - that we were heading towards a caravan that would lead us to Essaouira. Maybe it was true - but only maybe.

Anyway, on we must go, and on we went. The same smooth hard surface continued, broken only occasionally by groups of rocks forming small ledges in this bleak furnace. Near one of the rock groupings we stopped to rest, and also to let our camels rest, though these animals never seem to weary or tire, they just move on forever at the pace demanded by their riders.

We eased our thirst by drinking some of the camel's urine, which we caught in our hands. It was less salty than our own, for ours, which was now a dark colour, was a product of drinking urine itself and contained the salt that our bodies had expelled once before. Our masters did the same and told me not to fear, claiming that it was good for our stomachs. I vowed that if I ever returned home, I would not tell anyone of our drinking habits; people would be disgusted and would not understand. They would not point me out as the survivor of the desert; rather I would be the man who drank urine. Children would mock and adults would sneer. But would they do otherwise?

Now we were mounted and once more on our way. The camels took long steps and their motions were very heavy. As a result, our legs, unsupported by stirrups or anything else, flew backwards and forwards at every step of the animal, chafing against the beast's hard ribs.

Each day we found new ways to suffer pain. Every part of the body had its turn - and still the sun would not go down. Finally it did, but our masters had not yet found a place to stop for the night. Sidi Hamet explained that they wanted to carry on until we reached a place where there were some shrubs on which the camels could feed. Well, I suppose it made sense.

We stopped at long last, hours after darkness had arrived, in a very small valley and yes, there were some shrubs. I lay down with my men, all of us completely worn out. My companions said nothing; we had nothing to say to each other.

Our masters kindled a fire and gave us about a pound of roasted meat to share, which we greedily devoured. Next we allayed our thirst in the new manner we had learned. No one showed the least reluctance; this was now our way of life - our way of staying alive.

We had started before daylight and had stopped for only about fifteen minutes in the course of the whole day. So, trotting for over fourteen hours at say seven miles to the hour, we must have travelled over ninety miles. We were certainly making progress, but soon we would need to find food and water if we were to continue.

In our mangled state, we lay down to sleep on the bare ground, without the slightest shelter from the wind that blew violently from the north throughout the night. Sidi Hamet and his two companions thought nothing of this, nor did they even appear to be fatigued. How did they do it? But if they had been working day and night on board ship in mid-Atlantic, it would have wearied them, yet it would have been mere routine for us. How I longed to be back at sea; master of my vessel, facing danger, but loving it.

When I awoke in the morning, I asked Sidi Hamet to look at the condition of my companions. We were all so worn out, our skin hard and tight, like skeletons covered with parchment. He seemed genuinely concerned, and told me not to worry; we would come to water soon and be able to drink as much as we wanted. Sidi Hamet explained that this was why we were travelling so fast and far every day. After we had reached the spring of fresh water, we would no longer need to ride at such speed. I had heard of such miracles - oases in the middle of the desert; but Sidi Hamet said it would not be an oasis, yet it would be a miracle nonetheless.

Continuing on our journey at a long trot, we discovered in mid-morning what seemed to be high land. But as we approached, it looked more like the far bank of what was once a river or an arm of the sea.

An hour later, we came to the edge of the bank nearer to us. I looked down and saw the valley below. We were standing on the top of a massive cliff that continued as far as the eye could see to the left and to the right. The valley was about five hundred feet below us, and in the distance was the cliff on the other side. What a fearful sight. Could it really have been part of an inlet of the sea from which the waters had retreated long ago, or had the land parted as the result of an earthquake?

I looked down; the cliff was perpendicular and I could see no way to descend. Sidi Hamet then ushered us along the ledge, and we travelled on for an hour until we reached a place where the cliff had collapsed into the valley, leaving a rocky staircase all the way down.

We dismounted and slowly edged our way down with the camels. It was a difficult and wearisome route, but not dangerous; it was only necessary to encourage the camels step by step. When we reached the bottom, Seid and Abdallah went forward to search for the fresh water that Sidi Hamet had told me was not far away. The rest of us followed slowly with the camels.

It was so hot, the sun's rays blazing into the valley, unrelieved by any breeze, not even the slightest movement of the air. The rays seemed to be targeting each one of us, pushing against us, making every step a battle against this powerful enemy that resisted our advance. What an adversary; never beaten, never relenting -

just hiding every night, only to attack again completely rejuvenated the next morning.

As we walked on, Sidi Hamet came alongside and started to ask me many questions. He asked about my country, about my family and whether I had any property at home. He also wanted to know if I had really been to Essaouira and if I was telling the truth when I said I had a friend there who would pay money for us. Sidi Hamet said that he and his brother had parted with all their property in order to purchase us, and I should be truthful with him, for he was my friend.

"God will deal with you as you deal with me," he said.

Of course I persisted in asserting that I had a friend in Essaouira who would advance whatever sum of money I needed.

"Will your friend really pay for Clark and Burns?" he asked. "They are good for nothing."

The two of them certainly did look worse than the rest of us. I told Sidi Hamet that they were my countrymen, my brothers, and he could depend on me to ransom them if he would take us to the Sultan.

"No," he replied, "the Sultan will not pay for you, but I will take you to Essaouira to your friend. What is his name?"

"Consul," I replied. Goodness, I had not been prepared for that, but as the question went into my ear, the answer came out of my mouth without my brain coming into use. Sidi Hamet was very pleased to hear me provide the name so readily - but not half as pleased as I was.

He was so encouraged that he told me that I must give him ten *benduqis* for myself, ten for Horace and seven for each of the others. He also said that I must pay him the cost of all our provisions on the journey. As that had amounted so far to part of a dead camel - cost one blanket, and occasional camel's urine - cost unknown, I agreed to the extra payment.

Obviously I agreed too readily to the new bargain, for now he said, "You must swear to God that you will give me those amounts and a double-barrelled gun. Then I will take you all to Essaouira.

Otherwise I will take you that way," he continued, pointing to the south-east, "and sell you for as much as I can get. But if I take you to Essaouira and you do not keep to our bargain, then I will cut your throat and sell your companions."

It was rather easy for me to select the option I preferred. Nevertheless I was screaming at him inside my head: 'Why don't you just ask me for all the money in the world here and now, without all these daily increases? I will gladly swear to pay it to you'.

But calm prevailed. Anyway, he probably needed his expectations to be raised from time to time. If this was the way to get to Essaouira, then I must comply. I assured him that I had told the truth, and I called on God to witness the sincerity of my intentions. Although I was perfectly prepared to be dishonest and worse to get to Essaouira, I was not being dishonest. I did not in the least doubt that if only I could get to that town, then somehow I would find an American or European who would pay the reward demanded by Sidi Hamet.

"You shall go to Essaouira, if God pleases," he said.

Then he astonished me by reaching into a bag hanging from his camel and pulling out a piece of cloth, which he unfolded to reveal the broken pieces of my watch and a candlestick. He told me that before he had met me, he had bought those items from a man who had come across the wreck of my ship. The candlestick had belonged to Williams. Where was he now? Sidi Hamet wanted to know what he could get for these trinkets in Essaouira. I suggested ludicrous prices; he was well pleased and put the articles away.

We kept on walking along the valley, but now Sidi Hamet had run out of questions, so he just watched me as we proceeded. It felt as though his eyes would pierce my very soul in order to ascertain whether or not I was deceiving him. At length, he seemed to be satisfied that I was sincere, and we continued in silence.

Now I could see Seid and Abdallah in the distance clambering amongst the rocks at the base of the cliff. This was obviously where the water was meant to be. Sidi Hamet called out to them, asking whether they had found any water, but they had not. So he told us to stay with the camels, and he ran ahead to help Seid in the search, while Abdallah came back to wait with us. After about an hour, Sidi Hamet shouted to me to join him. I went towards him and clambered up over the fragments of rock that had fallen from above. I reached Sidi Hamet, but could see no sign of water. He saw the despair on my face.

"Look," he said, pointing through a fissure in the rock. I pressed my face against it and saw water flowing, but there seemed to be no way to reach it. Sidi Hamet then took me about thirty yards along the rockface where there was a much wider crack, wide enough for a man to get through.

"Go, it is sweet," he said, a broad smile spreading across his face. I squeezed through and reached the flowing water. He was right; it was sweet. I drank until I could drink no more. Then I went out into the open and shouted to my men to come and join me. They scrambled up and quickly sated their thirst.

When the eight of us had drunk again, we lay down. Then Seid and Abdallah went to get the camels, bringing them as near as possible. We were ordered to fill a large bowl and the goatskins with water and take them down to the camels so that they too might be replenished.

My men and I did this time and again. The capacity of the animals was amazing. For sure, the largest camel drank at least thirty gallons. I suppose that explains how they can go half a week without water and nearly two weeks without food. These creatures were everything to their owner: transport, money, food and drink. No wonder the Arabs call them 'ata Allah' – 'God's gift'.

After the camels had been watered, we filled the goatskins again and tied them to the sides of the beasts. Then we mounted the camels and continued along the valley.

It was clear to me that our masters were looking for a place where we might once more climb to the surface. Why did they have to be so adventurous? Why not go back to the place where we had descended? But an hour later, another area where the cliff had collapsed was presented to us. We continued on the camels until we were about two hundred feet from the top. Then we dismounted and slowly coaxed and pulled the reluctant animals upwards, and at last we were back on the surface of the desert.

Off we went again; we travelled about eight miles to the northwest and then, having eaten the remainder of the camel meat, we stopped for the night.

Although we were no longer thirsty, it was impossible to shake off the infectious melancholy inspired by this desolate place. As I lay down to sleep, I was depressed by the thought that despite something different happening each day, basically we were just travelling over the desert, with more desert to come the following day. I assumed that tomorrow would be the same; perhaps hunger, perhaps thirst, perhaps food, perhaps water.

But I was wrong - the next day there would be more humans.

CHAPTER ELEVEN

Across the desert

To awaken from a dream is always a shock; such a change and re-adjustment. Relief after a bad dream that things are not so bad, dejection after a good dream that things are not so good.

I had been dreaming of just an ordinary day back home, a sunny day in late Spring - the weather is always good in good dreams. The children playing, my wife running to me. Dancing in the sunlight. In my dream, it was everything to me, as it should have been in my real life.

When I awoke, it was indeed to sunlight, but it was a fierce sun. The morning of 1st October, and we started early. Sidi Hamet told us that he and his two companions would each ride a camel, and the five of us would have to take turns with the remaining animal, three riding and two walking. The camels travelled briskly as a result of their watering and we had to walk quickly in order to keep up with them, advancing all the while to the north-west. At least the direction was favourable.

Then, shortly after midday, Sidi Hamet turned to me and shouted, "I see a camel, Riley!"

He was excited, as were his companions; but being on foot

and therefore lower down, I could see no new camels. Frankly, camels and desert were all we had seen since leaving the tribesmen. More camels, more sand, neither was of much interest.

I noticed that we had altered our course, and were now heading due east once more. After travelling in that direction a little longer, I saw on the horizon the outline of a large drove of camels. We headed straight for them, and just before sunset we reached the camels and their masters. The men greeted my masters warmly, and we proceeded with them to their encampment.

When we reached their tents, we were told to dismount. Our masters had given us neither food nor drink all day. I begged for a little water, and they gave us a very meagre portion to share. Sidi Hamet saw the disappointment, almost anger, in my face.

"Wait, Riley," he said. "These people will bring you food. I will see to it."

My men's mood was not good. Savage was particularly angry.

"We should have killed them when we were five against three," he said. "Now it's too late. We may never have the chance again."

"Why kill them now, when we're lost in the desert?" I said. "We couldn't find our way to a city. We would either die out here or be captured and enslaved again. And what chance would we have had of finding that spring in the rocks?"

"I don't trust them," said Savage. "They have our lives in their hands. Why not kill two and keep one alive and bound. He could lead us to Essaouira or wherever."

"If you don't trust three, then it doesn't make much sense to rely on one as a guide," I said. "Anyway, we're now outnumbered again, so you're wasting your breath."

"Alright," Savage replied, "but if things change, I'll do as I think right."

The conversation was over, but I knew that I must be careful in future not to leave Savage with the other men unless I was present. Of course, there was something in what he said. The moment might come when we would have to take control of our fate.

At last, a young man came to us with a bowl of boiled meat.

The five of us ate this meat, which I think was mutton, and then we lay down on the ground to sleep. Less than an hour later, we were awakened by the same young man, who now brought us a large bowl of milk. These tribesmen, whoever they might be, were indeed kind and generous. Although that night we slept in the cold and on the sandless surface of the desert, we slept well.

Sidi Hamet woke me in the morning and told me that we must continue our journey. I was disappointed. A few days of being fed here was exactly what we needed.

"I have something to show you, Riley," he said, and he led me towards a large tent and then told me to wait. He went inside and came out carrying, believe it or not, my hand telescope.

"Is this yours?" he asked.

I took it in my hands. It was the telescope I had purchased in Gibraltar, which Antonio had found when looking for the buried money.

"Yes," I said. "Yes, it's mine. You should buy it, I believe it will be very useful for us." It might also be useful for me, if I could get my hands on it.

"What could I sell it for, Riley?" asked Sidi Hamet. I suggested a high price, hoping it would entice him into buying it with a view to profit; although I was careful to ensure that it would not be worthwhile for him to exchange one of us for it. He went back to the tent, but returned without the telescope, merely shrugging his shoulders and walking on. Presumably the telescope's new owner wanted too high a price.

So our masters took their leave of these hospitable people, and we pursued a course to the north-west. Anything north or west was a relief for me, but our masters were changing direction too often for my liking. Time and again they stopped and dismounted, now smelling the sand, now debating where to go, now pointing in various directions, before moving off again.

We took turns in riding and walking; but in the afternoon, our masters joined in the rota and walked, even as some of us rode. They were very uneasy throughout the day, clearly uncertain as to their route. If only I could be confident about the intended destination, the route would not worry me.

In the late afternoon, we saw, and soon caught up with, another drove of camels and their masters. We were invited to join them, and we rode alongside them for about two hours. Then we all went down into a large shallow valley where there were about fifty tents pitched, with many women and children awaiting our arrival.

We dismounted and walked up to the tents. Dozens of people milled around us. Whether we were heroes from afar or strange animals now captured and harmless was not clear. But the smiling and chattering between them encouraged me to believe that we were being welcomed.

As we walked along, men and women called out to me, '*El Rais!*', and gathered round with their children to look at us. Some questioned me about my men, our ship and our families, and then repeated my answers to the crowd.

It was now getting late, and the last rays of a red and glorious sunset were burnishing the desert. Having satisfied everyone's curiosity, we were allowed to lie down on an area of soft sand, and here we fell asleep. We were awoken at midnight for the customary meal, and each of us was presented with a good quantity of milk. Then we went to sleep again, and rested well into the next morning, when I was awakened by a commotion within the camp. I looked about and could see that everyone was busy dismantling the tents and loading the camels. So we were off again.

We all travelled north-west for about twenty miles. Then we stopped and the tents were pitched once more, and a shelter was made for our masters with two pieces of tent cloth joined by thorns and supported by several sticks. After a good drink of water at noon, everyone rested for the remainder of the day. At midnight, milk was brought and each of us had as much as he wanted. This tribe took no other nourishment; just sour milk and water in the day and milk at midnight. This must have been by choice; they had camels and many goats and sheep, yet they ignored the opportunity for a feast.

The next morning, we prepared to leave. First, our masters made a trade, exchanging our youngest camel for an old one that was slightly lame, plus a very young camel and one of the tribe's sheep. I hoped that our masters' transaction was intended to provide food very soon.

Having said our farewells, we moved off. We could only travel slowly, being held back by the slowness of the sheep. After two hours, we came to another valley with some small bushes at its lowest point. In the middle of the bushes was a well. Here we drank, and then we watered the camels.

The sheep could go no further, and anyway its slow pace had been hindering us and annoying our masters. So they cut its throat and strapped the carcass on one of the camels.

As we prepared to move on again, I tried to take a view of what was happening, but every thought was depressing. Although we appeared at each stage to be travelling with a purpose, overall nothing much seemed to be changing. Yes, things were certainly a little better, but for how long? It was as if fate was playing with us as a cat might play with a mouse before killing it. Were we actually getting anywhere?

CHAPTER TWELVE

Punishment and theft

We made slow, almost casual, progress all day until it was dark, when we dismounted and prepared for the night. Our masters lit a fire and roasted three of the quarters of the sheep and its entrails. The quarters were for our three masters; the entrails for the five of us. It was not much for five men, but with our shrunken stomachs it was quite filling, and we slept soundly all night.

In the morning we set off on foot, driving the camels in front of us. I noticed towards the middle of the morning that the nature of the desert floor had started to change. There were numerous patches of sand, rather than the arid hard surface of previous days. Although the sand was soft and kinder to our feet, it lay in large heaps that were difficult to walk through, as we sank almost to our knees at every step. Also, of course, the sand was scorching hot.

We trudged on through that sterile expanse, beneath the terrible and triumphant power of the sun, raising our eyes only rarely to see if, by a miracle, there was a new prospect before us other than sand, sun and sky.

Our progress was now desperately slow, so we all mounted the camels and rode forward. From our lofty seats, our view over the desert was widely extended; the quiet so intense. Very soon, we saw before us vast numbers of immense sandhills, all heaped up in the most terrifying manner. Some hours later, we arrived at those hills, and were struck with horror at the sight; massive mountains of loose sand piled up like drifted snow, towering two hundred feet above our heads, blocking our route. They seemed to threaten destruction to our whole party.

However, there was no choice; we would have to climb. Having dismounted, we began to drive and pull the camels up the sandhills after our masters, who went on ahead to look for a practicable passage. Just like us, the camels struggled to progress, and climbed only with the greatest reluctance and difficulty. Sidi Hamet, Seid and Abdallah were full of apprehension for their own and our safety, and they were also most concerned for the survival of their camels.

We drove on until dark, never stopping, never speaking. Then we came to a place where the surface was flatter, like a lake of sand surrounded by these sand mountains. Here, near a few miserable shrubs, we stopped for the night. We fettered the camels, which quickly ate all the leaves from the shrubs, and then ate the shrubs themselves.

Having taken the saddles and sacks from the camels, we made a ring with these items to shelter us during the night. We kindled a fire and roasted what remained of the sheep. It was sweet, but not very substantial.

As we lay down for our night's rest, I asked Sidi Hamet how he was able to find his way across the trackless desert. He immediately pointed out to me the north or polar star and the Great Bear. Then he told me the Arabic names of the principal fixed stars, as well as of the planets visible in the firmament, and his manner of finding his course and reckoning time by them.

His knowledge of the stars astonished me. He appeared to be much better acquainted with the motions of the heavenly bodies than I was. Bear in mind that I had made them my study for many years, and had navigated to many parts of the globe with their assistance.

To convince me that he knew the cardinal points, he drew two lines in the sand at right angles, one pointing directly towards the polar star. He then drew two other lines across them, dividing the circle into eighths, and then in a like manner into sixteenths. I was well satisfied that he knew the divisions of the compass, and I went to sleep much encouraged and impressed.

At daylight, I was ordered to fetch the camels. I took Savage and Clark with me. The animals were all nearby, their forelegs having been tied twelve inches apart. We started to untie the fetters. I made one of the camels kneel, and mounted it with a good stick in my hand. I had seen these desert travellers, who used neither bridle nor halter, guide and drive their mounts with a single stick. But it was not quite so simple.

Savage, having found the old camel, took off its fetters, intending to make it kneel down so that he could climb on to its back. But this lame creature, which had caused us so much trouble in forcing it to keep up with the others, now set off at a great trot to the south. The young camel followed its example, quickly pursued by Abdallah's camel, and then the big one also joined the escape, all three having already been unfettered by Clark.

I tried to stop the escape by riding my camel in front of the others. If we lost the camels, we were as good as dead. But they would not stop. As I rode in front of one, it dodged me to the side, another dodged me to the other side; I was slowing them, but stopping none of them as I turned to the left and the right, and they swerved and ran one way and the other. Now my camel, seeing an opportunity, tried to get rid of me by running, then jumping, then lying down, only to get up suddenly. But although I had lost control, I was able to keep on it - just.

Our masters had seen what was happening, and they started to run after the camels, shouting and waving their arms. I managed to halt my camel, and Sidi Hamet ran up to me and told me to make it lie down. Then he pulled me off and climbed on to the animal. The other camels were continuing their escape. Sidi Hamet told me to return to our camp and stay there with my men. He then rode off, Seid and Abdallah running after him.

I walked back to the encampment with Savage and Clark. We sat there with Horace and Burns, and I explained to them what had happened.

About an hour later, our masters returned with the camels. They had caught them after a long and difficult chase, and the creatures were covered with sand and sweat. Our masters looked exhausted, and they were clearly furious.

Now we would see their reaction, and that would tell me how they regarded us. I did not have to wait long. Seid and Abdallah strode forward, Seid carrying a large stick. They headed straight for Savage, for they had seen him let the first camel escape. I pleaded for him, but to no avail. Seid whipped Savage most brutally, bringing the stick down on his back again and again. Savage did not beg for mercy as I would have done, but took his punishment without a word.

When they had finished with him, Aaron just looked sideways at me and nodded twice. He was awaiting his moment. I showed no approval, but I did not attempt to reason with him. He needed the thirst for vengeance to keep him going.

Sidi Hamet had not taken part in this cruelty, but he had made no attempt to intervene. There was no doubt in my mind that he could have stopped it had he been prepared to confront his brother. I looked at him, but he would not meet my gaze. It was important not to get confused; my shipmates were my friends, not these people who wanted to sell us for profit.

Having settled this affair, for the time being at least, we reloaded the camels and watered them, and then we proceeded in silence, the animals resuming the same placid demeanour they had adopted before their attempted escape.

The hills were now so close to each other that great care was necessary to prevent the camels from falling over. Our masters went on ahead, two of them at a considerable distance, to select the path to follow. Abdallah was halfway between them and us, passing on directions and taking care to keep both groups within his sight at all times.

It was hard work trudging up and down the hills - like wading through gleaming embers spread over boiling mud.

We continued on our journey until late in the evening, and with the sun's decline we stopped to rest. But rest was all we got. There was no food for us, and no food for the camels either.

I was awakened late in the night by Horace. "What is it?" I asked.

"Listen," he replied. I listened. There was a huge roaring of the wind in the distance.

"My God," I said. "If this is a sandstorm, we're lost. We must try to protect ourselves. Wake the others."

Horace woke the other three, and we sat together trying to work out whether the noise was moving towards us. We were all terrified that we would be buried alive. But as we listened, it seemed that the noise was not coming nearer, nor was it going further away.

"Maybe the noise isn't the wind," I said, "but the sound of something else being carried by the wind. Could it be the sea?"

Everyone's eyes lit up. Were we really near the sea again?

If the sea was close, it suggested that our masters might well be taking us towards Essaouira. All were overjoyed at the possibility that we were not being deceived, for that was what we had all privately feared. We lay down once more, but none of us slept; we were too excited.

By morning the wind had fallen, and we could no longer hear the sea. Had it been our imagination? Was it indeed the sea? It was impossible to tell. Despite our hunger, we felt stronger and more determined. We continued on our journey, labouring among the sandhills until noon, but we did not hear the sea again. Then, mounting the camels, we turned a little to the east, and coming round a mound, we saw two loaded camels. We quickly made for them. Our masters held their guns ready as we all dismounted. But there was no sign of any humans; just the two camels standing there, as if awaiting further instructions.

Both animals had large sacks on their backs. The sacks were full, and our masters were excited by the opportunity. Sidi Hamet went in search of the owner of these two beasts, gripping his gun, which was cocked and primed.

The rest of us followed with the camels. As we rounded the next mound, we saw Sidi Hamet approaching a man who was lying on the sand, fast asleep. Sidi Hamet crept right up to him, keeping his gun ready to fire. He snatched some small bags from near the sleeping man's head and returned to us, where Seid and Abdallah had made the man's camels lie down. Seid untied one of the sacks - it was full of barley. He emptied about half the barley into a bag and put it on one of our camels, after which he tied up the sack and put it back on the sleeping man's camel.

Next, our masters began to examine the contents of the small bags which Sidi Hamet had taken from near the sleeping man. One of them was partly filled with barley meal. Seid immediately poured some of the barley meal into a bowl, mixed it with water, and ate it. Sidi Hamet and Abdallah did likewise. Then they gave us about two pints of water with a handful of this meal in it, which the five of us shared. When we had all eaten, we mounted the camels and continued on our way, leaving the two camels and the sleeping man where we had found them.

We had proceeded for about half an hour, when suddenly we heard a voice calling on us to stop. We turned round. There he was; it was the sleeping man riding after us, waving a scimitar as he closed in. My masters immediately urged the camels on, but the man was gaining on us. Sidi Hamet shouted at the man to go away, but he continued to advance, getting closer and closer.

Realising that the man would soon catch up with them, my masters stopped, took hold of their guns and prepared to shoot. Seeing this, the man dismounted and threw himself to the ground, declaring that he had lost part of his property, and he knew that they had taken it. It could hardly be denied; there was no one else around for miles.

The man then said that he was their brother and he would rather

...leaving the high sandhills behind

die than commit a bad action or suffer a bad action from others with impunity.

He continued, "You have guns and you believe that you can kill me; but the God of justice is my shield and will protect the innocent. I do not fear you."

I thought that a shotgun would now be used to good effect to test his shield; but I was wrong. Sidi Hamet told the man to put down his scimitar and approach. We all dismounted.

"Is it peace?" asked the man.

Sidi Hamet confirmed that it was, and all three of my masters went up to the stranger and hugged him. Then they sat down together and had a long discussion. Sidi Hamet justified the theft by blaming us. He said that he had taken the provisions because his slaves were in a state of starvation, and he could not bear to see us suffer.

In the end, my masters returned some small bags, some opium and all that remained of the barley. Then they prayed together and the stranger went off, carrying his goods back to his camels, and we resumed our journey, leaving the high sandhills behind.

I did not know what to make of this extraordinary episode. My masters were thieves but not murderers? Or they were opportunists but cowards? No matter. Further tests lay ahead.

CHAPTER THIRTEEN

A caravan, a storm and an attack

It was the turn of Savage and Horace to ride the old camel. As soon as the other camels started to move faster, it became impossible for the old one to keep pace with them. Again and again the others had to slow down to allow it to catch up. In the end, our masters became so exasperated that they rode alongside the old camel and beat Savage brutally on his back, and they also gave Horace a few blows for good measure. Of course it was no help; it was the camel that needed a beating - not that it would have done any good. I had little doubt but that the true reason for the flogging was the loss of the stolen goods. Ever since their return, our masters had been in a bad humour. But there was nothing I could do to stop Seid and Abdallah; although I would have loved to tell Seid that every time he struck Savage, he was shortening his own life.

We kept on as fast as we could until late in the evening, our masters finally accepting that we must always travel at the pace of the slowest. Then, as we eased to a walk, we heard men's voices to our left. Our masters were frightened. They immediately turned to the right, where they found a deep hollow. We descended its steep bank in silence. When we reached the bottom, we saw a considerable number of small bushes on which we allowed the camels to feed.

Down in this hollow, the head of the largest camel was some twenty feet below the level of the desert, so we were well out of sight of the men whose voices we had heard.

Despite our temporary safety, our masters were still very nervous. We fettered the camels, and then Sidi Hamet, Seid and Abdallah each took a gun and crawled up the side of the hollow. When they reached the top, Sidi Hamet turned round and motioned to us to join them. The five of us clawed our way up and looked over the edge, but we could see and hear nothing. We all slid to the bottom and fell asleep.

When I awoke in the morning, I found that we had been joined by an old woman and a young boy. The woman appeared to be friendly and she was talking to Sidi Hamet, who was asking her many questions. Then she called the boy over and gave him instructions, as a result of which he scrambled out of the hollow and disappeared from sight.

He returned about twenty minutes later with a large bowl containing the remains of a cooked sheep, consisting of the entrails and some bones. Our masters ate the entrails and gave us the bones. The boy had also brought a large skin of sour milk and water mixed together. Sidi Hamet allowed us half of this. By the time we had finished, the woman and the boy had gone. We loaded the camels and pulled and coaxed them out of the hollow and on to the desert surface. I looked about; there was no sign of the woman, the boy or the men.

But my attention was taken by the first sight of bushes that deserved that name. They were of the willow kind, some as thick as a man's leg, and rising to over six feet. We rode towards the bushes, but as we neared them we saw in the distance a man mounted on a camel. He was riding swiftly towards us, a second camel in tow.

Our masters stopped and dismounted. Then they furiously dug some holes in the sand. They were burying the small bags they had stolen from the sleeping man the day before and which they had not returned.

As he approached, I recognised the man whose goods had been plundered. He dismounted and confronted my masters, complaining bitterly that they had deceived him and not returned all that they had stolen.

The three thieves denied everything and showed the man that they had none of his possessions. They encouraged him to search them and their camels. He took up the challenge, but obviously found nothing, so he rode off without further protestation.

Our masters waited a few minutes in case the man returned, and then they dug up the stolen items. Now they smiled and danced with glee at their success.

Sidi Hamet showed me the two bags and their contents. In one there was a box that contained opium and several hollow sticks the size of a man's finger; each was filled with gold dust. The other contained tobacco stalks and the roots of a herb revered as a remedy for the evil eye or witchcraft, which they value greatly, even above the gold and the opium. They smoke this root through the leg or thighbone of a sheep or goat, having no other pipes, and then consider themselves invulnerable. No wonder the sleeping man had gone to such lengths to recover his property.

Whilst I was glad that my masters were now in a good humour, I confess that I was not overjoyed by their propensity for dishonesty; it did not bode well for my bargain with them. But at least they now had something with which they would be able to buy food and water.

I asked Sidi Hamet, "Where did that woman and child come from?"

"They are from the tail end of a caravan," he replied, "but it is not a caravan coming back from Timbuktu, it is going to Timbuktu, the great trading place in the south of the desert. Of course, it is not as great as it used to be because now your vessels can sail round the coast beyond Cape Bajador to trade directly with the countries that lie to the south."

"But that's no good for us," I said. "It's going the wrong way; we need to reach the sea, not the centre of the desert."

"I know, Riley," replied Sidi Hamet, "but we should join the caravan for a short time to get some food and water. After that we will leave and make for the coast and then Essaouira."

We rode on until we saw it, like a narrow forest in the distance, this great slow-moving mass of people and camels. Before long, we caught up with them; it was not narrow at all, it was a wide column, over fifty yards wide in parts, making its way to the hellish centre of the Sahara.

Our group just melded into the caravan, near the end; nothing said, nothing asked. Sidi Hamet rode ahead to speak with some of the leaders. As soon as darkness came we stopped for the night, and the caravan became invisible, except for the numerous campfires stretching into the distance and joining the sky as if an extension of one of the great constellations.

When he returned, I asked Sidi Hamet what he had discovered about this caravan.

"It is commanded by a sheikh called Sidi Ishrel," he told me. "They set off with about four thousand camels, having first fattened them with dates, barley and water for several days, and more than a thousand men, all well armed. They are carrying with them a huge store of barley and a great number of milk camels."

"Why do they need to be so heavily armed?" I asked. "Would anyone dare to attack such a great number?"

"Certainly they would," said Sidi Hamet. "Over the last ten years, several caravans have been totally destroyed."

That was not very encouraging. The caravan was obviously bait to bandits.

"After setting out," he continued, "they stopped and cut wood and burned charcoal for the camels, for caravans never attempt to cross the desert without this resource. Then they travelled south around the bottom of the Atlas Mountains."

"But do they have food and water to spare?" I asked.

"They brought much food and water with them," he replied.

"Of the four thousand camels, four hundred were loaded with provisions and water for the journey. The camels also carry hay, most of which they drop off on their way in the hope that it will still be there for them on the return journey. But they have a problem because many of the wells they came to were dry, so they have not been able to replenish their water. Nevertheless, they have sold us enough, and we will eat and drink tonight."

Eat and drink we did, before most of us fell asleep. I stayed awake, for I wished to speak more with Sidi Hamet, as I was curious about this caravan.

"What goods are they carrying to Timbuktu?" I asked.

He told me that they carried many types of merchandise for trading at Timbuktu with men who came from the south. Those men bought various things from the caravans, but mainly they wanted salt. They had no salt in their countries, and salt trading had driven these caravans south through the desert for hundreds of years. Apparently our caravan already carried some salt, but they were going to buy more on the way to Timbuktu at the salt mine at Taodeni, where the slaves work throughout their lives digging the salt out for sale by their masters to the caravans.

I asked Sidi Hamet what these people received in return for the salt and other goods they were carrying.

"Gold and ivory and slaves," replied Sidi Hamet. "They are happy to exchange anything for the salt; they value it as we value gold. They come from the Bilad as-Sudan, the southern country, to trade with us as they have always done."

"Are all the people in the caravan Berbers?" I asked.

"No, not Berbers," he replied angrily. "You call us Berbers, but we are Imazighen."

I understood that they preferred to be called 'free people', rather than 'barbarians'.

Sidi Hamet continued. "We are not of the same people as those who live in the south, nor are we of the people who now live in the north. Our ancestors came from the east of Africa; the land of Egypt. We conquered this country many generations ago, and

166

we took the land from the black people who used to live here, but then the Arabs came and took our land and drove us to the desert and the mountains. But we have always controlled the caravan routes; they are ours."

"But do you all speak Arabic as well as your own language?" I asked.

"Not all of us, but many. Our language has no written form. So, with the exception of the few tribes who are Jews, we have to learn Arabic to read the Koran," explained Sidi Hamet.

"Will this caravan pass by any towns?" I asked, hoping that we might be freed earlier.

"Yes," said Sidi Hamet, "but only small towns where there are no Christians; and anyway these will be walled towns. Not more than fifty unarmed men from a caravan can go into such a town at a time, and they must leave before others are permitted to enter. It would be long before it was our turn. Forget about that. In a day or two we will leave this caravan and make for Essaouira."

With that he lay down and went to sleep, and I did the same.

The next morning we all set off, and the caravan travelled laboriously in the intense heat, until shortly after noon a wind began to blow at us from the south-east. It was a dry warm wind to start with, but it became stronger and stronger and hotter and hotter.

"What's happening?" I asked Sidi Hamet.

"This is bad, Riley," he said. "This is the wind of the desert, the Chergui, a burning wind that brings death and destruction, although usually it does not come so late in the year. We will all have to stop."

Loose sand filled the air, and the whole caravan halted. We took the loads off the camels and piled them in one great heap, and then we made the camels lie down.

The flying sand was now so thick that it was impossible for us to see each other. Standing up, we could not resist the suffocating surges, so we lay down with our faces to the ground and prayed for the wind to calm. But the Chergui continued to blow unabated.

All of us huddled together, until the sand on our bodies grew so heavy that it almost prevented us from breathing. Then we turned over to dislodge the sand, and we found new positions. This procedure continued for hour upon hour.

The whole caravan was transfixed by this evil wind all day and all night. Then, as suddenly as it had arrived, the Chergui departed. We crawled out of the sand that had buried us for so long. But many must have lain alone and fallen asleep at some stage; for it emerged that over three hundred people were missing. The eight of us were amongst the survivors; anyone who had fallen asleep had been woken up by the others when they turned, and as a result each of us had dislodged the sand at regular intervals.

All the survivors now joined in thanking God for his mercy in sparing their lives - although He had had no need to send such an executioner in the first place. Then we proceeded to dig out the camels. Unfortunately, about five hundred of the camels towards the head of the caravan, where the wind had been strongest, were found to be dead. We were obliged to give the remaining animals a little water to wash their parched throats and some charcoal to eat.

Later in the day, the caravan set out once more, travelling through the deep and boiling sand. Many of the camels were almost expiring and could not carry their loads much longer. But now we arrived in a wide valley that contained a famous watering place where the caravan leaders planned to stop for some days to allow everyone to recover their strength and, more importantly, to allow the camels to recover theirs.

Can you conceive of the mass distress and disappointment when we discovered that there was no water in any of the wells in the valley? Not one drop of rain had fallen there for over a year.

The authority of Sheikh Ishrel could hardly restrain the desperate men; everyone was eager to save his own life and his property, and each sought the means of relief by running about the valley looking for water. This behaviour continued for the rest of the day, when finally accepting that nothing could be done without co-operation, everyone became obedient and joined together in great numbers in digging out the various wells.

After digging for another day without finding any sign of water, all subordination was entirely at an end. The Sheikh, who was a wise and prudent man, insisted that two out of every three camels should be killed, so that the little water to be found in them together with their blood might keep the rest alive as well as the people until, with the aid of Providence, we might find some water.

But the men would not accept his advice, as no one was willing to have his property sacrificed. Sheikh Ishrel then directed that thirty of the oldest and most judicious of the men should pick out the camels to be spared. They quickly selected the strongest; but when they began to kill the others, a furious quarrel ensued, which soon escalated into a battle.

The Sheikh was killed immediately. Then about a hundred of his supporters were butchered, and a general carnage ensued. We avoided the worst, for Sidi Hamet had directed us to take hold of our camels and withdraw to the edge of the valley until the fighting had subsided.

An hour later, we could see from a distance that exhaustion had led to a calming in the battle, but not before another two hundred men had been killed. About five hundred camels were also destroyed during the day, and now the other camels drank the water from their bodies and also their blood. So the Sheikh's purpose was achieved to a degree, but instead of the strongest camels surviving, it was the camels of the strongest men that triumphed.

Then, just as the caravan was preparing to reform, we saw a large body of wandering horsemen storm into the valley, shouting and firing their guns. They directed a most destructive fire of musketry at the caravan as they rode by like hungry tigers, with guns and scimitars in their hands, yelling dreadfully.

The attackers threw the whole caravan into confusion; but quickly the caravan formed a large circle about one of the dried-up wells. Then the defenders manoeuvred the dead camels into a barrier, and the men seized their weapons and rallied as one.

Now the battle raged furiously. It was becoming dark, the blaze of powder making only a faint light, whilst the cracking of musketry, the shouts of the combatants, and the bellowing of the wounded and frightened camels, together with the groans of the wounded and dying men, made the most dreadful uproar.

The fighting continued for about two hours, hand to hand and breast to breast, until as suddenly as they had arrived, the assailants gave way and rode off, leaving their dead and dying on the field of battle.

In the morning, we rejoined what was left of the caravan and counted the dead. Two hundred and thirty of the caravan members had been killed, and four hundred more camels were either slain or so badly wounded that they had to be put down. We found over three hundred of the enemy lying on the ground, dead or wounded. Those who were badly injured were put out of their pain; those who could still walk, about fifty, were taken as slaves.

Sidi Hamet explained that this was no victory, for with less than three hundred men left in the caravan, another attack could not be resisted. The weakening process had been successful. Next time the bandits could demand whatever they wanted.

Now it was time to leave the remains of this cursed group. The eight of us, with our camels, quietly sprinted away to the west as fast as we could ride. No one had any interest in challenging us, and our departure went unnoticed.

Early afternoon, and we discovered some camel tracks. We followed the tracks until we saw a large drove of camels feeding on scattered shrubbery in a small shallow valley. There were also several sheep and goats nibbling at some brown moss. The increase in the number of animals and plants encouraged me to believe that we were coming to the end of the desert - or at least the desert in its harshest form.

Several men came forward to greet us. After the usual salutations, they invited our masters to remain with them for the night, which they readily accepted. We were shown the way to the

Next time the bandits could demand whatever they wanted.

encampment, and one of the men rode with us at a full trot towards their tents, which we reached half an hour later.

There were between twenty and twenty-five tents pitched near a small thicket of thorn trees. I call them trees, but in truth none of the trunks had a diameter greater than four inches.

Our masters bought a kid from these people for the price of some of the stolen gold powder. Then they killed the kid, skinned it, tore it apart, and boiled the pieces over a fire. They ate the meat and gave us the entrails. Some of the meat was offered to four of the tribesmen who were sitting with us, but they had only come to gratify their curiosity by viewing us, and did not accept the offer. This was the first time since I reached Africa that I had seen someone refuse food. I took this as a favourable sign.

We went to sleep, to be awakened at midnight and given a skin of water to share, as well as a bowl containing a kind of pudding into which they poured some milk. We devoured this mixture in an instant. The effect it produced on my palate has never left my memory. We fell asleep once more; the sweetest of sleeps.

On the morning of the thirteenth, we set out in a north-westerly direction and travelled slowly on the camels for several hours without stopping. Now another improvement; we had come to a well. It was situated in the middle of a cluster of high bushes. There were a great many men with camels near and around the well. All those we passed greeted our masters in a friendly fashion.

I was about to walk forward to assist in drawing water for the camels, when Sidi Hamet caught hold of my arm and told me to stay with my men. So Seid and Abdallah performed this task.

While they were doing so, a tribesman came up with his camel and led it straight to the bowl into which Seid had poured water for our camels. Seid tried to stop him, but the man persisted. As a result, Seid gave him a heavy blow to the face with his fist, which knocked the man to the ground. I looked carefully and recognised the sleeping man whose property my masters had stolen. Rolling over and getting to his feet, he drew his scimitar and charged at Seid with the weapon raised. He slashed at Seid, who dodged out of the way, but not far enough. The tip of the blade drew a thin red line across Seid's robe.

Sidi Hamet had by this time drawn his gun and pressed it to the man's back, ready to kill him. But just as quickly, Sidi Hamet was seized by three bystanders, and others restrained Seid and his antagonist.

The sleeping man was taken away. A length of cloth was wrapped around Seid's injured chest, probably a reasonable price for the stolen items.

Having completed the watering, we quickly mounted our camels and rode off in silence, continuing until Sidi Hamet came alongside and told me that there were some goats ahead, and we would soon all have food to eat.

We hurried our camels up and down the gentle sandhills, but the exertion was too much for our old lame camel, which collapsed and died.

While we were transferring the dead camel's load to the other camels, we heard the sound of a musket being fired. We travelled on for several minutes, and then we saw Abdallah, who had gone ahead, approaching us with another man. They were driving a flock of goats towards us. The man looked very frightened; not surprising, because Abdallah had fired his gun in order to scare him.

As soon as the goats were near, our three masters ran into the flock and each grabbed a goat. The owner of the flock did not dare to complain; but his wife, who had now appeared on the scene, had no such problems. The woman ran towards our masters, screaming and cursing. She did not pause for breath; she just continued non-stop with her barrage of complaints, unimpressed by her husband's feeble efforts to calm her.

Sidi Hamet had had enough. He walked over to the woman, put his gun to her chest and threatened to blow her to bits. This compelled her to stop, and Sidi Hamet took advantage of the silence to tell the man that we had left a camel a little distance behind, as it could not proceed at our pace, so they could have it in return for the three goats. All perfectly true in a most dishonest way.

At first, these two people found it incredible that such a pathetic collection of people would leave a valuable camel behind. Sidi Hamet repeated the information, laced liberally with oaths in the names of his family and his ancestors, and at length the husband and wife reluctantly agreed to the bargain, provided that one of the goats was exchanged for a smaller one. Probably they thought that the prospect of one camel was better than death, because once calm prevailed, they must have realised that that was the choice.

So the business was settled, and the man and woman went their way with their flock on a route that would lead them to the dead camel.

Our new goats were tied together and given into my charge. Savage and Burns helped me in driving them, and Clark and Horace were ordered to drive the camels.

The heat of the sun, both from the sky and reflected from the sand, was intense; but as usual we had no choice. We continued behind the party of camels, struggling all the while with the goats. Then Savage found a short green weed, which he pulled from the sand and ate, telling me that it was delicious and as sweet as honey. I doubted that very much, although all food was delicious to us.

As we continued, I begged Savage not to eat any more of the weed until our masters had confirmed that it was not poisonous; but he ate on nevertheless. I refused to touch it, even though it looked very tempting. Our masters had not taken any, despite having reached it first - they had not even allowed the camels to eat the weed.

In his distressed condition, Savage believed that a green thing that tasted so good could do no harm, and he continued to eat it whenever he could find some. But in time, he began to vomit violently. I picked some of the weed and examined it. I was convinced that it was none other than what is called in America the 'Indian tobacco', or 'nicotinia'.

We had been trailing between ten and fifty yards behind the camels, and Savage was finding it hard to keep up. He would vomit from time to time, but I could not wait for him or else I would lose sight of the others. So every time Savage stopped to vomit, Burns went on with the goats, and I continued slowly whilst keeping Burns in view and ensuring that Savage could still see me. When he was done, he would run after me and gradually catch up, and then we would chase after Burns.

I told Savage what I thought the plant was, to convince him that he would not die, though I warned him he would have to carry on in this manner until his system was rid of the tobacco.

But then we were both enormously uplifted when we saw in the distance the sea as it came into view, dark and smooth, on the horizon. At first, I had thought it to be a high ridge of woodland, and hoped that it would prove to be the end of the desert. But Savage thought that it was too dark to be land, and he was right, for soon we saw that it was definitely the ocean. I could plainly distinguish the mountainous waves as they rolled forward, for the waters were fiercely agitated by the wind.

This was our first view of the sea since we were made slaves, and it was a hugely gratifying sight – this was my 'ata Allah', my God's gift. New dangers might not be far off, but new hope had already arrived.

CHAPTER FOURTEEN

New companions and a test

Our spirits lifted, though still nervous and fearing disappointment, we trudged on towards the sea. I recalled that several days ago we thought we had heard the sea, but we had not reached it; instead, we had headed inland. Would this happen again? I really hoped not, because last time it was probably wishful thinking; this time it was real.

Thankfully, our masters did not change direction. Shortly before dark, we reached the cliffs that separate the waters from the desert. As we came to the edge, we stood still, tears in our eyes; this was truly the way home. The roar of the waves welcomed us; we had defeated the desert.

Part of the cliff had crumbled, and we carefully clambered down over the broken rocks. Rushing forward, we threw ourselves into the cold waters. We felt reborn and strengthened. Now we could face anything.

Returning to the camels, we walked along the sands, and soon came upon four families sitting under shelters made of skins extended over poles sunk into the sand. Our masters greeted the families, and went to sit with them. We were told to fetter the camels and then to wander along the beach collecting the bush that was growing on the cliff face, so that a fire could be made to keep us warm throughout the night.

Savage was completely exhausted, so I told him to lie down while the rest of us collected the bush. When we returned, I found Seid beating him with a stick as punishment for not assisting us. I begged Sidi Hamet to intervene, explaining that Savage was sick and that I had told him not to help, adding that I had performed his share of the labour. Sidi Hamet grunted and told his brother to stop, and the two of them walked away.

Then we made a fire, and I poured some water into a large bowl and set it above the fire, but not before I had stolen some of the water for Savage. Now Sidi Hamet killed one of the goats and skinned it, throwing the pieces of the animal into the bowl. Our masters had the best parts and gave us the boiled entrails. We were also allowed to drink some of the soup in which the goat had been cooked. Then we were given a small drink of water to finish our meal, after which we lay down.

I looked at my men; they smiled at me. I could not remember any of them smiling since the day of the storm. We had been through so much since then. In the course of the night, one of the families gave our masters a large bowl filled with the kind of pudding we had eaten before, which was made of barley, fermented camel's milk and honey. They gave each of us a small portion, but as Savage was sick, they refused to let him have any, saying that he had already eaten too much of something, although they did not know what.

But we were shipmates; we had to share everything, both good and bad, so each of us gave Savage a share of our portions. However, he was feeling so ill that he decided he ought not eat any more, so he kept his share in a bowl for the morning. Our hunger and thirst being somewhat appeased, we slept well that night.

On the morning of 14th October, while we were busy making preparations to leave, Abdallah seized Savage's pudding and swallowed it in an instant. It was taking us so long to learn how to deal with these people.

Now it was time to move on once more. Before taking our leave of the families on the beach, our masters purchased two goats from them, so that we now had four. We were forced to drive these disobedient animals as we all wandered slowly along the seashore towards the north.

At about noon, we came across another encampment. Our masters went and introduced themselves to the man who appeared to be the chief, and whose name was Hassar. Sidi Hamet called me over and told Hassar who I was, and he seemed very pleased to meet me.

"These five families are travelling north and we will travel with them," announced Sidi Hamet. "You may sit with us."

I sat down with them, and Hassar's wife began to speak with me in broken Spanish. She told me that she had saved the lives of some Spanish seamen who had been wrecked on this coast several years earlier. A vessel had come to collect them, and she went with the rescued sailors to Lanzarote in the Canary Islands to receive some goods that the Spanish captain had promised to deliver to her father. He had retained three of the sailors until she had been brought back with the reward. To me, the arrangement had the unmistakable odour of ransom rather than altruism.

We all journeyed together in the afternoon, climbing to the top of the cliff and heading north along its edge. In the evening our masters killed another of the goats, and this time they gave us some of the meat as well as the entrails. Hassar's wife also gave us a small quantity of their pudding, which she called '*lhash*'. Travelling gently and eating, even though the quantities were tiny - if only this improvement would continue.

Early on the fifteenth the tents were struck, and the five families proceeded with us until late afternoon, when we came to a very deep gully that we could not pass without going down to the beach once more.

We descended slowly, and on reaching the shore we found yet another family sitting outside a tent at the base of the cliff. Having talked with Sidi Hamet, the owner of the tent came to talk to me.

He told me that he knew I had promised Sidi Hamet that my friend in Essaouira would pay him a large amount of money.

This man then asked me, "Have you a friend in Essaouira?"

I answered that I had.

"Do not lie," he said, "for if you do, you will have your throat cut."

I protested that there was no problem, my promise would be kept.

"If you have told Sidi Hamet that you have a friend there so that you will get something to eat and be taken from the desert, and it is not true, he will pardon the deception and will sell you and your men. Your throat will be safe, but only if you confess your deceit now. Before long you will find buildings and a river. If he discovers your deceit then, you will surely lose your life."

I made this man understand that I would never lie to Sidi Hamet, that everything I had told him was true, that he was the man who had saved my life, and that he would be well rewarded by my friend and by the Almighty.

As I spoke, I wondered what this man's interest in us could be. Was he making these investigations for his own benefit, or had he been put up to it by Sidi Hamet? Either way, he was going to get the same answers. My question was dealt with when Sidi Hamet came out from behind a boulder, beaming with joy on discovering that I was not deceiving him. He put his arm round my shoulders and told me that I would be in Essaouira in a few days' time.

We carried on with our journey, the new members of our band accompanying us. Hassar had two young sons. Savage pointed at one of them in sheer disbelief; the child was wearing Savage's shirt. I immediately told Sidi Hamet, and asked him to buy the shirt. After a long session of bargaining, wholly disproportionate to the value of the garment, Sidi Hamet agreed the purchase with the boy. The price? A piece of blue cotton cloth. Sidi Hamet handed me the shirt and said that it should be given to Clark or Horace, but I gave it to Savage, despite Sidi Hamet's insistence that he was a bad man.

Having climbed the steep bank and reached the surface of the land once more, we stopped for the night. After dark, our masters returned to the shore with Horace and came back an hour later with a large quantity of mussels, which, although very salty, tasted excellent.

Horace sat beside me. "Captain," he said, "we're going to survive aren't we?"

"Yes, Horace," I replied, "I think we are. There are difficulties to come, but I think we've passed the worst."

Now Seid killed the remaining goats. All were boiled, and we shared the meat and the entrails with our new travelling companions.

We started out slowly on the morning of the sixteenth, keeping close to the edge of the cliff at all times. Our masters seemed unusually fearful that day, looking around and travelling all the while. Sidi Hamet told me that there were many robbers and bad men in this area who would try to seize us and carry us off.

I noticed that when it became dark, our masters held their guns in their hands whilst riding. Savage, Clark and Burns were on a camel, whilst Horace and I walked behind them. From time to time, Horace and I had to stop for a rest. Whenever this happened, one of our masters stayed with us until we had recovered, and then hurried us on as fast as possible.

We carried on until midnight, and then we came to another steep gully. Savage and Clark dismounted, and Horace and I took their places on the camel. We had never travelled after midnight, and I could not understand the urgency of continuing non-stop, albeit at a slowish pace. But anything that brought us to Essaouira sooner rather than later would get no objection from me.

Descending slowly, we reached the bottom of the valley and found it covered with high sand drifts. We continued for another two hours, weaving around and in between the drifts. Although the five of us shared the one camel, no such arrangement applied to the families travelling with us. The men rode and the women and children walked alongside. No sharing there.

Clark and Savage had fallen some way behind us. After a while, I heard Clark shouting, "Captain stop! Savage has fainted, and they're flogging him with sticks."

I slipped off the camel and ran back to Savage as fast as my legs would carry me. When I reached him, I saw Seid striking Savage's apparently lifeless body time and again with a heavy stick. Then Hassar lifted Savage's head by the hair with one hand; in the other hand he held a scimitar with which he was about to cut Savage's throat. I dived at Hassar and caught him around the waist, knocking him to the ground. Then I ran to Savage, raised him in my arms and called for water.

I knew that I was risking my life, but I was determined to save Savage. Hassar now stood up and took hold of his scimitar; no doubt preparing to run me through. Fortunately Sidi Hamet came to my rescue. He grabbed Hassar and held him still.

All the men, women and children had stopped and gathered round us. Several explained that they believed Savage was perverse and obstinate, and that he would not exert himself to proceed at a time when they were in haste to go forward, fearing that they might be attacked by robbers. That was why they had decided to kill him.

I made them understand that Savage had fainted through hunger and excessive fatigue, and that in this instance he was not being perverse. I told Sidi Hamet that from now on I would ensure that Savage was always on our camel, and the four of us would take turns, two by two. Our camel was then brought forward, and after Sidi Hamet had given Savage a drink of water, Burns and Clark mounted the animal, and we lifted Savage on to sit between them, with Clark holding him steady from behind.

Sidi Hamet told me to get on the small camel with Horace, and then said with a sneer, "The English are good for nothing. You see even our women and children can walk and run."

Wrong on three counts. The women and children would not have walked and run if they had been starved and beaten as we had been. Two, the English are good for a great many things, at least compared with savages who steal barley and drink urine. Three, we were not English anyway. But, as usual, silence was the wisest option.

I told Sidi Hamet that I had no problem walking, and I continued on foot alongside him as our whole troop set out once more. He looked down to me and said, "Good, Riley, you shall again see your children if God pleases."

What should I think of these people? One minute they were starving and beating us, the next they were feeding and saving us. More to the point, what of Sidi Hamet? Was he an evil person with a good streak, or a good person with an evil streak? I could never relax, never lower my guard. The nearer we came to Essaouira and freedom, the more I must be watchful and resourceful. We had come so far; we must not fail now.

Continuing on our journey, we moved to the east and away from the sea once more. We were travelling along the south side of a string of high sandhills. In the silence of the darkness, we suddenly heard a dog barking some way ahead of us. Our masters immediately turned sharply to the left and set us once more towards the north, having instructed all of us to proceed without making a sound.

We kept on in this manner until it was almost daylight. It then became clear that our masters were unsure of the direction they should follow. Fearing to go too far off our course, they decided that at last we should stop. Anyway, rest and sleep were long overdue.

They made the camels lie down, forming a circle with their bodies, and placed all the people within this living barrier. Some of the men kept guard with their muskets whilst we slept. Apparently we were now a valued commodity that had to be kept safe. I was, however, acutely aware that such a valuation had not stopped them from trying to kill one of us only a few hours earlier.

CHAPTER FIFTEEN

A reunion and a name

On the morning of 17th October we set out once more towards the north, with the sea to our left. Though we trudged on as before, we now definitely felt that there was a purpose to our efforts other than merely surviving for another day.

In the distance we could see hills rising and presenting a new aspect, so that I was convinced we had left the desert behind. I had great hopes that we had entered another phase of our journey, and that very soon we would come to cultivated lands, or at least running water.

When it was completely dark, we stopped, and the women set up the tents. Then they cooked two goats belonging to Hassar, which were divided amongst all of us. Although the portions were again rather small, we now felt almost like members of the group, not just miserable slaves. But I knew we could not rely on this being a permanent situation; I had already been taught that several times. Yet I wondered whether people might behave in a more civilised manner, the nearer they came to civilisation. Certainly, one or two of our group would need a lot of civilising before it became noticeable.

The following morning, we mounted the hill under which we had spent the night, climbing up a winding path. When we reached the top, we could see that we were in fact back on the surface on which we had previously been travelling.

At about noon, we came to the foot of the mountains we had seen the day before, and we turned to follow a path between two of them towards the east, entirely losing our view of the sea. We went up through a chasm in the bank, over rocks and along a narrow footway formed no doubt by years of passage by camels, horses and humans.

We carried on, and just before sunset we came to a small area of land that had been cultivated. It had to be a sign of better things.

Now we stopped for the night, and our masters gave us the remains of a goat that had been hanging on one of the camels for the last four days - perhaps not one of the better things I had hoped for; but after we had roasted the goat, we ate it and found it to be very tasty. In fact, this meat was tender and needed no seasoning. My shipmates all declared that putrid meat was by far preferable to fresh meat, in that it needed neither salt nor pepper - of which we had none - to give it relish. Clark rather wildly added that if he ever reached home, he would always prefer putrid meat to any other food. His family might not agree with that. And, of course, he might need to starve for a few weeks in order to appreciate the taste.

Having finished our savoury supper, we lay down on the barley straw that was scattered about the cultivated land, and enjoyed a sound and refreshing sleep.

On the nineteenth we resumed our journey, each of us travelling on foot, with the exception of Burns. Up to that point he had been walking without complaint, but he must have been suffering, because all of a sudden he was unable to maintain the required pace. We sat him on a camel, and as he slouched down we strapped him to the beast so that he would not fall off. At least Savage had now recovered. I prayed that not more than one of us would be unwell at a time; two or three to look after would really be a problem.

We continued to wind our way through the mountains as the path dictated, until about two hours after midday we saw a wonderful sight. A valley lay in front of us, with several rough huts alongside a stream of clear water meandering through banks covered with green bushes and shrubs in full blossom. On the far side of the stream, cows, asses and sheep were grazing on the plentiful grass, and in the midst of these animals I saw a number of date trees growing.

I fell to my knees. Then my thoughts raced to my dream. Oh no, would I be awoken at any moment and returned to misery? I looked up from the ground; it was there, it was real.

"Let's go!" I shouted. I stood up and ran with my men to the stream. There is something in the Bible about God advising Gideon to rely in battle only on men who drank water with cupped hands and to ignore those who put their heads in the water and drank like beasts. But battle was not our concern. We wanted fresh water and our faces went straight in, drinking and bathing our faces at the same time; pure relief.

We were on the right bank of the stream, which was no more than five yards wide and very shallow. Not far from the bank were the barren date trees. Barren, but not useless, for at least they could give us some shade. We lay down and enjoyed two hours of refreshing sleep.

Sidi Hamet awakened us and told us to go towards one of the huts. We followed him there, and waited outside whilst he went in. A few minutes later, he came out and showed us, to our inexpressible joy, about four pounds of honey in the comb.

Hassar and his men pressed around us, watching enviously, doubtless intending to steal this nourishing food, given half a chance. But Sidi Hamet was insistent that they should have none. He sat down and placed the honeycomb in a bowl on his knees, passing it to us piece by piece with one hand, while he held his gun with the other, ready to fire on anyone who should attempt to deprive us of our meal.

With the hungriness of greedy bears, we devoured it, comb and all, together with a host of young bees not yet ready for hatching, which filled many of the cells.

I was finding Hassar increasingly tiresome. He had nothing to do with us, yet he seemed to be assuming rights over us, as if he was one of our masters. I could see his eyes flash fire at the preferential treatment we were enjoying, and I dreaded the effects of his malicious envy.

An hour or so later, we were given some pudding of the same kind as we had eaten before, though this time mixed with a strong-smelling oil. Now we could rest. About fifty yards away, we found a burial place with a small square stone building in the centre, whitewashed and covered with a dome - a sanctuary or saint house, which they call a '*koubba*'. We found good shelter nearby, and we lay down for the night.

On 20th October it soon became clear that we would not be leaving that day. We went to the stream to revive ourselves by drinking the water and bathing our entire bodies. Then we returned to the shade of a palm tree to watch what was going on. This place appeared to be a great thoroughfare. I watched a large number of people arriving and leaving: Berbers, Arabs, Moors and other tribesmen, several of whom talked with our masters.

Many droves of camels were travelling south-eastwards in the direction from which we had come, no doubt heading for the desert. They carried barley, salt and iron, as well as other merchandise.

From the south came camels carrying goods obtained from the countries beyond the desert. There must have been plenty of gold hidden away somewhere. But our hearts fell at the sight of the numerous black slaves following the camels. The male slaves were entirely naked, but the women were allowed to wear a piece of cloth. All the slaves were strongly ironed; it was an awful sight. What was to become of those hapless people? We had been bought for cloth; they had been bought for salt. Where was the sense in all this?

While I was watching, I had not noticed a slave walking furtively towards me. Then I saw him. I was astonished to see that he was wearing part of an American flag - it was Robbins!

The five of us jumped to our feet, ran over to him and hugged him warmly. I asked Robbins to sit down and tell us what had been happening to him.

"Well," he said, "a few days after leaving you, we were travelling through a gigantic valley, and I was informed that there was an *ensahrau*, or Christian, in a nearby tent. I was told that I could go and see him, and I was delighted to discover that it was Porter. He said that Hogan and Dick were not far off. Unfortunately, I was summoned by my master, and I had to leave.

"We went on our way, but we soon stopped and then I saw Hogan. Porter had looked quite well, but Hogan was in a terrible state, and he was totally depressed. He said that his sufferings were too much to bear and he expected to die very soon, as did Dick, who was owned by the same master. My mistress gave Hogan some milk, but he was then forced to leave us.

"Later that day, Dick came to speak with me. His condition was desperate; and when his master found him, he pulled him away and beat him viciously. The next day, my mistress gave me part of our flag. I tore a hole in it and put my head through, and since then, as you can see, I have worn it as a cloak."

Robbins told us that he had travelled on day after day, often changing direction, drinking camel's milk and occasionally eating camel meat. At last he had reached the coast and seen the Atlantic. They stopped at some wells, and at that place Ganus sold Robbins to a man called Mahomet Meaarah. This man fed Robbins well and treated him reasonably. He told Robbins that they would go to Essaouira, as that was where Christians could be ransomed.

"I assisted my master in fishing for several days," continued Robbins, "and then I saw Barrett. He didn't just look healthy, he was positively overweight. He said that he'd been there for some time, and had been given plenty to eat. Barrett said that George Williams had the same master, and that Williams' health and spirits had been completely restored. I told him of your good fortune, and that he must try to get to Essaouira where we could all be redeemed.

"My new master then decided that it was time for us to leave. We travelled with his entire family, as well as a teacher and a black female slave. After two days we stopped near a group of tents, and I again saw Porter. I spoke with him several times before we moved on. Like me, he is determined to regain his freedom.

"We then travelled to the sea again, and proceeded along the coast to the north. The teacher often denounced me as a *kellup en-sahrau* and pressed upon me the necessity of renouncing the heresy of Christianity and becoming a good Mussulman. He promised me wealth, power, wives on earth, and eternal happiness and sensual pleasures in Paradise with the divine prophet. I resisted, but I have a feeling our lives would be easier if we became Mussulmans.

"I saw Porter again a few days later. He had been sold to a slave trader, and said that he now had great hopes of getting to Essaouira. He told me that he'd seen Hogan, who'd been sold to another trader, but that Dick had become totally worn out and been left to perish while Hogan went to the south-east with his new master. Then I journeyed on with my master, and now I've reached this place."

"So," I said, "another of my men has died. Poor Dick. But the rest of us must still have hope. You must convince your master that if he takes you to Essaouira, the English Consul there will pay good money for you; much more than he will get from anyone else."

"I will, I will," said Robbins. "I won't give up. I'll see you in Connecticut once more."

"Yes, be strong," I replied. "Never give up, and if you come across any of the others again, you must encourage them to get to Essaouira as well. But maybe my master can buy you now. Wait here; I'll look for him."

But there was no time. Robbins' master was calling him. He pressed our hands and walked away with tears in his eyes. I was proud that so many of my men were surviving in the face of such appalling treatment; it gave the five of us strength to see those who were now on their own showing such fortitude. But the news of Dick's miserable death in the solitude of his abandonment saddened us greatly.

We rested for some time, our thoughts with the missing members of the crew.

Later in the day, a very respectable-looking old man walked over towards us and sat down in front of me. He spoke to me in Spanish and said that he had learned from our masters who we were, and had been given permission to speak with me.

The man asked all the usual questions about my men and our shipwreck, and I told him of our troubles in this land.

"What friends do you have in Essaouira?" he asked. But before I could reply, he continued. "But I suppose you still call it Mogadore."

So that was it. Essaouira was the same as Mogadore. I had never been there, but I knew of the place. It was a substantial town on the coast, and there were bound to be foreign consuls there as well as some European traders. Even if traders did not live there, they must visit from time to time to buy goods, so there would eventually be ships to take us to Europe or America. That had to be the case, because Mogadore was the major trading port in these parts.

"Yes," I said, "Mogadore. I know the consul there."

"I know all the consuls there," he boasted, "Renshaw and Joseph and Estevan and Corte. Which one do you know?"

From the names, I guessed that Renshaw was the English Consul, so I replied, "I know Mr Renshaw; he is the English Consul."

"Yes, yes," said the old man, "I know him too, Mr Renshaw. I am going to Essaouira; I will be there in ten days' time and will tell him of you."

"Please tell him you met five enslaved Englishmen here."

The old man nodded, got to his feet and hurried back to Sidi Hamet. I could see him talking excitedly and nodding his head. No doubt he was confirming to my master that I knew the English Consul in Essaouira, and had been telling the truth.

Then I saw the old man climb on to his mule and set off. But he had served his purpose. What a piece of luck. We were going to Mogadore, and Mr Renshaw was the man to save us. I told all this to my four companions, and we grew very excited - not just hopeful, but confident that we would survive and return home.

Sidi Hamet came over to sit with us. It was clear that the old man's visit had cheered him as well.

During the afternoon, many of the people passing through came over to speak with Sidi Hamet. They appeared to be very friendly, and all wished to know our story. Several of them asked for my opinion of their horses, their saddles and muskets, and other things. I told them that their possessions were of the best possible quality, and they were very pleased with my answers.

The next morning, a much happier Sidi Hamet told me that he was going to buy another hive of honey, and that he would share it with us. He returned half an hour later with his purchase; but he was not able to carry out his generous intentions, for just as he was handing the comb to me, Hassar's men rushed forward, snatched the hive, ran off and ate all of it. Sidi Hamet went to find Hassar, and a fierce dispute began. In the end, Hassar bought another hive for Sidi Hamet, who then gave us about three pounds of the poorest part of the comb.

I could not understand why Sidi Hamet wished to travel with Hassar and his despicable colleagues. They were nothing but trouble, and they were a threat to our safety.

Setting aside these worries, I tried to summarise our position. We had been wrecked, reached land, been enslaved and then sold, survived the desert and promised a route to freedom and home. But now, vitally, I had discovered that Essaouira was Mogadore and that there was an English consul there called Renshaw. It was a distant light in the gloom of our despair. Now let it get closer and brighter.

CHAPTER SIXTEEN

Fever and a challenge

Sidi Hamet now came to tell me that it was time to leave. We mounted our camels and awaited instructions. I was disappointed to see that Hassar and his group would again be coming with us. We started off together, but soon divided into three groups. Two of Hassar's men and their women and children and many of the camels set off to the east. Hassar and the remainder of his men took the rest of the camels, including ours, in a north-easterly direction, and we, with our masters and two other men, started to walk along the river bank and then turned to the north.

After a short time, we began to ascend the craggy mountains. The labour of clambering up these steep precipices is indescribable. We climbed as fast as we could, pulling ourselves upwards with our hands, fighting for a firm footing with each new step. It was desperately slow progress. I was convinced our masters were taking this route so that they would not be followed. Probably the others were taking an easier path, but one where any robber could catch up with them. We were apparently prize possessions that had to be kept from thieving hands; no doubt the identification of Mr Renshaw had made our value more tangible.

Several hours later, we had climbed over the peaks of the

mountains and started to descend the slope on the other side. We stopped and waited for some time, and were then joined by Hassar and his company, whose two groups had come around the mountain by slower but gentler routes.

It was now near nightfall, but we continued to travel through the mountainside, assisting one another over the most difficult parts, while Hassar again sought out easier ways with the camels.

At last we came to a small area of level ground where there were several tents pitched in a semi-circle. We approached to within a hundred yards, and then Sidi Hamet told all of us to sit down as he did, with his back to the tents. I found this a rather odd way of introducing himself to these people and befriending them.

While we waited, the camels wasted no time in finding food. These small valleys furnish them with subsistence, acting as basins to catch the little water that falls here. Most of the rain is immediately dried away by the intense heat of the sun, yet some moisture escapes that fate and causes the growth of dwarf thorn bushes and two or three other types of prickly plants.

One such shrub grows in a bunch at the base, which is as thick as a man's leg. Then it spreads out in every direction up to a height of about two feet, being roughly five feet in diameter. At the top, the branches are armed with small spikes, over two inches long, which, when broken off, leak a whitish liquid that is very nauseous and sharp to the tongue; but the camels are happy enough to nip it off when they are hungry. The plant looks rather like a chandelier, and is covered once a year with red blossom. It is from this blossom that the bees make their honey, for which we had been so grateful.

After a while, a woman came from one of the tents carrying a bowl of water, and she presented it to our masters. She stood there waiting as they drank the water; but no words were exchanged. Then she went back to the tent, and returned with a bowl of dates. Sidi Hamet took a handful for himself and stood up to bring the remainder to us; but by the time the bowl reached my hands, Seid, Abdallah and Hassar had each snatched as many of the dates as they could, leaving us with about a dozen each. Well, at least we had something to eat. With that, we all stretched out for the night.

We never saw any more of the people in the tents, because we left before dawn the next day, even before the stars had faded from the heavens. We moved speedily to the north, and soon our path veered westwards, bringing us once more near to the sea, passing through numerous steep gullies, until at midday we reached a plain at the far side of which we could see the ocean. It was amazing how whenever we saw the sea, a sea that had caused our shipwreck, our hearts were lifted.

Here on the small plain, we came upon yet another group of tents. This time we went right up to them to meet their occupants. About twenty young men came forward, and they seemed to recognise Sidi Hamet and Hassar, for they smiled and waved as they approached us.

My master walked over to the tents with some of the young men, but then I saw him stagger and fall to the ground. The men immediately cleared a tent, carried Sidi Hamet inside, and put him down on a blanket. I stood near the entrance to see what was happening. My thoughts were not just for Sidi Hamet, they were also for us. If something serious should happen to him, we could not rely on Seid or Hassar to take us to Essaouira.

Sidi Hamet clearly had a fever, and he was complaining of violent pains in his head and in his limbs.

Now one of the young men took charge of proceedings. On his direction, some of the others made a small fire at the entrance to the tent and moved Sidi Hamet next to it, keeping his head close to the heat and almost roasting his brains - or so I thought. Not surprisingly, Sidi Hamet obtained no relief from this extraordinary treatment.

He was then subjected to another attempted remedy, equally bizarre. A large knife was put into the fire and heated red hot. The men then made Seid draw the knife slowly across the top of

Sidi Hamet's head, an inch from his scalp. When the knife had cooled, they heated it again, and it was then stroked along Sidi Hamet's legs and arms about two inches from his skin. Sidi Hamet screamed and twitched throughout this treatment, five men being needed to hold him still. In the end, he lost consciousness and was allowed to sleep.

Burns was also unwell. He had been ill for some time and was so weak that he could not stand, and had therefore been carried on a camel all day. As Sidi Hamet had survived his medication, they now applied the same remedy to Burns' limbs. From want of bodily strength, Burns was unable to resist; he could only cry repeatedly for mercy. Eventually, he too was allowed to sleep.

I sat in the open with Savage, Clark and Horace.

"They may have killed Burns," said Clark.

"No," I replied, "I think he's just sleeping. At least they only did to him what they did to Sidi Hamet, and they left his head alone. I think they were genuinely trying to help both of them. We just have to wait and see."

"Never mind Burns," said Savage, "what about Sidi Hamet? If he dies, your bargain is gone and our future goes with it."

"He's right," said Clark. "If we're lucky, we'll be sold and taken back to the desert. We have to act."

I agreed. "If Sidi Hamet dies, we must try to escape. At least we know that we can reach Essaouira by following the coast to the north for several days. We'll go at night, once we're sure he's dead."

All were in favour. We were somehow fortified by the thought of taking action at last and putting our fate in our own hands, although carrying Burns would be a problem - if he was still alive.

Now we were hungry. I asked Seid to let me go to the beach to look for some mussels, but he refused, saying that I could do so in the morning. My disappointment was reduced when we were later given a good supper of pudding, and we were then allowed to pass the night in the tent where both Sidi Hamet and Burns were fast asleep.

Imagine my surprise when I was awoken by Sidi Hamet the next morning. He seemed to be fully recovered, and as I looked across the tent, I saw Thomas Burns get to his feet unaided. Incredible! We were all amazed and relieved. Our intended escape, which would have been fraught with danger, could be postponed.

"Are you well?" I asked Sidi Hamet.

"Yes," he said. "I have recovered; it was the food. Many of the people here live solely on camel's milk. Those who live on nothing else have no sickness and are favoured by Heaven. But if the same people leave the desert and live on meat and bread and fruits, they suffer every kind of pain and sickness.

"A great many of the food-eaters die very young, and not one in ten lives to an old age. I always feel well when I live on the milk of the camel alone. Then I am strong and can bear heat and cold and fatigue. If it was possible, I would always have as much camel's milk as I could drink, and I would never taste meat again. But," he added with a sigh, "I love food, especially honey, very much."

I told Sidi Hamet that I thought they had killed him. He laughed, and explained that different people had different ways of treating illness. Usually, for internal complaints a bitter weed was administered. For cramps and pains in the bones, the patient was made to lie down on his belly, and a man would jump up and down on his back. Tar and grease were applied to flesh wounds, and a headache was cured by pinching the forehead and temples with the fingers, or biting them. I was in no position to criticise; maybe it worked.

We were given some water, and then we left, driving only our own camels. Hassar and his people had stayed behind with the young one, so the eight of us had three large camels between us.

Riding in turns, we crossed deep hollows until the afternoon, when we were forced to travel along the beach in order to avoid some of the larger hollows whose sides were so steep as to make our passage impracticable.

When we came to the sea, my men once more followed my dash into the water, where we lay in ecstasy as the surf crashed over us. But the incoming waves were strong, and our masters feared that we might be swept away by the receding current, so they ordered us to come out and not go in again. That was no problem, we were now refreshed.

We journeyed along this narrow beach for some time, the cliffs overhanging us on our right and the ocean to our left. Suddenly, as we turned round a bend in the beach, we saw four men, each armed with a musket and a scimitar, spring out from beneath the jutting rocks and challenge us, barring our way.

Sidi Hamet, Seid and Abdallah leapt off their camels and unsheathed their guns. Neither side fired, neither side advanced. No one knew what to do next. Our masters could not retreat; it would disclose their fear and lead to instant pursuit and death - so they advanced three against four. Sidi Hamet, still in a weak state after his illness, now ran at the four men, his musket aimed at them. Seid, that cruel coward, lagged behind with Abdallah.

The enemy stood in a line, neither moving nor speaking. Sidi Hamet stopped about ten yards in front of them, still aiming his gun at the strangers, and demanded to know whether they would let us through. One of them smiled, nodded and held out his hand to Sidi Hamet, who walked forward, offering his own hand, expecting no treachery. But the fellow grasped Sidi Hamet's hand fast and would not let go. No doubt the others were now prepared to fire at our masters, but at that critical juncture three of Hassar's men came into sight, running from behind us along the sands, each brandishing a double-barrelled gun, ready to shoot.

When the robbers saw them, the alarm showed in their faces, and the one holding Sidi Hamet's hand instantly let go, laughing weakly and implying that it had all been a joke. Our people accepted this because they still did not feel sufficiently strong to show their resentment at the insult.

So we moved on as the four bandits stood aside. After we had passed, they followed us in a most threatening manner. Sidi Hamet ordered us to keep close together and proceed as quickly as possible. The bandits soon accepted that there was no booty for them here, and they turned round and ran along the beach away from us, firing in the air, as if asserting their imaginary power.

Having continued further along the beach, we again ascended the bank, leaving the ruffians in control of the shore, to which they were now welcome. Once back on the high level, we sat down to rest and recover our composure. Sidi Hamet told me that these bandits were very bad men who would have killed him, Seid and Abdallah if Hassar's men had not arrived, and we would have been taken for sale as slaves.

He then asked me if I would have fought to save his life. I told him I would have. "No one shall kill you while I am still alive," I said, rather grandly. Pleased with my answer, he patted me on the shoulder and walked away.

CHAPTER SEVENTEEN

Horsemen and a cure

We trudged on without thought, just hoping that something new would come into view. Near evening, we caught up with a man walking alongside a mule that was laden with fish. These fish, which they call '*shebbel*', were quite large and looked rather like salmon. Our masters tried to buy three of the fish from this man, but he said he had already agreed to sell all of them to someone else, and could not part with any regardless of the price they might offer. It seemed to me that this was a reasonable way for him to open negotiations; but nothing of the sort. He would not sell and that was the end of it.

My masters muttered a little amongst themselves, but to my surprise they did not pursue the matter, and we overtook the man and carried on as it quickly grew dark. We climbed a gentle hill near the cliffs, and there we found Hassar's tents already pitched and the rest of his group waiting to greet us.

The shadows of evening were fast falling, and we dismounted and lay down to rest. I noticed that Seid, Abdallah and two of Hassar's men were having an animated conversation. Then each of them took a gun, and they left the encampment on foot.

About two hours later, now in complete darkness, we heard footsteps approaching. Sidi Hamet and Hassar seized their muskets, ran to the edge of our encampment and called out, challenging whoever was there, and demanding to know their purpose. But it was only Seid and the three others carrying a large blanket that was carefully folded. They brought it before one of the tents and opened it. Out rolled seven large fish of the type we had seen earlier in the evening.

"Riley," said Sidi Hamet, "these are good to eat. Put them in the pot. You and your men may have one of them, but do not choke on the bones."

I took the seven fish and cut them into pieces. Then I put the pieces into a large earthen pot, added some water and set it to boil.

We were allowed our one fish, which we shared, and then we lay down to sleep close to the tents. Sidi Hamet warned us not to stray, for there were many evil robbers in this area who would try to seize us and carry us off. A little strong, I thought, for I doubted that our party had acquired the *shebbel* by their fishing skills.

On the twenty-fourth, we set off at daybreak together with Hassar and his party. In the afternoon, a company of men on horseback, all well armed, rode towards us, shouting out as they approached. As the horsemen came near, our masters sprang from their camels, unsheathed their guns, and took station before their possessions, standing in a line ready for action.

The horsemen rode up to within five yards of our masters, and then stopped their horses abruptly. I expected to see a battle, though I rather feared that our company would be trampled to death before any fighting could take place.

Then the chief of the horsemen demanded in a very imperious tone who our masters were, where they came from, if they knew who Sidi Ishem was, what country we slaves came from, and where they had found us. Sidi Hamet replied to their questions in a sharp manner and as briefly as possible. He then demanded in turn who they were, where they came from, and by what right they approached so fiercely.

A loud dispute raged for half an hour, although fortunately it

... a company of men on horseback, all well armed

was limited to shouting. Then the noise ceased; it was obviously not getting anyone anywhere. The horsemen rode off, and we were allowed to continue on our way.

Experience was showing me that when few were involved, safety lay in having almost equal numbers to any adversaries. No one would risk a battle unless he believed that he had overwhelming superiority.

We travelled on until long after dark, and came to a collection of pitched tents where we stopped for the night.

I looked round at the encampment. It was the usual arrangement: men dealing with the camels, women seeing to the tents. Amongst these people, the women have all the management of what may be called domestic economy, including the preparation of food. However, the different sexes never eat together; both eat sitting on the ground, taking the food with their hands from wooden dishes, the men in one group and, a few yards away, the women in another.

The families consist of the father, one or more wives and the unmarried children, as well as their slaves, who are all black. Each family has a mat, which serves as a bed for all of them. They all lie down on it, wrapped only in their *haicks*, which may be used as a cloak, carpet or blanket.

Polygamy is allowed, but the people of the desert seldom have more than one wife. Only the rich ones, who need more servants, sometimes take a second or third wife, the wives and daughters being considered as little more than slaves. The father of the family is its absolute chief in every respect, though he seldom inflicts punishment.

Many of the richer men own two or three slaves, both male and female. The slaves have to carry out all the daily chores, including taking care of the camels, but most of them refuse to obey the women.

Whilst we had been travelling in the desert, I had never seen any sick people. However, since we had come to the cultivated country, I had noticed that many people were unwell. Some were

202

afflicted with swollen legs, and some with what I took to be leprosy.

Now Sidi Hamet came over and told me that he had informed these people that I was learned in the ways of curing illness. No doubt this raised his status with them. He had promised that I would treat one of the women in the tents. I was surprised at this, but not in the least worried. It was worth a try; it might improve matters for us if I had a little success.

Sidi Hamet and I walked over to the tents, where we found a woman sitting on a blanket, looking extremely distressed. Another woman lowered the sitting woman's clothes to the waist. One of her breasts was swollen and astonishingly large and inflamed. The slightest touch caused her to cry out in pain. There was little I could do to examine her, apart from feel her forehead to determine that she had a fever.

I told her to lie down flat, and I advised them to keep her in the shade at all times and to place a piece of wet cloth on her forehead. I knew that I had to offer further advice, and that I must make use of whatever resources they had. So I then recommended that they apply a poultice of their barley pudding to the woman's breast, and renew it often until the swelling subsided or burst. They did this and were very grateful to me. As payment, I was given a handful of mussels and a drink of water.

The confidence I had portrayed encouraged these people to believe that I could indeed cure illnesses. Now the woman asked me to treat her brother, and he was brought before me. The man had a badly swollen leg. No skin was broken, so I directed that a thick plaster of sea salt should be applied and held fast by a cloth. As soon as this had been done, the man indicated that he felt immediate relief.

When we had returned to our group, Sidi Hamet asked me if the remedies would work.

"I don't know," I replied. "It would be wise if we left in the morning." I could see that he understood.

CHAPTER EIGHTEEN

An accusation and a dispute

I was in a deep sleep when Clark pushed me to wake me up. It was very early on 25th October.

"What is it? It's still night-time," I said.

"We have to get up and leave right away," said Clark.

"What's happening?" I asked.

"I don't know," he replied. "We just have to leave now, and no more talking."

It was well before daylight. This was very strange; I suspected some roguery.

We journeyed for about two hours when, just as dawn was breaking to our right, we heard the sound of horses coming up behind us at full speed. The clanking of the riders' spurs against the stirrups made a great noise, and it was made doubly frightening by the thumping of the horses' hooves. Expecting trouble, our masters immediately stripped the covers from their guns and prepared for battle.

The horsemen rode to the front of our camels, halted, and blocked our progress. I noticed that the two sides were evenly matched; would this prove my theory that no fighting would take place if the numbers were similar?

Sidi Hamet told me that we must keep close behind him. Then our masters charged at full speed. We ran behind them, going as fast as we could, fearful that we might be separated from our masters and then fall into the hands of the bandits.

The two groups were now very close to each other, all shouting loudly, the mountains ringing with the sound of their noise, the horses restless and straining to move away. Despite my theory, I still expected slaughter to commence; but no, instead the two sides stopped five yards apart and started to hurl insults at each other, my masters being accused of a breach of hospitality. Eventually, this war of words subsided a little, and one of the horsemen asked Sidi Hamet his name. In reply, my master demanded to know the horseman's name. After a considerable delay, each insisting that the other should disclose his name first, Sidi Hamet broke the impasse by telling the man his name. The horseman then announced that his name was Ali Mohammed. There followed a long dispute between them with much pointing of fingers and waving of fists.

I noticed that daylight had now arrived. Without the darkness, the scene looked less ominous. But not for long, because our adversaries gained strength as they were joined by many armed and unarmed men. Now I was most concerned. I could no longer rely on my theory - and nor could Sidi Hamet. As the enemy increased in force, so our party's arguments lowered in tone and volume.

One of the unarmed men pushed his way to the front. This man was really angry; the veins in his forehead were near to bursting, his eyes ready to pop out. He did not limit himself to shouting abuse and insults; he had an accusation to make. Now everything became clear to me. Our masters had set off with two of the man's camels; this was the cause of our early departure and of the uproar that was now raging. The purloined beasts were with our camels; I had not even noticed them in the dark. The odd thing about camels is that unlike dogs, horses and many other creatures, they do not recognise their owner, and that makes it easy to steal them, as they neither resist nor bellow at the thief.

Our masters were defeated by the deadly combination of truth and superior numbers. Now that they knew there was no hope of keeping what they had feloniously taken, they had nothing more to say. Seizing advantage of the situation, the aggrieved man ran over and drove his two camels away.

I was worried. Would the others now attack? Although our masters were ready to fight, I had no doubt that they would be overpowered, in which event we would fall to the conquerors. There was no reason to suppose that these men would treat us more humanely than Sidi Hamet. Nor could I be certain that we would not be slaughtered as the horsemen and their companions gave vent to their rage.

Our situation was perilous; what would happen? Then Sidi Hamet went over to Ali Mohammed and spoke to him in a low voice, inviting him to walk away from the others so that they could speak in private. They came near to where I was standing, still trembling with apprehension. Sidi Hamet now explained to Ali Mohammed that his group had not had the slightest intention of driving off any camels but their own, and that the mistake had been a result of the darkness. He blamed himself for causing the error by leaving before daylight, something he should never have done and would never do again. My master went on to protest that he was incapable of committing an unworthy action, that he abhorred robbers and thieves and that, as he was entirely innocent of intentionally driving off the man's camels, he was prepared to lose his life in maintaining his character, and would sell it as dearly as possible.

Next he told the man that he was relying on him to convince the others, because he now knew the truth. Ali Mohammed seemed to be satisfied by this preposterous story. He said to Sidi Hamet, "I am your friend because you are a brave man."

Ali Mohammed then walked over to his companions and addressed them on behalf of Sidi Hamet. He repeated Sidi

Hamet's excuse, sounding considerably more convincing than Sidi Hamet himself. They accepted my master's defence, and all of them went off back to their camp in silence.

We could now proceed once more in clear sunlight; but, of course, without the stolen camels. By noon we reached a plain, and moved a little way from the coast. Hassar and his party with their camels, and Abdallah with his, filed off to the left, leaving us with Sidi Hamet, Seid and their camels. Our party was on its own.

Soon we discovered land that was very high a good way to the east, stretching as far as the eye could see.

"There is Essaouira, Riley," said Sidi Hamet, pointing to the north. I asked him how long it would take to get there.

"Six days at our slow pace," he answered.

Six days to freedom? Perhaps.

The mortifying result of the morning's failed enterprise had rendered Seid extremely ill-tempered. He was forever scowling and turning round to glare at us, all the time muttering to himself.

Sidi Hamet was riding on the big camel in front of us, when Seid turned his camel and rode between us and Sidi Hamet, and ordered us to halt. Sidi Hamet turned round and ordered us to continue. Seid then jumped down from his camel and took hold of Savage and Horace.

"These two are mine," insisted Seid.

Savage had been Seid's slave for some time, there was no disputing that. In addition, Seid had always claimed that Horace was his property, as he had provided the price of Horace's purchase. Perhaps because Horace was young, Seid had a good opinion of his worth.

But Sidi Hamet claimed that he had purchased Horace and had sworn that Horace would not be separated from me. Seid might have provided the price, but that was a loan to Sidi Hamet, no more. In return, Seid was to receive a share of the ransom. Seid warned Sidi Hamet that they were entering dangerous territory with powerful chiefs, and that many groups of men, intent on plunder, were scouring the country in every direction. For that reason, Seid was determined to take his slaves and make the most of them before they were stolen. By that, I assumed he wished to sell Savage and Horace at the first opportunity.

"I have made a bargain with Riley," said Sidi Hamet. "We will get much more for these people by taking them to Essaouira."

"No you will not," said Seid, "and a bargain with an infidel is worthless," he added. "Anyway, that miserable wretch will not find anyone to pay you money."

Seid was Sidi Hamet's younger brother, and had always submitted to his views, though not without a good deal of resentment. But now Seid looked ready to defy his brother. It was a worrying time for us. How would this be resolved?

I could see that Sidi Hamet's wrath was kindled. He would not accept this insubordination. Leaping from his camel, he ran at Seid, grabbed hold of him, and pulled him from Savage and Horace. The two of them grasped each other fiercely, as each strove to throw the other to the ground. Seid was the taller man, but Sidi Hamet was the stouter. They writhed and twined in every shape, until both fell to the ground. Seid was above Sidi Hamet and this gave him the advantage. Fire seemed to flash from their eyes as they held each other tight. Then they rolled round and round like two serpents, until Sidi Hamet by superior strength or skill, managed to disengage himself from his brother's grasp, and both of them sprang to their feet.

Instantly, they ran to the camels and snatched their muskets. Then both took a few paces backwards as they tore the cloth from their guns. Each pointed his gun at his brother's breast.

They were not more than fifteen yards apart, and both would surely have fallen dead had they fired.

"Stop!" I shouted in despair, but at that instant I heard two shots fired. I expected to see them lying on the ground, but no; Sidi Hamet had intentionally fired both his barrels into the air. Then, walking forward, he threw his gun to the ground. He tore open his *haick*, and presented his breast to Seid, inviting him to fire and kill him. Surely there were few people on this earth less appropriate for such an offer.

Seid hesitated.

"Go ahead," said Sidi Hamet looking to the sky, "our mother and father are watching you."

Savage and Horace were still close to Seid, afraid to return to us. Now Seid pointed his gun at Savage and Horace, threatening to fire if they moved.

Sidi Hamet told Seid that he could have Clark in place of Horace; but Seid would not accept the exchange, signifying his refusal by spitting on the ground. So then Sidi Hamet offered both Clark and Burns for Horace. Seid's response was to make Horace lie on the ground and then place a foot on Horace's chest to prevent him from moving. Sidi Hamet now ordered Savage to go over to me, although I was not sure if Savage understood the instruction. Seid held his gun to Savage's head, threatening to blow his brains out if he moved. He had no intention of moving, but Sidi Hamet ran over, took hold of Savage and dragged him towards me.

The two brothers then sat down on the ground and started a violent, though non-physical, negotiation. They bargained and calculated in every way; the greater the reasoning behind a proposal, the greater the contempt with which it was dismissed. Whatever was offered, Seid was not interested. He insisted that he would keep the slaves who had been bought with his money.

But Sidi Hamet would not accept this, at least as far as Horace was concerned. "You shall not separate him from his father, for I have sworn it."

"Then I will destroy him!" exclaimed Seid furiously and, springing to his feet, he seized Horace, lifted him in the air and hurled him to the ground with all his might.

Horace lay there motionless, the impact having beaten the breath from his body. As I saw him stretched out and apparently dead, I sank to my knees in an agony of despair.

Sidi Hamet, observing my anguish, said, "Go, Riley," pointing to the north. What was this? Was he releasing me from my bondage because he had broken his word to me? I told him that I would go because Horace, my son, was dead. I was distraught, but now I must think carefully. What was I meant to do? Was I to walk off into the distance and leave my men behind? This was nonsense. I must stop bewailing the death of my adopted son; I must look after myself and my remaining shipmates.

"We shall stay together, and my bargain will be kept," I said.

Sidi Hamet went over to Horace and pulled him to a sitting position. To my astonishment, Horace was breathing, and he opened his eyes. He quickly revived and, although dazed, seemed to be uninjured. Sidi Hamet melted into tears at the sight, saying to me in a tender tone, "Go to your son."

By chance, the area where Horace's head had hit the ground happened to be clear of stones, otherwise his brains must have been dashed out. I knelt down beside him, and asked if he was in pain. He said that he was sore and a little unsteady, but no more than that. Within half an hour, he was as fit as he had been before the attack.

Having watched Horace's recovery in silence, and with obvious relief, Sidi Hamet and Seid once more sat down on the ground to continue their debate. Tempers and voices rose until, fortunately for us, they saw men riding in the distance. This reminded the two brothers that their mutual priority was the defence of themselves and their property. They agreed that we should move off immediately and stop at the next village on our route. There they would find someone to advise what should be done about their dispute.

We did not have to travel far. As soon as we had passed over the next hill, we came to another walled village or *dourham*. The gates were open, and we rode in.

Proceeding to the far side of the village, we were greeted by a respectable looking old man. He was a Moor of light olive colour, and he welcomed Sidi Hamet and Seid very warmly. The man told us to sit down in the shade given by one of the walls of his house and to rest there.

Our host came and sat with us and our masters. He wanted to know all about us. Not realising that I could speak some Arabic, he addressed all his questions to Sidi Hamet.

My owner told the old man our story, and explained to him the details of the bargain, although he was careful not to mention the amount of money I had agreed to provide. The old man then asked how Sidi Hamet had been able to discuss the bargain with me. Now the man was told of my knowledge of Arabic, so he asked me the questions all over again. I was also required to repeat my oath of payment, but Sidi Hamet interrupted me before *benduqis* were mentioned.

The old man also wanted to know what property I owned, if I had my own house, if I had any money there and how many animals, children and wives I had.

I thought that my masters were being surprisingly trusting in allowing their host so much information; but perhaps they were more interested in impressing him. Anyway, that was up to them. Having answered the questions to everyone's satisfaction, they made me tell them what Savage, Clark and Burns were worth to me, how much property I thought they had in their own country and what families they had. As usual, I supplied answers that I thought would make them happy and would cause us no problems.

Our host asked me if Essaouira was called Mogdoura by the English. This was a new name for me. "I have heard Mogdoura used by some," I said, "but usually we call it Mogadore."

"Yes," he said, "the town's name has been changed often. It is an old town, and whoever owned it changed its name. The Berbers were the first, and they called the town Amogdoul after Sidi Mogdoul, who is buried not far from the town. The Phoenicians called the town Migdol, which meant a lookout tower. When the Portuguese came, they changed the name to Mogdoura; then the Spanish changed it to Mogadour and the French to Mogadore. Not many years ago, Sultan Sidi Mohammed Bin Abdullah had the town rebuilt, and he re-named it Souira, which soon became Essaouira- 'the fortified place'."

211

Now a bowl of boiled barley was brought to our masters, and another was brought for us. The old man presented the bowl to me, saying, "Eat, *Rais*."

We rested for a while. During that time, Sidi Hamet left us, returning about an hour later with a large young man named Bo-Mohammed. Sidi Hamet told me that he had hired Bo-Mohammed for protection, as he could no longer trust Seid. He had been advised to do this by our host, who had also told him that the dispute between the brothers should be dealt with by a wise man who lived in a nearby town, where we should go immediately.

The old man wished us well, and we set off, leaving the *dourham* and travelling towards the coast. We reached the sea, and then we turned and walked parallel to a sandy beach. Continuing until it was almost dark, we came upon the town where Sidi Hamet expected to find the wise man. We entered and wandered along, barking dogs announcing our arrival to the inhabitants.

Sidi Hamet was looking for a particular house, and we soon found it. A most respectable and serious-looking man came up to us, and bade our masters welcome.

Our new host was called Sidi Mohammed. Mohammed is the name generally given to the first male child and he is always addressed as Sidi, meaning Sir, Monsieur, or Senor, as well as saint; whereas those with other names have to earn that address. Sidi Mohammed placed a large mat next to the wall of his house, sat down on it and invited my masters and me to sit with him, whilst my men rested several yards away. We were grateful for the opportunity to rest, as we were all suffering from pains in the stomach, caused no doubt by eating too much boiled barley.

Then the routine started once more. Sidi Mohammed made the same enquiries as our last host. Again, I satisfied his curiosity as well as I could, trying to appear neither bored nor tired. He then asked me to repeat my promise to Sidi Hamet, which I did - *benduqis* and all.

When you say something funny to an adult, he is likely to laugh. If you retell it later, it is no longer amusing and the more often you repeat it, the more tiresome it becomes. But if you say something amusing to a young child, every repetition is just as funny and the child will invite you to repeat your words again and again. It seemed to me that my bargain with Sidi Hamet fell into that second category. The more often I made my promise, the more he beamed in self-congratulation.

By this time, some cakes had been baked, and they were presented to our masters, who gave me a share to take over to my men. These cakes were made of barley meal ground coarse, but it was really a form of bread. We ate a little of it, even though our stomachs were not yet ready to savour such a treat.

After Sidi Mohammed and my masters had eaten and then washed their hands and feet, they sat talking for a while. Then Sidi Hamet called me over to join him.

"We have discussed our problems and agreed on what to do. Tomorrow, Riley, I shall leave for Essaouira with Sidi Mohammed," he said. "With God's blessing we will be there in three days. We shall travel on Sidi Mohammed's mules, which will be quicker than the camels."

"Can I go with you?" I pleaded. "I need to organise the money with Mr Renshaw."

"No," he replied. "You must write a note to your friend, which I shall carry to him. If your friend fulfils your promise and pays the money for you, then you will be free. If not, you must die for having deceived me, and your men will be sold for whatever I can get for them. I have fought for you and have suffered hunger, thirst and fatigue in order to restore you to your family. I have paid away all my money on your word alone. Seid and Bo-Mohammed will stay and guard you while I am away. They will give you bread and *lhash*. So now go and sleep."

I spent that night in a state of anxiety. To whom should I write? I knew nobody in Essaouira. Certainly I had Renshaw's name, but how would he react to a note from me? I had to think carefully. I had to take my chance. We had survived through all this; now we would take the final step.

CHAPTER NINETEEN

A letter and news

Early the next morning, Sidi Hamet called me into the house. "Come Riley," he said, "write your letter."

What now? Composing the letter would not be much of a problem, but addressing it was another matter.

Sidi Hamet presented me with a piece of paper about four inches wide and eight inches long, and a scrap that was part of a Spanish bill of lading. He also gave me a reed to write with and some black liquid. Once more I begged to go with him to Essaouira so that I could deliver my message in person, but he would not agree. I told him that he could trust me and that I would leave my son as hostage; but it made no difference.

So I took the reed in my hand; then before I could do anything, Sidi Hamet seized his last opportunity to improve the bargain.

Now he told me, "Riley, what you have agreed to pay me is not enough. You must tell your friend to pay twelve *benduqis* for you, the same for your son, ten for the one who was so much trouble, and eight for each of the other two. You have promised to give me a double-barrelled shotgun and you must also give one to Seid. He is a bad man, but he helped to save your life and must have a gun."

215

There was no negotiating with this man. So I took the reed and wrote.

"Sir, The brig Commerce, from Gibraltar for America, was wrecked on Cape Bajador on the 27th August last. Myself and four of my crew are here nearly naked, in barbarian slavery. I conjure you by all the ties that bind man to man, by those of kindred blood, and every thing you hold most dear, and by as much as liberty is dearer than life, to advance the money required for our redemption, which is 50 gold benduqis and two double-barrelled guns. I can draw for any amount, the moment I am at liberty, on Batard, Sampson & Sharp, London, or Cropper & Benson, Liverpool, or Munro & Burton, Lisbon, or on Horatio Sprague, Gibraltar. Should you not relieve me, my life must instantly pay the forfeit. I would leave my wife and our helpless children to deplore my death. My companions are Aaron Savage, Horace Savage, James Clark and Thomas Burns. I left six more in slavery in the desert. My present master, Sidi Hamet, will hand you this and tell you where we are - he is a worthy man. Worn down to the bones by the most dreadful of all suffering - naked and a slave, I implore your pity, and trust that such distress will not be suffered to plead in vain. For God's sake, send a guard for us, if that is possible.

James Riley,
late Captain of the brig Commerce.

I folded the pieces of paper carefully. I intentionally did not mention that we were Americans, as I was not sure if there would be an American Consul in Essaouira. Now to address the letter. Of course, Sidi Hamet could not understand English; it would not be difficult after all. There was no need to limit myself to one addressee, so I wrote on the back of the larger piece of paper the widest range of relevant addressees I could think of: 'Mr Renshaw, the English Consul, or the French, Spanish or American Consuls, or any Christian merchants in Mogadore or Essaouira'.

Sidi Hamet stood over me, hurrying me on as I wrote. Both he and our host were surprised to see me use Arabic numerals. Sidi Mohammed remarked that I must have been a slave before to an Arab master who had taught me to use their numerals, contrary to their law.

I handed the letter to Sidi Hamet. He looked straight into my eyes, as if to say: 'I know this is serious for you; I hope you have been truthful for both our sakes.' But he said nothing. He mounted one mule, Sidi Mohammed mounted another and, pulling a third mule laden with provisions, they set off for Essaouira.

We remained in the small town awaiting our fate. Nothing much happened for three days. During the daytime we were shut up in a yard where usually cows, sheep and asses rested. At night, we were locked up in a dreary cellar.

Seid and Bo-Mohammed guarded us day and night. I do not think they feared that we might attempt to escape; rather they were concerned that the neighbouring people might try to steal us.

So our imprisonment was unpleasant, but at least we were not in fear of our lives. As for food, we had barley bread twice a day, *lhash* once a day, and plenty of water. The rest, the shade, the food and drink - all these things allowed our bodies to recover, and the sores on our skin started to disappear. But, as ever, a new torture came to torment us. The food, although palatable, produced and kept up a constant dysentery, our bowels seeming to ferment like beer, and we were tortured with colic.

There was nothing for us to do during the day; we could only wonder whether my note would lead to freedom. Would Sidi Hamet come back in a good humour with our redeemer, or would he return enraged and intent on punishment?

Many of the people who lived in the town and the surrounding areas, on hearing that Christians were there, came to see us. These people refer to all Europeans as Christians, or *Nasrani*, meaning 'followers of the man from Nazareth'.

On the fourth day after Sidi Hamet's departure, one of our visitors gave me some documents to read. I examined the first one carefully; it was the Register of a Spanish schooner called the Maria, issued by the custom-house at Cadiz in May 1814. The second document was a bill of sale for the Maria, made out at Grand Canary in 1812. The man could see that I was interested, and he was very pleased with himself. He left and returned two hours later, carrying several items of clothing that he was eager to show to me. They were obviously from the Maria's crew. Then he took me by the arm and showed me around my prison, pointing to the wooden pieces that supported the floor above us - they were parts of the topmast, the jib-boom and other small spars of that doomed vessel.

I asked the man what had happened to the vessel. He told me that in the previous year the schooner had anchored near the coast to catch fish and to trade. Men from the town had managed to get alongside her during the night, and after killing the captain and three of the crew, the others surrendered. Having taken the money and other valuables on board, the assailants cut the vessel's cable and ran her on to the shore. Next they made the surviving crew-members assist them in tearing the wreck to pieces and then carrying the timbers to the town, so that they might use them to build houses.

By now the man had been joined by others who gloried in their capture of the Maria and jabbered excitedly, happy to show off their great victory. I asked how many sailors had been on board and what had become of them. He told me that the vessel had a crew of seventeen; four had been slain in the battle and five had died later. The remaining eight were, so he said, a great way off to the south-east, where they were employed on the land and in building houses. That sounded to me like slavery in the salt mines in the middle of the desert. But others said no, the survivors had gone to Essaouira and from there back to their country. The smiling faces suggested that this was a huge joke, and I was sure that those men had either been massacred or else were in slavery, where neither the voice of freedom nor the hand of friendship was ever likely to reach them.

Some of the people who came to visit us, both old and young, knew quite a number of Spanish words and phrases, though they did not know their meaning. These were mainly the roughest and coarsest words and phrases in the language, which had no doubt been spoken by those desperate Spanish sailors who were being tormented by their captors. Their only relief must have been to execrate their persecutors with the foulest expressions imaginable. The townspeople had learned those phrases, and now used them smilingly to one another, without a clue as to the abuse they were uttering.

One young fellow knew several words of English, such as 'good morning' and 'good night'. He was also the master of a good collection of curses. One afternoon, he walked up to Savage and said, "Button, cut it wid a nif." Who had taught him these words? Had the crew of another vessel met with disaster here? I never found out.

Amongst the people coming to view us were several black men, who came from the countries beyond the desert. Some of them were free men and some were slaves who came in attendance on their masters. Seid asked me what we called black men, and when I told him 'negroes', he repeated the word to each of them, smirking and pointing at them, at which they were very indignant.

Late in the day, a tall and impressive-looking man with dark skin, coloured somewhere between a negro and an Arab, came to

219

stay with our guards. When he arrived, the man was greeted with great respect by Seid and the others, who addressed him by the name of Sheikh Ali. This must have been the man whom Sidi Hamet mentioned when I first saw him; the same Sheikh Ali who had sold goods to Sidi Hamet and Seid, and who was to be paid by them after their travels. Seid seemed to be severely shocked by the Sheikh's arrival.

Sheikh Ali possessed talents of that superior caste that never fail to command respect and at the same time inspire dread, awe and reverence. He raised his voice terribly on occasions and spoke in tones of thunder. Yet when he wished to please by condescension and courtesy, his voice was like the sweetest music. But either way, when he spoke, all the company observed the most profound silence.

He questioned Seid about me and my men, and I heard him tell Seid that he believed me to be a very artful fellow and capable of any action, either good or bad. So the Sheikh did not like me; I had better take care. But at least he did say that he had no doubt that my friends would raise any sum of money that might be demanded for our ransom.

Sheikh Ali also said that he very much regretted that he had not seen Sidi Hamet before he had set out for Essaouira. He had matters to discuss with Sidi Hamet, and he would remain here until my master returned.

There was something threatening in what Sheikh Ali said, and I would have been happy to see him leave. But there was no chance of that; he was determined to wait for Sidi Hamet for as long as it took. Now Sheikh Ali came over and spoke to me. He questioned me very closely about my country, my crew, my property and generally as so many others had done. He also wanted to know all about our shipwreck. Finally, he asked me for details of the property and the precise amount of money that had fallen into the hands of those we first encountered after our vessel was wrecked.

He said that he knew the group of people we had met on the

beach. He was their lord, and they had, as their duty required, delivered to him everything they had taken from us, of which he had handed back part as their reward. In reply, I told him exactly what had been taken, except that I increased the amount of money tenfold.

"What!" he shouted. "How much in money?"

So I told him again. He stormed away, furious, his eyes on fire, muttering threats of violence and retribution. Now that elderly villain would get justice for his murder of Antonio.

About an hour later, Sheikh Ali returned to continue his enquiries. He examined our bodies, and on one of Savage's arms he noticed a tattooed cross and some other Christian insignia. The Sheikh immediately pronounced him a Spaniard and said that he should not be redeemed, but must be taken to the mountains to work for him. I feared the Sheikh's power, and I wondered whether Sidi Hamet would be able to resist his will; everything this man said seemed to carry with it a weight that bore down all opposition.

We were now in constant expectation of Sidi Hamet's return, or at least some message from him. Whenever someone arrived in the town, our keepers asked if they had seen him, but the answer was always no. Then, on the fifth day of Sidi Hamet's absence, one of the fiercest-looking men I had ever seen approached and called for Seid to come out and meet him immediately. Seid came forward and demanded to know who this man was. He replied that his name was Ullah Omar, that he had come from Essaouira, that he had met Sidi Hamet near that town, and had been asked by him to tell Seid that God had prospered his journey so far.

Ullah Omar was almost as tall as Sheikh Ali, with a similar dark complexion. He was about forty years old and extremely muscular. He wore a cream-coloured robe, and had iron spurs fastened to his yellow leather slippers. In his hand he held a musket, and he boasted a pair of pistols in his belt and two long knives at his side.

Sheikh Ali knew this man and strode forward to welcome him. After they had finished their greetings, Ullah Omar asked for me.

221

I was pointed out to him, and he came over and told me that he had met Sidi Hamet one day's ride from Essaouira.

"I hope that you will be as true to Sidi Hamet as he has been to you," he said, before turning away and going back to Seid and Sheikh Ali. Seid gave him a bowl of food that they called '*couskusu*', with some slices of squash spread over it. It looked very tasty and would have been a nice change from our *lhash* pudding; but we were given none.

After they had finished their meal, they washed, drank some water, and then prayed together. Then, Ullah Omar left.

This felt like good news - but only because there was no bad news. It was no surprise that Sidi Hamet was getting near to Essaouira, and I hoped that the confirmation would encourage Seid and Bo-Mohammed to see to our safety, for the time being at least.

Now, more than ever, I was desperate to know my fate, although I must admit that I trembled at the thought of what it might be. If Sidi Hamet should find no one willing to pay the money for our redemption, my fate was sealed. I had already agreed to have my throat cut; this could not be prevented. Yet, when I had made that bargain, I had been naked in a vast and dreary desert without a drop of water to quench my burning thirst, nor anything to satisfy the cravings of hunger. My life had been fast wasting away, and I and each of my comrades would have sold our lives for a drink of water or a morsel of bread.

In that situation, who would not have done the same? It was not from a desire to deceive Sidi Hamet; it was from my desire to do whatever I could to obtain liberty for my shipmates and for myself. But the thought of Sidi Hamet's return produced in me an uneasiness that bordered on panic. Would his return lead to my freedom or to my death? There seemed to be no other alternative.

CHAPTER TWENTY

A Moor and hope

The sixth day of Sidi Hamet's absence passed tediously as we sat around drinking water, eating, resting - like beasts in a stable.

Then, after dark, we heard people approaching. Seid went outside to see who it was. He came back with Sidi Mohammed and a very tall Moor. The Moor was a man of noble stature, with stalwart limbs. His face was fearless, and he had very marked features: a sombre complexion with a dark beard, piercing black eyes and an aquiline nose. He had the look of desert blood and breeding about him, with a refinement of appearance and superior manners. Sidi Mohammed and the Moor had arrived from Essaouira. They came straight to where we were sitting, trembling with apprehension. Where was Sidi Hamet? What had become of him?

The Moor came right up to me and said in English, "How you, Capetan?" I felt as though my heart was forcing its way up my throat and preventing me from breathing. Taking hold of the Moor's arm, I asked him who he was and whether Sidi Hamet had come back with them.

In reply he asked me in Spanish if I spoke that language, and I told him I did. He then addressed me in Spanish, telling me that he came from Essaouira. By chance he had met Sidi Hamet and Sidi Mohammed as they entered the town. Having recognised Sidi Hamet as a member of a tribe called by the Moors 'sons of lions', he had approached him and greeted him, asking 'Where do you come from, son of a lion?' Sidi Hamet had told him our story and shown him my letter.

When Sidi Hamet mentioned the word 'consul', the Moor had replied that he knew the English vice-consul, and Sidi Hamet had asked to be taken to him. As a result, my letter had been handed to one of the best men in that town, an Englishman whom the Moor was proud to call his friend. This man had shed tears on reading the letter, and had instantly agreed to pay Sidi Hamet the amount demanded. He had then given the Moor instructions and had asked him to set out immediately, which he did, travelling with Sidi Mohammed as fast as possible, day and night, until they had reached us.

Other than Savage, my shipmates spoke little Spanish, and they interrupted to find out what had been said. So I translated the Moor's story. We were full of joy, yet still apprehensive as to what this meant for us. At that moment, the Moor handed me a letter. My hand was shaking so violently that I could not read it. I gave the letter to Savage, who read it out aloud by the light of the fire.

My Dear and afflicted Sir,
I have this moment received your note from Sidi Hamet, the contents of which, I hope you will be perfectly assured, have called forth my most sincere pity for your sufferings, and those of your companions in captivity.
By a Gibraltar paper I have discovered under Arrivals from the 5th to the 11th August the name of your vessel, and that she was American, from which I conclude that you and your crew must be

subjects of the United States.

I congratulate you most sincerely on the good fortune you and your fellow sufferers have met by being in the hands of a man who seems to be guided by some degree of compassion.

I can in some measure understand the severe and dangerous sufferings and hardships you must have undergone; but, my dear sir, console yourself for, thanks be to God, I hope there will soon be a happy result, for which purpose I pray that you and your unfortunate companions will be given the health and strength once more to visit your native land.

This letter will be delivered to you by Rais bel Cossim, in whom you may place the fullest faith. He speaks Spanish, and has directions to pay attention to your orders and render you every care.

I have agreed to pay the sum of 50 benduqis to Sidi Hamet on your arrival in this town with your fellow sufferers. He remains here as a kind of hostage for your safe appearance.

I have been induced to trust implicitly to your word and the respectable references you have given, in confidence that those gentlemen or yourself will readily reimburse me the whole of the expenses incurred in obtaining your redemption.

I have the most sincere pleasure to inform you that you will be at liberty to commence your journey for this town on receipt of this letter. I have sent with Rais bel Cossim shoes and clothes which I have no doubt you will find very useful in preserving you on your journey. I have also sent some provisions and spirits, so that you may have a foretaste of your returning liberty.

I beg to advise the greatest secrecy of your

circumstances until your arrival here, for should your captors suppose that you are able to pay more, you will face further severe difficulties.

I shall send a message tomorrow to the United States Consul General in Tangier, and a letter to Mr Sprague in Gibraltar, informing them of your loss and of the favourable hopes I have for your immediate release and return.

I have told Rais bel Cossim to take you to a place that is a short distance from Mogadore. Then he will send a message to me and I will immediately set out to meet you.

I need hardly say how truly I commiserate and feel for you in all your misfortunes. I beg you to assure your crew of my truest intentions, and I trust that they will set out not with sentiments embittered by the thoughts of the miseries you have undergone, but rather with the most sanguine hope of a happy end to all your sufferings.

I am, dear Captain Riley, your friend,
William Willshire

Our captors could not, of course, understand any English, so the Moor explained in Arabic that he and his friend, an Englishman, had agreed to pay the ransom, and Sidi Hamet was waiting with his friend until he had delivered us to Essaouira.

We could only raise our eyes and hearts to heaven in silent gratitude, while tears of joy trickled down our haggard cheeks. But joy is rarely pure and untroubled for long. In the midst of those happy moments, we were interrupted by the thunderous voice of Sheikh Ali, who was furious to learn that Sidi Hamet had given us away for what he called 'such a paltry sum'. He said that Sidi Hamet must be a fool and a madman to put himself in the power of a villainous Christian, who would undoubtedly murder him and take back the money as soon as we arrived in Essaouira.

The Moor was angered by these remarks, and he spoke out in a very spirited manner, telling Sheikh Ali that although the Englishman had agreed to the payment, he, Rais bel Cossim, had provided the money, and he would do with us as he wished. The price was not paltry; as the Sheikh well knew, you could buy a strong black slave for a *haick*; and Sidi Hamet remained in Essaouira not as a hostage for the slaves, but as a hostage for Rais' safe return.

He continued, "We are of the same religion and owe these Christian dogs nothing. We have the right to make merchandise of them and oblige them to carry our burdens like camels. That fellow there," he said, pointing at me, "calls himself the captain of a vessel; but he has deceived his master and he has deceived you. He was nothing more than the cook. The captain died in the wreck."

This man was either the blackest villain or the cleverest, shrewdest man on earth; but which?

Still Sheikh Ali would not believe Rais bel Cossim. If what he said was true, how could I write a note to induce a stranger to pay so much money for us?

"I fear," said Sheikh Ali, "that you, although a Muslim, have conspired with a Christian against Sidi Hamet, first to rob him of his slaves and then to take his life."

"No, it is not so," replied bel Cossim. "I am incapable of such an act of treachery. Anyway, what is it, a paltry amount or so much money?"

He then told Sheikh Ali that it was obvious that I was the cook. That was why I was stouter and stronger than the others. "As to the letter," he added, "give them each something with which to write, and you will see that they can all write as well as Riley."

This controversy continued for some time. Rais bel Cossim was no villain; he was fighting for our lives with his brain and his cunning. He was eventually successful in depreciating my value as a slave and in checking the Sheikh's avaricious and malevolent intentions.

The argument was at an end, though not resolved, and Sidi Mohammed led all of us into another building. Seid and Sheikh Ali insisted that we slaves should remain where we had been confined on the previous nights, but Rais would not agree, and declared that his slaves would stay by his side at all times. They had cost him a great deal of money, and he was determined not to lose them.

Now we were in a more comfortable building, and Rais brought us robes, and we put them on. Mr Willshire had sent us some cold meat and biscuits, as well as tea, coffee and sugar. There was also a bottle of rum, a kettle, a teapot, cups and saucers and honey, all packed neatly in a box.

Rais assisted me as I gave each of my men a slice of the meat, a biscuit and a drink of rum, and I also had a share.

Next we were given some very fine watermelon. Then, having put on our new shoes and wrapped our hooded robes, or *djalabas*, tightly round our bodies, we stretched out to sleep. Rais, Seid, Bo-Mohammed and Sheikh Ali lay down on a low platform made of boards that had probably come from the wreck of the Maria or some other vessel.

We should have slept well. But yet again the food and drink caused such violent pains in our stomachs that we passed a troubled night.

Early in the morning, Rais bel Cossim asked me in Arabic to make some tea, quietly telling me in Spanish that I must do so without assistance. So I took the kettle and filled it with water, then gathered some sticks and made a small fire, and soon we had tea ready for drinking.

Several men, hearing of Sidi Mohammed's return, came to congratulate him and to see the Moor. Rais directed me to pour a cup of tea for everyone in the building, and he then made the liquid thick with sugar. None of them had seen such a thing as a teacup, nor knew the taste of tea. It was with some difficulty that they would be persuaded to drink it.

I waited on them until they had finished. Then Rais turned to Sheikh Ali and said, "I told you last night that Riley was the cook, and now you see with your own eyes that he is the only one who can wait upon us." Sheikh Ali did not reply.

Next I made a strong cup of tea for myself and for each of my men. This had a most remarkable effect in composing and restoring our stomachs.

Now, at last, it was time to leave for Essaouira. We packed what remained of Mr Willshire's gifts, loaded them on mules, and set off. Our company included Sheikh Ali, Sidi Mohammed, Seid, Bo-Mohammed and Rais bel Cossim.

As we went along, Rais asked me to tell him the story of our survival in this country, and I gave him a detailed history of what had happened to us.

When I had finished, he looked upwards and exclaimed in Spanish, "Praise be God for his goodness." Then, addressing me, he remarked, "You have indeed been wonderfully saved. You must be a particular favourite of Heaven. Never before has a Christian survived such a time in the desert. It is true what Sidi Hamet said - that God is with you."

I asked Rais who this Sheikh Ali was, and why he was accompanying us, admitting that I feared him. Rais told me that he had asked the same questions of Sidi Mohammed, who had told him that Sheikh Ali was the chief of a large and powerful tribe that inhabited the hills to the south, near the borders of the great desert. Apparently, Sidi Hamet had married one of the Sheikh's daughters, but had later been at war with him. This was because the Sheikh had given Sidi Hamet and Seid goods to sell for him, and when they returned ther had handed over only part of the proceeds, withholding two black slaves, pretending that they had been received in exchange for their own goods. In the war, Sheikh Ali had taken back his daughter and had destroyed Sidi Hamet's village. However, they had eventually made peace, and the daughter had been restored to her husband.

Rather more frighteningly, Rais told me that Sheikh Ali could bring a thousand men into battle whenever he pleased, and that he was a man of the greatest talents and influence, both in war and in peace.

"But why is he travelling with us to Essaouira; is it just to see Sidi Hamet?" I asked.

"I do not know," replied Rais, "but I agree that it is worrying and unlikely to be for any good purpose. But do not fear, Riley, the power that has protected you so far will continue to protect you. God will not forsake you until he has achieved his purpose."

Amen to that.

CHAPTER TWENTY-ONE

Widnah and Shleema

We travelled on through sandy country with a scattering of small hills and also some cultivated areas. Then, after about five hours, we came to the shattered walls of a large town - a town of some size, but now deserted, having been destroyed with obvious violence.

The walls, insofar as they still stood, were fifteen feet high. They had been built with rough stones laid in clay or mud, and partly daubed over with the same material. On the north side there was a large gateway handsomely arched over with stone and furnished with a strong wooden gate that was now shut. Over the gate there was a platform, doubtless used to station men who were to defend the entrance. Two massive battering rams stood silently outside the town, and there was a large breach in the western wall, evidencing the effect of the weapons.

We stared at this battle-scene from which all life had been removed. The cause of its removal was there for all to see - the place was strewn with human bones. It was a most gruesome sight, and it needed little imagination to appreciate the bloodshed and death that had occurred here.

I asked Rais to tell me the history of the place, but he did not

231

know the full story. So Rais asked Sidi Mohammed, and he told us what had happened.

"That city," said Sidi Mohammed, pointing towards it with his staff, "was built by Omar Rashid about forty years ago. He named it Widnah. Omar Rashid was a brave and pious man, and the number of his family and friends consisted of no more than five hundred souls when the city was built. However, their numbers increased so rapidly that within a few years the inhabitants amounted to several thousand.

"They were industrious and planted those fig, date, pomegranate, olive and other trees that you can see about the walls, and they cultivated fields and gardens. Within a few years, they had an abundance of food and beasts of every kind, and had become rich and powerful.

"These people were respected by all their neighbours, because they were also just and wise. Omar Rashid came to be known as Omar el Milliah, Omar the Good. He was my friend, and helped me when my fortunes were low. But even the best of men have enemies, and so it was with Omar.

"From the days of his youth, Omar had an inveterate foe whose name was Sheikh Sulmin. About twenty years ago, this Sheikh came down from the hills with a great army and laid siege to Widnah. The Sheikh's men took positions all around the city, so that none of the food in the surrounding fields could be used to support the citizens and nobody could enter or leave - or so the Sheikh thought. But Omar Rashid had planned for every eventuality. When times were good, he had spent part of his wealth in preparing for bad times; famine, siege and so on. One of those preparations was the construction of secret underground passages to places well beyond the city walls.

"So it was that after two weeks of siege, Omar Rashid and his forces sallied out of the city through these underground passages and fell on the besiegers from behind their ranks. The Sheikh and his men were caught totally unaware, and a huge number of them were killed, the remainder being put to a shameful flight. From that time until his death several years later, Omar Rashid and his city enjoyed a profound peace.

"After Omar's death, his eldest son, Ismael, took upon himself the government of Widnah. He assumed the title of prince and called himself Mulay Ismael. But this man was different from his father, enjoying the pleasures of power, but observing none of its responsibilities. He was a very effeminate man, entirely devoted to sensual pleasures, and he had a great number of wives and concubines.

"Under Mulay Ismael, the people of Widnah continued to enjoy the peace and prosperity that Omar had brought to them, and they were confident in their strength. But about three years ago, Mulay Ismael fell out with one of his younger brothers. That brother, named Kesh-bah, was very ambitious, and he resented the way in which Mulay Ismael had taken the entire benefit of their father's rule.

"Kesh-bah's hopes were raised when he was betrothed to the only child of the ruler of another town. Although he still had no power, he now found himself a step away from it in two places. Imagine his delight when his betrothed, Fatima, arrived in Widnah and he discovered that, in addition to improving his chances of gaining power, he had been presented with a beautiful and voluptuous bride.

"In his joy, he soon set out to visit his future father-in-law, laden with gifts. His visit was a great success, and Kesh-bah returned to Widnah glorying in his new position and expectant of the future. But when he returned to his home, he could not find Fatima. No one would tell him where she was, until the threat of his knife induced one of her attendants to disclose, to his horror, that his betrothed had been taken to join his brother's collection of concubines.

"Now Kesh-bah was enraged. He rushed to his brother's palace and forced his way into the quarters of the concubines. Bursting into the main room, he found Fatima not merely there, but actually being used at that moment for Mulay Ismael's gratification in the presence of the other concubines, whilst being watched over by two large guards.

"Kesh-bah drew his dagger and ran forward, but he was seized by the guards who held him firm while his brother finished with Fatima. Then, Fatima and the other concubines laughed as Mulay Ismael mocked his helpless brother. Mulay Ismael left the room, telling the two guards that they could do as they wished with both Fatima and Kesh-bah. They did not need a second invitation. First they tied Kesh-bah to a pillar, and then they joined the willing Fatima on a pile of cushions on the floor. She was only too pleased, and she satisfied their lust as Kesh-bah looked on.

"The guards were now too busy to pay any attention to what was going on in the room, so they did not notice one of the concubines as she sidled up to Kesh-bah offering to help him if he would take her as his bride in place of Fatima. Kesh-bah agreed immediately, and the concubine cut the rope that held him fast.

"In an instant, there were three dead bodies on the floor. Kesh-bah stood there, his dagger ready for further use, his hand and arm bright red with blood. But in his rage, he was still wise enough to realise that the screams of the concubines would put his life at risk within seconds. He ran to the window to climb out, but his accomplice grabbed hold of his leg, reminding him of his promise and begging to be taken with him. Kesh-bah's knife did its work once more. He climbed through the window, escaped from the city, and headed for the mountains.

"Now he had to deal with his brother; it was kill or be killed. He raced to his late father's enemy, and he found Sheikh Sulmin still alive and bitter at his defeat. Kesh-bah had no difficulty in stirring the Sheikh up to war against Widnah.

"The old Sheikh soon collected a powerful army of young and bloodthirsty men. They came down from the mountains, bringing the battering rams that you see before you. But even more usefully, this time they came with full knowledge of the city's defences, the locations of the tunnel exits and all the information an invader could want.

"When this host approached the city, it was the dead of night. The army drew near to the walls in perfect silence and prepared the battering rams totally undiscovered.

"As soon as it was daylight, both machines were put into action at the same moment. The first strokes against the walls shook them to their foundations and awakened the slothful inhabitants. Many of them raced to the parapets to defend their city, but it was too late. The enemy was thundering against them, and the city was filled with confusion.

"The defenders concentrated on the gate, and they repulsed the attackers, slaughtering those who mounted the platform over it. But by then the gate was irrelevant; the wall was already shattered. The assailants poured in, climbing over their dead and dying enemies.

"It was now full daylight, and the indiscriminate slaughter of the inhabitants commenced. All was carnage and blood. Every male was put to death, except for two who escaped to carry to their neighbours tidings of the fall of the city. The women and children shared the same fate, except for two hundred virgins, who were spared for the use of the conquerors.

"Next, the victors plundered the slain of their ornaments, gathered up all the spoil to be found, and departed, leaving the place in a heap of ruins and covered with the mangled carcasses of its once proud and prosperous people.

"On hearing of the fall of Widnah, the inhabitants of the neighbouring towns, many of which were under the lordship of Widnah's ruler, collected their men and pursued the Sheikh's army with great vigour, catching up with them where the mountains begin. It was a long and bloody fight, but Sulmin's men were fighting from the higher position, and the advantage was theirs.

"They rolled down great boulders from the precipices on to their pursuers, who were forced to retreat, leaving over half their number dead and wounded on the ground. I know; I was one of the pursuers."

Sidi Mohammed then showed us a large scar on his chest caused by a wound he had received from a musket ball.

"But," continued Sidi Mohammed, "that is not the end of the story. Sidi Ishem, a very powerful prince, had been told of these events, and he would not suffer that such brutality should go unpunished. He assembled a large army, which pursued the Sheikh and his men for five days, killing many and driving the rest into the desert. And when they reached the desert, the Sheikh and his men kept running, for they knew that the alternative was certain death.

"Sidi Ishem waited until he was satisfied that the Sheikh's men were continuing deep into the wilderness. Then he returned to Widnah with his army. But all they found were dead bodies that were so decayed that none could approach to bury them. Instead, they were devoured by dogs, wild beasts and birds of prey.

"They had offended the Almighty by their pride," observed Sidi Mohammed. "Thus perished Widnah and its haughty inhabitants."

It was a cruel epitaph, but Sidi Mohammed clearly saw everything as the will of God and done for good reason.

After leaving the ruins of Widnah, we continued until we came to the bank of a stream now no bigger than a brook. We travelled along the bank for several miles as the stream gradually became wider and deeper, and on the far side we saw a town.

On our way to the town, we passed large fields of Indian corn and barley, and then we saw dates and figs, pomegranates, oranges and other fruits growing in great numbers, as well as clumps of vines. Many oxen and cows, sheep and goats were feeding in newly cleared fields, their thin and famished appearance a testament to their scanty diet during the summer months.

After sunset, we arrived at the town and entered through the gateway with our camels and mules. There was one broad street that ran the entire length of the town. The houses were built of rough stones laid in clay or lime, and they were all one storey high and flat roofed. Each house had a stout wooden door with a large iron lock, but there were no windows facing the street, except

236

for a small aperture about one foot square, presumably to let in some light.

We stopped next to a smith's shop near the gateway, and were told to sit down and wait. The inhabitants were returning to their homes, bringing their animals into the town, and then the gate was shut and barred with four pieces of timber.

Rais bel Cossim and Sheikh Ali had been to see the ruler of this town, which was called Shleema, as was the river, and had obtained permission for our party to stay within its walls for the night. When they returned, they told us that we might go inside the smith's house, and Rais gave us some dates for our supper, together with some *harira* soup. We watched in wonder as he handed out bowls of this broth containing cubes of mutton as well as chickpeas, lentils and onions, all mixed with spices and rice.

The shop was about twenty feet square. There was a kind of forge in one corner, and two animal skins had been curiously applied so as to form a bellows with which to blow the fire.

We sat down, and were visited in turn by what seemed to be every single man and boy in the town. They all wanted to look at us and ask the usual questions. The people looked like so many others we had seen, but their manner was much more friendly. Several spoke a few words of Spanish, but again they were mainly vile oaths.

These meetings were now becoming quite relaxing; I almost enjoyed them. But there was a new matter that troubled me. Ever since we had left Sidi Mohammed's house, Sheikh Ali had been in a world of his own. He would stare long and hard at us, saying nothing. He seldom spoke to anyone, and when he did, it was in a low voice to Seid. This was a big change from the overpowering and vocal character we had first known. Clearly he was unhappy with the situation and, just as clearly, he intended to do something about it. I strongly suspected that he and Seid were hatching some sort of plot. While those two men were about, we were in danger.

On 2nd November, we made ready before daylight. As soon

as it dawned, the gates were opened and we left the town, proceeding once more on our journey.

Sidi Mohammed told me that there had once been a large and flourishing Christian town only thirty miles away, near the mouth of the River Shleema. But this town had been taken by storm long ago, and all the Christians were massacred.

Rais said that he had known Christians for much of his life, and had often been to their countries when sailing under the Moorish flag. "I visited many countries, transporting wheat and olive oil; but now I assist Mr Willshire with his purchases," he told me.

Travelling on, we came to a large plain, over whose surface were scattered a few shrubs and weeds and clumps of trees, their boughs bent under the weight of bright yellow fruit. I learned from Rais that these are called argan trees after the nearby town of Argana, and that they grow only in this part of the world. The fruit, when ripe, resembles a yellow date, and from it they extract oil. I picked one, and a sticky milky juice covered my fingers. Then I bit into the fruit, and I found it to be fleshy and very bitter. The nuts, which comprise half the fruit, have a hard stone containing two kernels from which strongly scented, orange-coloured oil is extracted. We even saw some goats that were able to climb the twisted and gnarled trunks of these trees and graze above the ground, eating the argan leaves and fruit.

The Atlas Mountains now came into full view. They stretch for over five hundred miles to the north-east in three parallel ranges, the High Atlas, the Middle Atlas and the Anti Atlas, the most northerly range starting far to the east. We had seen these mountains for several days on the distant horizon, but now from this wide plain we saw them in all their magnitude. Their summits, towering high above the clouds in sharp peaks, appeared to be covered with never-melting snow.

The chilling blasts of wind that blew directly from the mountains made our frames shake, despite the clothes and shoes with which we had been provided. Seid and the others were also shivering with cold, and often glanced at the sky, which was overcast and obscured by heavy clouds, threatening torrents of rain.

Sheikh Ali had been very attentive to me all morning, calling me Captain and being incessantly charming. He tried to convince me that I should go with him to the mountains in the south, where he had large possessions. He even went so far as to offer me one of his daughters for my wife, and to promise to make me the chief of the area where I would live. Of course I did not believe a word he said, and I politely turned down his generous offers, explaining that I must return to my country and my family. Once he had given up this attempt, Sheikh Ali stopped the whole of our company so that he could have a discussion with Seid. I was now sure that he and Seid were bent on doing me and my men some mischief.

Late in the afternoon, we approached another walled town, which was called Stuka. We waited by a well about a hundred yards from the gate while Seid and Sheikh Ali went inside, presumably to buy some food, or to obtain permission for us to enter. Several minutes later, Sidi Mohammed and Rais were invited to join them, and they went into the town, leaving us outside in the charge of Bo-Mohammed.

Soon a great many men and boys came from the town to have a look at us. There was no doubting their curiosity. The boys, by way of amusement, began to throw stones and dirt, and to spit at us. Fortunately, Bo-Mohammed was there to protect us. He ordered all the townsfolk to go back to the town, threatening them with violence if they disobeyed, and cuffing a few of the boys around the head as they went past. Then he drew some water from the well and gave it to us.

While we were resting, the winds from the mountains, driving before them thick masses of dark clouds, released a heavy discharge of rain. Rais came out of the town and shouted at us to come through the entrance and get some shelter. We went in and sat down just inside the walls, where there was cover from the downpour.

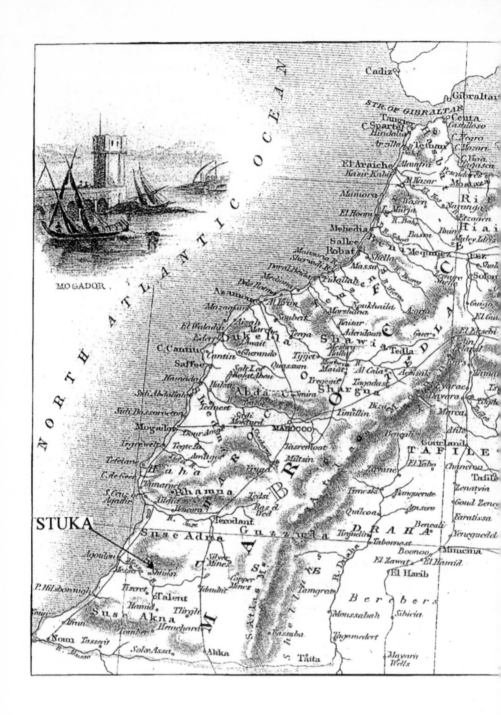

STUKA

Rais and the three others were in a small house just across the path from where we were sitting. We waited patiently for Rais to come and tell us what would happen next. I began to fear some form of disaster or treachery by Sheikh Ali, because I could hear his voice roaring loudly inside the building.

This tremendous clamour between Sheikh Ali and the others, but presumably not Seid, continued for two hours. Then Rais bel Cossim came out to talk to me. His expression revealed fear, grief and indignation. He called me aside from my companions.

Rais told me that Sheikh Ali was the intimate friend of Mulay Ibrahim, or Prince Abraham, the ruler of Stuka. Rais felt that he had been tricked into coming here. Now we were in trouble.

"What's happening?" I asked.

"Sheikh Ali has told Mulay Ibrahim that you and your compatriots belong to him. He says that Sidi Hamet is his son-in-law and owes him a great deal of money. As I cannot prove that Sidi Hamet has been paid, Sheikh Ali says that you are still owned by Sidi Hamet, and therefore he is entitled to take you in repayment of the debt. I have argued against this. But Sheikh Ali has also told Mulay Ibrahim that Sidi Hamet is now held as a hostage by a Christian in Essaouira. He says that none of us should be allowed to proceed further until the five of you or the agreed fifty gold *benduqis* are handed over, and Sidi Hamet, the husband of his daughter, is delivered to him. Seid has confirmed everything that Sheikh Ali has said."

So this was the result of their conspiracy. Sheikh Ali and Seid had finally been able to stop us with the help of the Prince's power. To me this information was like a clap of thunder.

"What can be done?" I asked Rais.

"I do not know, Riley," he replied.

Rais was deeply upset. He told me that he had argued the matter in every way, but to no avail.

"Is a *benduqi* of great value?"

"We have three types of coin under Sultan Sulimaan," said Rais, "the bronze *falus*, the silver *dirham* and the *benduqi*. The *benduqi* is small, but it is made of gold and it is possible to buy much with just one.

"I promised to pay Sheikh Ali fifty *benduqis* as soon as we reached Essaouira, but this was rejected," continued Rais. "Next, I offered to have the money delivered to him after we had reached Santa Cruz in the Sultan's dominions; but it made no difference. I also suggested that Mulay Ibrahim and Sheikh Ali should go with us to Santa Cruz and wait until the arrival of the money and Sidi Hamet. But," said Rais, "whatever I said, they would not listen to me. I can do no good for you here. I must set off immediately and tell all this to Mr Willshire. May God preserve you in the meantime from their evil plans."

This was more than I could bear. My companions could see that something was wrong. They came over and asked me to explain what had happened. When they heard, they were even more distraught than I was. This time I could not make the effort to encourage them or raise their spirits. I was the one who needed that help.

Rais brought his mule over and was about to say farewell and leave, when Sidi Mohammed came up to him and said, "Mulay Ibrahim and Sheikh Ali have decided that you may not go to Essaouira. They fear that when you report what has happened, it will cause a war to break out between them and the Sultan."

"Aha!" exclaimed Rais. "So they know that what they are doing is wrong."

"Do not be angry," said Sidi Mohammed. "It is not me who is against you."

Sidi Mohammed then came over to me. Seeing that I was almost in tears, he took hold of my arm and said, "You must not be sad, Riley. I will go to Essaouira carrying a message from Rais and also a letter from you to Mr Willshire. If he needs a hostage, I will stay with him. I have two wives and seven children, houses and land and herds of cattle. I will be a more valuable hostage than Sidi Hamet. He is your friend and will come immediately to rescue you. God is great and good and will restore you to your family."

This man owed me nothing. So far he and Mr Willshire were the only people acting without any self-interest. Perhaps Rais as well. I kissed Sidi Mohammed's hand in gratitude, and told him that I prayed that the Almighty would reward him for his goodness.

Sheikh Ali, Rais and the Prince, with many attendants, were now seated on the ground in a circle near the city gates. Here they debated the matter again. Rais insisted that we were his slaves, that neither the Prince nor the Sheikh had a right to interfere with his rights over his own property, much less to stop him as if he were a criminal. He complained that it was contrary to their religion, which made them brothers, to commit such an outrage.

Rais maintained that he had paid for us with his own money and he had nothing to do with the Sheikh's claim. If the Sheikh had a claim, it was against Sidi Hamet, not against property he had sold or its new owner.

Sheikh Ali, on the other hand, contended that even if Rais had paid the fifty benduquis, as Sidi Hamet owed him a large amount of money, we were their joint property. Therefore Sidi Hamet was not entitled to sell us without his consent, and consequently he had an undoubted right to detain us and carry us off to his lands.

Both Rais and Sheikh Ali agreed on one thing; they extolled the virtues and justice of Mulay Ibrahim. Seeing Mulay Ibrahim's pleasure at hearing this, they agreed - not that they had much choice - to let him decide what should be done.

Mulay Ibrahim asked Sidi Mohammed and Bo-Mohammed what they knew of this matter. They both supported the claims of Rais bel Cossim. No doubt this required considerable courage.

Then Mulay Ibrahim declared, "You, Sheikh Ali, my old friend, and you Rais bel Cossim, both of you claim these five Christian slaves as your own property, and each of you has some reason on his side. Yet, as it is not in my power to be able to determine for certain whose claim is best founded, I have decided, with strict regard for justice and without going into further evidence, to keep the five slaves in my own city carefully guarded until messengers

243

can be sent to Essaouira. These messengers will bring Sidi Hamet back here, and when the three of you are before me, I shall settle your claims once and for all."

He then proposed that Rais should remain with him as a friend and guest, and without having anything to fear. The Prince's plan was agreed by all parties, and the meeting disbanded.

We were then led to a small building next to the Prince's house. A mat was spread on the floor for the Sheikh and Rais to sit on, while we were ordered to sit in a corner of the room. Guards with guns and scimitars were stationed at the door of our room and throughout the house.

It was all very threatening. But now it was dark and time to eat, so they prepared a meal of *couskusu*. They made this dish by softening hard wheat with water, and then forming it into semolina-like grains that they coated in flour. This was then steamed in the top part of a two-tier cooking pot, while a chicken and vegetable stew with cinnamon, tomatoes, carrots, onions and dates cooked slowly underneath. After some considerable time, the contents of the two sections were combined and coated in *harissa* sauce, a spicy mixture made from hot red peppers, olive oil and garlic, which when tasted alone burned the tongue and the roof of the mouth. A dish of the *couskusu* was brought forward, and we ate this excellent meal. But good food was not enough to cheer us; my companions and I were very downcast.

As we lay on the floor, I could hear the sighs of my men, and I fought to think of something to raise their spirits. I tried to convince them that it was better to be detained for a short time, as it would enable all of us to regain our strength; but it is hard to sound convincing when you believe the opposite of what you are saying.

We slept fitfully that night. I was aware that Mulay Ibrahim, the Sheikh and Rais were conversing for some hours, but I was too tired and depressed to make the effort to listen in to their debate.

When daylight came, Rais gave me a quill, some ink and a piece of paper, and told me to write to Mr Willshire, explaining the present situation. I did this while a scrivener wrote a letter from Rais, as he did not know how to write.

I saw the scrivener writing from right to left like the Hebrews, and I asked him why they did this. He explained that the written forms of ancient languages were created before the days of parchment or paper, so they had used a hammer and chisel on stone. Holding the chisel in the left hand and the hammer in the right, moving from right to left was the natural direction.

As soon as the letters were ready, Seid, Sidi Mohammed and Bo-Mohammed set out for Essaouira, taking our letters and promising to return as soon as possible. I watched them leave, knowing that each of my men was thinking the same thing I was thinking: what would happen when they came back? More worryingly, when they returned, would we still be here?

A few hours after they had gone, Sheikh Ali left, saying that he would be back within two days. What was he up to?

Stuka was built in a quadrangular form near a stream
bordered by palm trees.

CHAPTER TWENTY-TWO

A gift and a granary

Now that Rais bel Cossim was alone with us, I started to question him about our detention. He tried to encourage me in the same way that I had tried to encourage my men. Rais said that we would only be here for a few days; we needed some time to refresh and strengthen ourselves; we needed to be stronger in order to bear the hardship of the remainder of the journey. Now I knew how my men felt when I invented reasons for optimism.

It all sounded so unconvincing. I told Rais that I almost despaired of ever regaining my liberty.

"What!" he shouted. "Do you dare to doubt the power of the God who has preserved you for so long? No, my friend, your God will not forsake you; but in his own time He will restore you to your liberty and to your family."

There was no point in arguing. I just sat silently. As we both rested with our own thoughts, Mulay Ibrahim came in to check on us and to speak with Rais. The Prince was a man of slight build, almost six feet tall, and about sixty years old.

He took Rais and me outside to show us his town. Stuka was built in a quadrangular form near a stream bordered by palm trees. Its walls measured about three hundred yards on each side. These walls were made of rough stone laid in clay and were four or five feet thick at the base, about twenty feet high, and tapering to about two feet thick at the top, with turrets at intervals. There was a single gate on the north side, very strongly made and swinging on the ends of its back posts, which were held in large stone sockets at the bottom and at the top. The gate was made up of two leaves, and at night it was secured by four heavy wooden bars.

This town was occupied by about three hundred families, and contained a total of over five thousand people. The houses were built of the same materials as the walls, one storey high and flat roofed. The Prince's house looked like the others, without any distinction or ornament, but was considerably bigger.

When we were once more in our room, Rais asked the Prince about his wives and children, and Mulay Ibrahim told him that he had only one wife and no children. Next, Rais asked him if his wife had any tea or sugar, and was answered in the negative.

After a while, Rais and the Prince left us, Rais returning several minutes later with a skin of water, and accompanied by a small negro girl who carried some wood. We lit a fire and boiled some coffee. This small girl was a slave to Mulay Ibrahim. Rais gave her as a bribe a lump of sugar, in exchange for which she agreed to take a large sugar lump and a cup of coffee to her mistress.

She soon came back to tell Rais that her mistress was much obliged to him and would keep the cup and saucer, for she had never seen such items before and thought they were very pretty. How, she wondered, could she serve Rais in return for his gifts. Rais asked the girl to tell her mistress that she could serve him by helping to make the Prince his friend.

No word came in reply, but about half an hour later Mulay Ibrahim came to our room and said to Rais, "You had no need to try to gain my friendship through my wife's influence." For a moment I thought that he was angry, but on the contrary. "You had my friendship already," he said. Mulay Ibrahim was pleased that his friendship was so important to Rais.

Rais then asked me to make some more coffee, which I did.

We all had some, as well as a share of the biscuits Mr Willshire had sent. However, all the remaining cold meat had been stolen.

The Prince and Rais spoke for some time, after which the Prince left us for the night. Now Rais brought me some good news.

"Riley," he said, "God has made Mulay Ibrahim my friend. The Prince has given me his word that he will protect me and my slaves, and, if possible, he will settle the dispute by ordering Sidi Hamet to pay part of the ransom to Sheikh Ali. He has promised that when the payment has been made, we will be able to continue our journey, and he will provide an escort for us until we reach the Sultan's dominions. He will send us chickens and eggs in the morning. Tell your men they have nothing to fear and that tomorrow, if it is God's pleasure, they will have good food."

I reported this promise to my shipmates, and it certainly cheered them. Now we could sleep soundly.

Early in the morning of 4th November, Mulay Ibrahim came to our room. Three of his servants followed him and placed before us six live chickens, several eggs and some salt. Rais took one of the chickens, turned to face the east, shouted out aloud *'Besmillah!'* – 'in the name of God!' - and cut its throat. He repeated this procedure with the remaining chickens, after which we plucked them, put three of them in an earthen pot with water, and set them to boil.

Mulay Ibrahim then gave one of his servants some instructions. The man left, and returned a few minutes later with onions, turnips and several small squashes, with which we enriched our soup. He also gave us some green peppers to season our stew. This meal would have been a delight under any circumstances. For us, a more wholesome dish could not possibly have been prepared.

After we had eaten, Rais told me that a large market was being held that day not far from the town, and he had the Prince's permission to visit it with me. He said that he would try to find a way to get us out of this place without having to await Sidi Hamet's arrival.

I went to the *souk,* or market, with Rais...

I went to the *souk*, or market, with Rais later in the morning. The *souk* was a gathering of peoples from all over the region. Everyone was on their best behaviour there, with double fines applying to crimes that broke the peace of the market. Along an array of stalls and tent coverings, men were trading crops, beasts and all manner of things. Numerous types of vegetables were displayed for sale, as well as olive and argan oils, and a thick white oil made from small red berries called '*d'hent*'. There was honey and various meats, including beef, mutton, camel and goat, as well as cooked locusts. Bread, called '*khobz*', baked into heavy black cakes was also on sale.

At the *souk*, I saw many articles of clothing for sale: blankets or *haicks*, blue cottons, slippers, belts, turbans and every type of trinket. There were also spices, powder, tobacco and tar. The tar was in great use for healing camels and killing the bugs that afflict them. But most of all, the market was an opportunity for the exchange of news, a meeting place where talk was the most traded commodity. Rais and I looked around for a while, and Rais spoke with several people. Then he told me that my presence was attracting too much attention, and it would be better if I returned to my companions. He took me to Stuka, and then went back to the market on his own.

Later in the afternoon, when he was once more in Stuka, Rais informed me that he had found out that a man of great influence lived near the town. This man was revered as the Shariff, a descendant of the holy prophet, and he was also called El Hajj, the pilgrim. He was regarded by all as possessing supernatural powers, and was obeyed - almost worshipped - as a superior being. I asked Rais what was implied by 'pilgrim', and he told me that this was the title that could be used by all people who had made the pilgrimage to the Kaaba shrine in Mecca, acknowledged by Mohammed as the location of the altar built by Abraham and his son. It was an extremely hazardous journey, and those who went granted their marriage partners a temporary divorce in case they

251

did not return and could not be proved to have died.

Rais had bought a bullock at the market. It had been slaughtered for him, and he had sent half to the Shariff by a messenger on a mule.

"I sent with it a message," said Rais, "saying that this is a gift from a pious man who has recently come from Essaouira and is now a guest of Mulay Ibrahim. He wishes to be remembered in your prayers."

Rais had given the other half of the bullock to Mulay Ibrahim; and he had high hopes that his thoughtfulness in offering the gift at such a difficult time, rather than its value, would place Mulay Ibrahim under a moral obligation to him.

But now Rais was called away. He came back beaming. The Shariff had come to see him and had asked what favour he wanted that made him give this present to a stranger. Rais told him our story, emphasising that he had paid all the money himself for me and my companions. He begged for the Shariff's assistance in forcing Sheikh Ali to allow us to be removed quietly to Santa Cruz, where we would be safe. The Shariff promised to use all his power and influence to protect Rais and his property, which meant us. He told Rais to let him know as soon as Sheikh Ali returned. Then he would deal with the problem in his own way.

The Shariff did not have long to wait. On the following day, Sheikh Ali came back. Relying on his friendship with Mulay Ibrahim, he was accompanied by only one attendant. Rais immediately sent a message to the Shariff, who came to see Sheikh Ali, embracing him as an old friend.

After they had finished their greetings, the Shariff took Sheikh Ali aside and told him that he had come as soon as he could, because he had some vital information for him. He warned Sheikh Ali that Sidi Ishem, whom he knew the Sheikh feared, was planning to arrive the next day, with the intention of seizing the Christians. I had heard of this Sidi Ishem as the prince who had chased the conquerors of Widnah into the desert.

The Shariff told Sheikh Ali that to save himself and his claim on the five slaves, he should take us to Agadir (which was their name for Santa Cruz) as soon as he could.

Seeing the fear in the Sheikh's eyes, the Shariff continued, telling him that if the slaves were not in the dominion of the Sultan by dawn, the Sheikh would not only lose his slaves, but would risk a war with Sidi Ishem that would set the whole country ablaze.

Sheikh Ali wasted no time. He thanked the Shariff profusely for his help, and rushed off to find Mulay Ibrahim. The Shariff then said farewell to Rais, and left Stuka for his village.

Now one of Mulay Ibrahim's servants came to summon Rais. I had the feeling that matters were proceeding very quickly.

About half an hour later, Rais returned to tell me what had happened.

"When I entered the room," said Rais, "I heard Sheikh Ali trying to persuade Mulay Ibrahim to let him leave this evening with the five of you, so that he could take you to his own lands. Before I could speak, Mulay Ibrahim rejected the request, saying that you were within his walls and he had given his word that you would not be removed until the disputed right of property was settled by all parties face to face.

"Sheikh Ali saw that he was not getting anywhere with the Prince, so he came over and said that he had found me to be a good and honourable man, and he wished to be called my friend. Knowing my fine character, he did not doubt my word and would therefore go with me and my slaves to Agadir in the morning. We could all wait there for Sidi Hamet and settle the property dispute amicably. He must really be afraid of Sidi Ishem."

"Good, so you agreed," I said.

"No," replied Rais, "at least not straight away. I told him that I was content to keep to our agreement. I said that he had stopped me and my Christian slaves contrary to the laws of justice; but now that we had been kept here for so long, I was not in a hurry to leave, and would wait with patience until Sidi Hamet arrived. Sheikh Ali carried on with his flattery and his conciliatory remarks, and I allowed myself to be persuaded that we should go to Agadir

- but only on condition that it was with Mulay Ibrahim's blessing, and that the Prince would escort us all the way with an armed guard."

"Did the Prince agree?" I asked earnestly.

"Of course," said Rais, a huge smile on his face, "all this had already been agreed between the Prince and the Shariff. You shall all ride on camels and be escorted by two hundred horsemen to prevent any treachery by Sheikh Ali, who might well have troops waiting to seize us and carry us off to the mountains. These horsemen will take stations along the route, so as to keep us in continual view."

This was good. Now we were once more inching our way to liberty. Rais told me to boil the remaining chickens together with the eggs we had left. I did this with the assistance of my men, at the same time relating to them all that Rais had told me.

While the food was cooking, I asked Rais to tell me more about this Sidi Ishem, the mere mention of whose name could inspire such fear.

"Morocco is divided between the Bled al Makhzan, the governed lands, and the Bled al Siba, the untamed and uncontrollable lands," Rais explained. "These uncontrollable lands are the territories of the Berbers; they comprise the desert, the Rif and the Atlas Mountains.

"We are in the country of Suse, or South Barbary, and it is bounded by the Moorish province of Hah-hah, by the Atlas Mountains, by the great Zahahra Desert to the south, and by the Atlantic Ocean. Its length from east to west is about two hundred and fifty miles.

"Suse used to be an independent kingdom, but was later united to those of Morocco and Fez, which now form the Moorish empire. But though the Sultan of Morocco claims jurisdiction over the whole of Suse, and indeed over the whole of the desert as far as Soudain, his true power extends only a short distance south and west from a line drawn through Santa Cruz, or Agadir, and Tarudant, south-east of the Atlas.

"This Sidi Ishem," said Rais, "is a descendant of the former kings of Suse before it was conquered by the Moors. He is over six feet tall, a powerful man with a white beard. I saw him once when I was in Widnoon. He was wearing a *haick* and a turban of the finest texture, and had a blue cloak trimmed with red silk. He also wore a broad red leather belt and carried an immense silver powder horn and a long cutlass. His chest was covered by a scarlet sash, and he held a musket decorated with silver and ivory.

"Sidi Ishem is between fifty and sixty years old, and is possessed of great wealth and power. This man is very crafty and very brave; but he is also rapacious and cruel. He has under his command fifteen thousand horsemen, all well armed. They are of the race of the ancient inhabitants of this country from whom the region derives the name Berberia, corrupted by the Europeans into Barbary. The Berbers are not really west-Africans; they came from north-east Africa and gradually slaughtered or enslaved the original black peoples. Before the Arabs came, all of the north of Africa was Berber. But when the Arabs arrived, they took this land by conquest and occupied it, driving the Berbers to the Atlas Mountains and south towards the desert.

"The Berberians, or Berbers, are extremely fierce and warlike, and those under Sidi Ishem's command have been joined by all the renegade Moors who have escaped from the Sultan's lands to evade punishment for their crimes. These men are always ready to join Sidi Ishem in any of his enterprises, for they invariably receive a share of the spoils.

"Sidi Ishem lives in the gorge of a mountain near the town of Widnoon, on the route from Morocco across the great desert to the city of Timbuktu and to Soudain, the country beyond the desert. The caravans that travel to or from the desert on the western trail are obliged to go close to Widnoon, and as the Atlas Mountains are to one side and the ridge next to the sea is on the other side, they find it highly necessary to secure Sidi Ishem's friendship and protection by delivering up to him a proportion of the goods they carry in each direction.

"But between Sidi Ishem and the Sultan of Morocco there exists the most implacable hatred and continual jealousy, which a few years ago broke out into open war. The Sultan despatched a powerful army of thirty thousand men against Sidi Ishem, but Sidi Ishem was forewarned of this and sent off every man, woman and child with all they could carry to the south of the Atlas Mountains and into the desert.

"The Sultan's army marched into Sidi Ishem's territory, but they found nothing to subsist on. They met no resistance, so they carried out their work of destruction by burning all the towns. But there was no one to kill and nothing to steal; the whole territory was empty.

"Then they chased around the land, looking for Sidi Ishem and his people until they were exhausted by fatigue and hunger, whereupon Sidi Ishem fell upon them with his infuriated followers, who had been rendered doubly desperate by the sight of their ruined cities. They slew more than ten thousand on the spot; those who escaped this carnage were hunted down, and nearly all were killed before they could reach the city of Tarudant, which is the southernmost town in the Sultan's dominions. Those who were taken prisoner uninjured were executed; those who were maimed were encouraged to return to the Sultan's lands to spread terror and dismay throughout the empire by the accounts they gave of their disasters, and by their awful appearance. As a result, it became impossible for the Sultan to raise another army to continue the conflict.

"All the inhabitants were soon recalled by their leader from the mountains and the desert, and they took possession of their homeland once more, rebuilt their towns and their dwellings, and are now more powerful and more respected than they were before the war."

Well, now I understood why this man was feared.

Our food was ready, and we were allowed a short sleep before we left. At daylight on 6th November, we were placed on five camels that were well saddled and loaded with bags of barley, which made quite a comfortable seat for the rider.

We left Stuka and set off to the north, accompanied by Rais bel Cossim, Mulay Ibrahim with his two servants and four armed men, and Sheikh Ali with his attendant, all riding mules or asses. Each of our camels was led by a driver. I noticed that as yet there was no sign of the two hundred guards; but I said nothing.

The plain on which we were travelling looked very fertile, and was planted with numerous groves and orchards of fig and other fruit trees. We proceeded rapidly, so much so that the drivers often had to run in front of the camels. After about six hours, we came to the ruins of several small towns on our left, and near their shattered walls we could see more battering rams. The gardens near the towns were still green with vegetation, so these towns must have been inhabited until quite recently.

Mulay Ibrahim saw us looking at the ruins, and he explained what had happened. "There was a family quarrel about a year ago between the chiefs of two towns," he told us, "which soon broke out into the most dreadful warfare. Each claimed that he had been insulted by the other. Both sides engaged their allies to assist them in the fighting, which was considered a righteous battle by all. Within days, the neighbouring towns joined in, some on one side and some on the other, and soon the plain was deluged in blood.

"As the quarrel was only of a domestic nature, Sidi Ishem did not interfere. Anyway, he realised that if he stopped the warfare, the argument would continue until fighting broke out once more. He knew it was better that the matter should be resolved; and he was right. In a short time the war was settled by the destruction of seven of these small towns and the massacre of their inhabitants. The matter was concluded, and there was no one left to seek revenge or to start the fighting again."

I could scarcely believe the devastation and death that had been wreaked on such trivial grounds. But Rais bel Cossim assured me that feuds of this type were common in these parts. He had known of many himself, and they seldom finished until one family or the other was exterminated and their names and memory were erased from the face of the earth.

We continued our journey until midday, when we saw in the distance Santa Cruz, or Agadir (a word that Rais told me meant 'a fortified granary'). The town is situated on the summit of a mountain; its walls are white and can be seen from far away.

I asked Rais what he could tell me of this town.

"The word Agadir is Berber," he told me. "Agadir has long been a harbour for the Berber fishermen, and they use the spring and the cave that was the original fortified granary. But Agadir became the centre of Suse independence, so Sultan Sidi Mohammed ben Abdullah decided to close the port to all foreign trade and banned merchants from visiting the town. He ordered the European consuls to move to Essaouira and also sent the wealthiest families and many of the Jews to live there. The Sultan then closed the ports of most other towns on the western coast, other than Essaouira. In that way, he also limited contact with foreigners in much of his country, and he ensured that all trade was dealt with by those who had been most successful in the past and who could speak the languages of the foreigners."

As we approached the city, many unarmed men with cattle or asses loaded with salt and other merchandise passed us. We also saw several bands of armed men on horseback, about thirty in each group - these were the men Mulay Ibrahim had instructed to ride guard and to be ready to act in case of treachery by Sheikh Ali.

In the early afternoon, when we were near the coast, we passed the edge of a series of huge drifts of sand to our left, which extended all the way down to the sea. This sand had been driven up from the beach by the constant trade winds, and had been slowly but surely making its way inland.

The sand drifts had buried several villages and towns; the tops of their walls were still to be seen. Mulay Ibrahim told me that Rabeah, whose ruins we had passed, was his birthplace and had been a flourishing town not many years before. However, the sand had attacked the western wall and in time made its way over

258

the wall and into the town. Within one year all the inhabitants had gone; there was no fighting the elements.

Now we were only two miles from Santa Cruz, and before the city we saw Santa Cruz Bay and the ocean. There were over a hundred fishing boats hauled up on the beach, out of the reach of the sea. Many fishing nets had been spread out to dry on the sand and over some of the boats, with men repairing the previous night's damage.

I asked Rais if there might be some Europeans here who would come to our assistance, but he explained that all the Europeans had left when the port had been closed to foreign trade. They had gone to Essaouira; that was why Sidi Hamet had wanted to take us there.

The sun had not yet set, and Rais told me that he did not want to enter the city until after it was dark, for fear of arousing too much interest. So Mulay Ibrahim and Sheikh Ali and their attendants went on ahead, leaving us behind with Rais, the camel drivers and the Prince's four armed men. We stopped and rested, and then, a little after sunset, we entered the lower town and port. This was in effect a large village on the seashore at the base of the mountain on which the upper town was built; a town withering in the absence of foreign trade.

It was not yet completely dark when we entered, and the street was soon filled with men and boys. They saluted us by spitting on us and pelting us with stones and sticks, accompanied by another selection of Spanish vulgarities. But some of the men welcomed us with, "How you, Christianos?"

Having walked to the far end of the street, we were told to rest alongside a shop, while our camels were fed with barley. The shop was a bakery; but a bakery in the true sense of the word rather than simply a bread shop, although there was some bread and many types of biscuit, as well as pastries covered with almonds and honey, displayed for sale. However, in general, the women of the town would prepare the dough at home and then send a child to deliver it to the shop, where it was baked for them for a small fee.

...a large village on the seashore at the base of the mountain
on which the upper town was built...

The people inside the bakery cooked a rich meal of fish and *couskusu*. After they had eaten, they gave us the remains, and although the portions were small, we found it excellent food.

We were still slaves, still prisoners, and the threat of Sheikh Ali had not disappeared; yet we felt that we were now very near to freedom. All the same, I knew that we still had to clear some dangers before we reached our redeemer, Mr Willshire.

CHAPTER TWENTY-THREE

Treachery and two meetings

After we had finished eating, Rais came over and told me to keep a good look out. He said that he was going to the nearby building where Mulay Ibrahim and Sheikh Ali were eating, and would watch Sheikh Ali, whom he feared was plotting something. With that, he left us.

I told my men that we were now out of danger. We were over fifty miles from Stuka, and were at last in the Sultan's dominions. Within a matter of days we would be liberated, so we had to maintain our remaining strength and determination in order to reach Essaouira. They now believed me, and there was an air of optimism within our group. We were allowed into the shop to sleep. My men lay down to rest. They had only the bare floor for beds, but being wrapped in cloaks and having eaten nourishing food, they soon fell asleep.

But anticipation troubles one's rest. Anyway, Rais wanted me to keep a watch; so as the four guards, the drivers and my men slept, I sat outside leaning against the building, looking up and down the deserted street, fear and hope keeping me awake.

Soon after midnight, Rais returned. He was in a serious mood, and very anxious. Rais awakened the five camel drivers, taking care not to disturb the sleeping guards, and told them to prepare their animals quickly and quietly, so that we could leave straight away. He then knelt down beside me and told me that while he had been busy feeding his mule, Sheikh Ali had slipped away into the main town to visit the Governor. Relying on whatever Sheikh Ali had told him, and having received a gift from Sheikh Ali, the Governor had agreed to take us into custody at daybreak. Then, if Rais did not pay Sheikh Ali the money he demanded, the Governor would assist the Sheikh in taking us to his own possessions.

"I have learned this," Rais said, "from an old friend of mine who is a servant of the Governor. Awaken your men; you have to depart this instant. The drivers know the way; it is very rocky, and you must all take the greatest care when riding. Remember, if you can get a good distance from this town before daylight, your liberty is secured. If not, you will again be the most miserable of slaves. Encourage your men to make this last effort. I hope, with God's blessing, that in three days' time you will be in Essaouira with your friend. I will join you as soon as I can. I still have things to do here."

"So this is what Sheikh Ali was up to when he left Stuka in such a hurry," I said.

"Obviously," replied Rais, "but never mind that now; just get your men ready to leave."

I awakened my men and explained the position to them. We were placed on the camels, and immediately set off, proceeding in the most profound silence.

Looking up at the summit of the mountain, we could see the walls of the town - or rather fortress - of Santa Cruz fifteen hundred feet above us. No one heard us as we went. The camels were so unlike horses with their noisy clattering hooves. You could scarcely hear the measured and monotonous impress of the camels' feet, broad and soft as sponge. The only sound was the roar of the surf breaking on the rocks, drowning any slight noise we made as we scurried away.

We pressed on, our hearts beating hard in our chests, until we had put Santa Cruz some distance behind us. Our only thought was to keep going. No words were spoken, no questions asked. As long as we were going north, as long as we were getting nearer to Essaouira, we wanted only to go faster.

Then, after a few hours, we heard a thundering of hooves on the ground. Within seconds, a considerable number of men riding mules came upon us from the north. They stopped alongside us in the dark. Not a word was uttered on either side. We were only a few yards apart, yet neither side could distinguish the faces of the others.

The short silence seemed to last an age. Then a wishful thought darted across my mind. "Sidi Hamet?" I called out.

I was quickly answered, "*Ascoon* Riley?" – "Is it you, Riley?"

All of us dismounted and ran to greet the others. I had the joy of grasping the hand of my old master.

Sidi Hamet was accompanied by Sidi Mohammed, Seid and Bo-Mohammed. He also had with him four Moors who had been sent by Mr Willshire, bringing the money for our ransom and mules to carry us to Essaouira.

The principal Moor, who introduced himself as bel Mooden, told me that he was carrying the money, and he would hand it over when we were securely delivered to him. Just like Rais, this man spoke perfect Spanish. He asked me where Rais bel Cossim could be found, and I told him that Rais was still in Santa Cruz.

Sidi Hamet was concerned about someone else. "Where is Sheikh Ali? Sidi Mohammed has told me of his claims." I told him that I had left Sheikh Ali in Santa Cruz with Rais bel Cossim and Mulay Ibrahim.

"There has been trouble with Sheikh Ali," I said.

"Of course," said Sidi Hamet. "He is a bad man and he does not fear God. Nevertheless, I must resolve matters with him now."

Sidi Mohammed was overjoyed to find us in the Sultan's lands and on our way to liberty, and the same emotions were displayed by Seid; but I had no doubt that he was still playing his game of artful duplicity. I would be watching him.

Now Sidi Hamet formally delivered us into the custody of bel Mooden, who handed Sidi Hamet a small bag containing the agreed amount of money in payment. We then said goodbye, mounted the extra mules and set off for Essaouira with bel Mooden and his three companions, followed by the drivers who could now ride their camels. The others proceeded towards Santa Cruz.

All the mules bore large saddles made of coarse cloth stuffed with straw. These saddles stretched from their heads almost to their tails. Over the saddle was placed a *shwerry*, which is in effect a double basket and is formed of palm leaves woven together like mat-work. In this *shwerry*, which hangs down on each side of the mule, they carry provisions and merchandise, and the rider sits on top on his saddle.

Unlike the camel's rocking motion, the mules' steady walk allowed us to relax to such an extent that we found it difficult to stay awake. Unfortunately, Burns was just too tired and he fell off his mount, bruising himself quite badly. As a result, we had to stop for some time, and when we set off again one of the Moors had to ride with Burns, holding him on. This slowed us down, but there was no alternative.

We proceeded in this way for some time. Then, in the afternoon, we heard riders approaching from behind. It was Rais bel Cossim, Bo-Mohammed, Sidi Hamet, Seid and Sidi Mohammed.

I asked Rais what had become of Sheikh Ali and Mulay Ibrahim. To my profound relief, he said that they had set out for their respective homes. This was a very unexpected abandonment by Sheikh Ali of his so-called rights over us, so I asked Rais to explain exactly what had happened after we had left Agadir. He said that we should press on, and promised to tell me everything later in the day.

Riding on together for about an hour, we reached a well where we dismounted. We had a meal of biscuits, butter and fresh water, and then set off once more.

Rais rode alongside me, and said that he would now tell me what had happened with Sheikh Ali.

"You remember that my friend had told me what Sheikh Ali had agreed with the Governor of Agadir. Well, after I had sent all of you out of the town, I went to Mulay Ibrahim and explained everything to him.

"Mulay Ibrahim said that he would go immediately to Sheikh Ali and sleep in the same room as him and try to delay the Sheikh's discovery of your escape in the morning. I followed him, and lay down across the doorway so that Sheikh Ali could not leave the room without disturbing me.

"Shortly after dawn, I was awakened by Sheikh Ali. He told me that as a courtesy we ought to visit the Governor. Now he was ready to put his plan into operation, so I agreed to accompany him. But as we were about to leave, Sheikh Ali stopped me and said that first he wanted to see the slaves and have you make some coffee for him."

"What did you say?" I asked.

"Wait, Riley," said Rais, "you will see how I was happy for him to find out that you had left. We went to the house where you and your men were meant to be sleeping. Of course we discovered that you had gone and that your camels and their drivers had also gone. I immediately launched into an oral assault on Sheikh Ali, accusing him of having stolen my slaves during the night. I told Sheikh Ali that I would have him arrested and brought before the Governor, and I would insist that he was punished according to Moorish law for having stolen my property. You may be sure, Riley, that our punishments for theft are severe.

"Mulay Ibrahim had heard my shouting, and he came rushing into the room. I repeated my accusation. Of course, Mulay Ibrahim knew the truth of what had happened, both the Sheikh's plans and your escape. He agreed that Sheikh Ali should be taken to the Governor, saying that he could no longer maintain friendship with a man who was capable of committing such an act. He considered what had happened to be one of the worst breaches of faith that had ever disgraced a man of the Sheikh's high standing.

"As you can imagine, Sheikh Ali was thunderstruck by this unexpected development. He declared in the most earnest manner that he knew nothing of the slaves' escape, and begged us not to bring him before the Governor. However, he confessed that he had indeed made a plan to take the slaves, but he insisted that he had not put it into operation. Now we had him, because he had acknowledged the proposed theft.

"The Sheikh said that we must find the slaves, and he suggested that I leave for Essaouira straight away, because you must have been trying to get there in order to reach Mr Willshire. Sheikh Ali added that he was now in my power, and would go with me and Mulay Ibrahim to prove that he was innocent.

"I did not want him with me at all," said Rais, "but I preferred to know where he was and what he was doing, rather than leave him in Agadir to prepare a new plot."

"But Rais," I said, "what was wrong with delivering him to the Governor as you had threatened?"

"No, Riley," Rais replied. "Remember that the Governor was party to Sheikh Ali's intended theft. No doubt he had been promised a handsome reward. He would have to ensure that Sheikh Ali was exonerated, and that could bring problems for me.

"So the three of us agreed to set out together to try to catch up with the supposed runaway slaves. I hoped that somehow I could prevent our party from reaching you, but even if we did, you would have left Agadir far behind and would be much closer to Essaouira.

"Mulay Ibrahim took a conveniently long time to prepare for our departure, infuriating Sheikh Ali by reciting lengthy prayers, and then we set off and mounted the hills to the north of the city. Within a short time, we came across Sidi Hamet and his company, who said they had met you.

"Now Sheikh Ali was faced with a dilemma. Should he take this opportunity to sort matters out with Sidi Hamet and let the slaves get further away, or should he pursue the slaves and let Sidi

Hamet escape? Fortunately, he decided to deal with the quarry that was now before him. We all dismounted so that the discussion could commence.

"Sheikh Ali insisted that Sidi Hamet had treated him very badly, and that Sidi Hamet and Seid owed him a large amount of money, which they had agreed to pay on their return from the desert. He complained bitterly that the two of them had defaulted and had passed around his lands without even calling on him to eat bread together.

"Sidi Hamet admitted that they had taken a roundabout route, but said that they had only done so in order to keep away from Sidi Ishem. Sheikh Ali rejected this defence, and said that he would have accompanied them himself, together with an armed guard, to prevent Sidi Ishem's men from taking their property. 'You were not concerned with Sidi Ishem at all; you wished to cheat me of my money as you cheated me of my daughter', the Sheikh said.

"But then the mood changed. Sidi Hamet, whose voice had been very loud before, lowered his tone and said that he always believed that it was better to resolve differences rather than to quarrel, and he would be happy to agree a settlement now. He acknowledged that he owed his father-in-law twenty *benduqis* for the goods and camels he had given him, even though they were not worth half that amount. He would pay the sum now, but he would pay no interest. The Sheikh agreed to this compromise, provided he was paid immediately.

"The twenty *benduqis* were counted out and paid by Sidi Hamet to Sheikh Ali, who said that he would now return to his home. With that, he abruptly took his leave of everyone and rode off. Mulay Ibrahim was now ready to depart. We vowed everlasting friendship to each other, and he set off for Stuka. Then I was ready to follow you, as was a much relieved Sidi Hamet. "

"Have we seen the last of Sheikh Ali?" I asked.

"Yes, I think so," said Rais. "We can now continue on our way to Essaouira. We only have future dangers ahead of us; those of the past are gone. But we should go forward with all speed."

Our company now consisted of me and my four men, plus Rais, Bo-Mohammed, bel Mooden, Sidi Hamet, Seid, Sidi Mohammed, the three other Moors and the five Berbers who had brought us from Stuka on their camels.

We proceeded along the sandy beach, but later took a steep winding path over a mountain, and descended into a deep valley. The track we then followed took us high again. To our left was a precipice reaching down to the sea at Cape Greer. In some places the path was no more than three feet wide, and the smallest slip of camel or mule would have plunged it and its rider down on to the rocks and inevitable death. Fortunately for us, there had been no rain for a considerable time, so the ground was dry and firm. Nevertheless, my men and I dismounted, as did Rais and most of the others. Only Sidi Hamet and Seid continued to ride.

Rais told me that when it was wet, the route could not be attempted, and there had been many fatal accidents here. He said that he would tell me the story of an incident that happened to the north, where there was a similar path. Rais and I walked near the back of our party as he recounted the tale. Behind us rode Seid, followed by Savage, both of whom were also able to hear Rais' tale - though only Savage, and not Seid, understood Spanish.

"Some years ago," began Rais, "a company of Jews, six in number, came to a path such as this, along the side of a cliff, with their loaded mules after twilight. They were very anxious to get beyond such a dangerous place before it was dark. Thinking that no other travellers would dare to pass that way at night, they did not bother to shout out aloud to announce their progress, nor did they look carefully for people coming in the opposite direction.

"A company of four Moors had started from the other end. They also supposed that no one else would attempt to pass at that hour, so they too failed to take the usual precautions.

"About halfway along, at the most difficult place, the two parties met. There was no possibility of passing each other, nor of turning and going back. Although a human could turn round, it was completely impossible for the animals to do so, nor could they be guided to walk backwards.

"The Moors were outraged, and threatened to throw the Jews over the edge. The Jews found themselves in a perilous situation. Their own country having been taken from them and been occupied, they have to live in the countries of others and are therefore used to submitting to constant insults and indignities. However, they were unwilling to break their necks merely to accommodate the Moors. The foremost Jew dismounted carefully over the head of his mule, with a stout stick in his hand. The nearest Moor also dismounted and came forward to attack with his scimitar. Both knew that they would be fighting for their lives, and neither would retreat.

"Being armed with a scimitar and fighting a man holding only a stick, the Moor was confident. In the struggle, the Jew's mule was pitched over the edge and was killed by the fall. Next, the Jew's stick was hacked to pieces by the scimitar. The Jew, realising that he could not possibly save his own life, rushed at the Moor, seized him in his arms and, still clutching him, threw himself off the precipice. Both instantly hurtled to destruction.

"Now the second Moor came to the front; but the second Jew knew what he had to do, and as before, both lost their lives. The two remaining Moors advanced together. But the third Jew did not hesitate; he advanced on his own. The two Moors could not fight side by side because of the narrowness of the path; also their confidence was reduced because of the willingness of the Jews to stand fast and to suffer death rather than retreat. As they hesitated, the third Jew rushed forward, grabbed both of them, and leapt over the edge.

"The three remaining Jews were then able to continue their journey unopposed. That place has ever since been called 'Sharf-al-Youdi' – 'the Jew's Cliff'."

Rais added that the relatives of the Moors had of course hunted down and killed the three Jews who had escaped. However, as no Moors had lived to tell the tale or identify the three surviving Jews, this postscript seemed like an effort to save face.

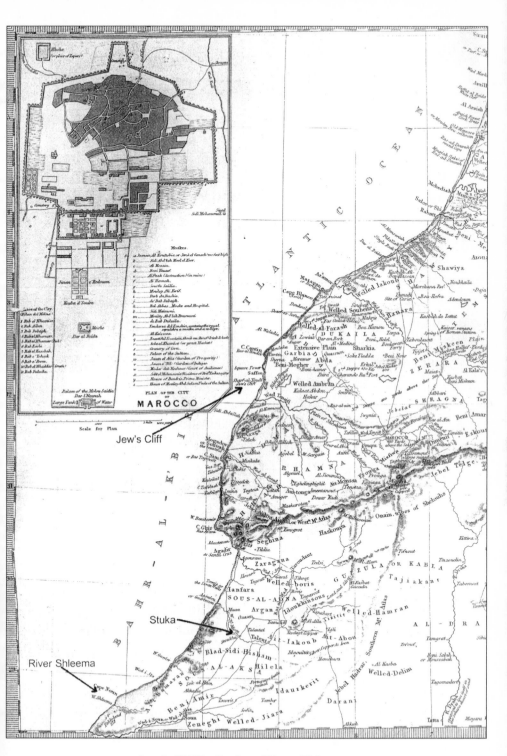

Jew's Cliff - Stuka - River Shleema

271

Even without this grim story, the path was dangerous enough to produce dizziness in the head of a sailor. If I had been told the story before getting on to this frightful ridge, I am not sure that my imagination might not have disturbed my faculties to such a degree as to render me incapable of proceeding along this perilous way.

I looked over the edge of the precipice and down to the tumultuous sea. In the early evening, the moon reflecting on the waters outlined the cape, which had been shattered over the years by waves and tempests, resulting in masses of rocks having broken off and tumbled down one upon the other, forming wild and disorderly heaps in the shallows at the base. I could not help shuddering at the sight, which was made more frightening by the sound of the surf as it came thundering in on the trembling front of the cliff.

As we continued, I heard Seid behind me shouting at Savage, and I stopped and turned my head to see what the problem was.

"What is it?" I asked Seid.

"He is too slow," he replied. "He must keep up with us."

Sidi Hamet and Seid had been paid, and they no longer owned us; but Seid was right, Savage was over thirty yards away and was becoming detached from our group.

"Aaron," I shouted at him, "try to stay with us. What's the problem?"

"This animal is frightened and tired," said Savage.

"Fine," I said. "Let the driver lead the camel. You encourage it from behind."

"No," Savage responded very firmly. "The driver can go behind. I'll walk in front of the camel and behind Seid"

"Very well, as you please," I said, "but let's get moving." It made no difference to me whether Savage walked before or after the animal. Why was he so insistent about walking in front? I soon found out.

We proceeded in silence. A few moments later, I heard a scuffling noise behind me, and then a shriek. I turned to see Seid and his mule flying through the air towards the rocks below, his piercing scream stopping us in our tracks; and then silence as man and beast met their deaths. There was nothing anyone could do; we had to continue.

Soon the path widened, and we were able to stop.

"What happened?" I asked.

"His mule must have lost its footing," said Savage.

"This path has claimed another victim," said Rais. "It is the will of God."

Sidi Hamet was most upset at his brother's death. But he accepted it as pre-ordained, and after a short prayer, we all mounted our animals and set off again. As I rode forward, I could not help thinking that God's will had received some human assistance. God's will, justice, or perhaps it was simply retribution. Was I the only one with these thoughts? Anyway, at least one of us was happier; perhaps more than one.

After an hour's ride we were beyond the cape and at the bank of a river. We stopped for a rest next to a cistern of water, one of a series available to travellers, and had a meal of biscuits and butter, as well as dried figs, dates and nuts, all of which had been brought by bel Mooden.

Having finished our repast, we mounted our beasts and crossed to the opposite bank. Rais told me that the river was called 'el Woed Tensha'. He said that it used to be very wide and deep, and emptied into the sea. In the rainy season it had been impossible to cross without going twenty miles inland. However, for the past four years there had not been enough rain to force open the river's mouth to the sea, so now a bank of sand separated the river from the ocean.

After leaving the River Tensha, we entered a plain and headed towards the high land in the distance. We soon reached a mountain, and followed a path to its summit. By now it was well into the evening, and we descended by another narrow path, although this time there was no precipice at the side.

We travelled for an hour on this winding route, which later

became very steep. The animals had great difficulty in keeping their footing, so we had to remove all the burdens from them and carry the loads ourselves. It took us another two hours to complete our descent, and on reaching the next plain, we could once more place the loads on the camels and mules.

Having progressed in an easterly direction until about midnight, we came near to the walls of a small town, and we dismounted alongside a cistern from which we could take as much water as we wished. The chief men of the town, alerted by the barking of their dogs, came out and welcomed their visitors.

For a modest payment they provided our company with a supper of *couskusu*, and we also ate some dates and dry figs. We slept for a few hours, and as soon as it was dawn we proceeded once more. Our rest was short, as Rais was eager to keep on the move towards Essaouira. With the departure of Sheikh Ali, there seemed to be no obstacle between us and Mr Willshire, other than the passage of a limited number of hours. Our hearts were racing at the thought of the end of our miseries, and we wanted only to continue our journey with the inevitable counting down of the miles between us and freedom.

We went forward towards the north-east for some time, and then we climbed a hill. At the top of that hill we saw two mountains before us to the north, and Rais told me that we had to pass those mountains in order to reach Essaouira.

No problem, we were happy to proceed. We headed straight for the nearest mountain and took a gentle meandering path to its summit.

As we came down the mountain, the path widened, and we passed large droves of camels, mules and asses on their way south, laden with salt and other merchandise. Some were driven by Arabs, but mostly the people we passed were Moors. The Moors were easily distinguishable by their dress. Besides a cloak, each of them had a *kaftan*, or close jacket, and many of them wore turbans. They were armed with daggers or scimitars, suspended from their necks by a cord of red woollen yarn thrown over the left shoulder.

Although there was nothing green to be seen as we passed through the valley between the two mountains, I noticed more and more of the argan trees on the hillsides, and I asked Rais how the oil was extracted from the nuts.

He told me that the argan trees grow in great numbers because they require no cultivation, and that most of the argan fruit is eaten by goats. I remembered having seen goats climbing the trees in order to reach the fruit. Rais said that the nut passed through the animal after it had digested the fruit, which although very bitter was relished by the goats. The women and children who tended the animals would then collect the nuts, carry them home, crack them between two stones and extract the kernels. Then they express the oily juice by roasting and later grinding the kernels down in a stone rotary quern. Finally, they boil the ground remains in a jar until it becomes of a proper consistency, when it would be poured off and then be fit for use in lamps, for cooking, or as a cosmetic. I wondered who had first thought of this extraordinary procedure. At first it sounded rather unpleasant, but I ended up thinking it was ingenious.

We were now at last at the foot of the next mountain. We ascended it, winding up its steep side. Although we had been riding, we were becoming extremely weary. Despite the realisation that Essaouira was now very near, there was no visual evidence of this, and I could see no excitement amongst any of my men. But we could not relax, we had to keep wide awake in order to stay on our mounts and to ensure that the animals did not take a wrong step.

On the highest part of the mountain that we reached, I was surprised to find a large flat area covered with several hundred stacks of salt. I looked around to see how such a great quantity of salt should come to be in this unlikely place. Then I saw a large number of shallow saltpans formed of clay, into which water issuing from a spring on the mountainside was conducted by numerous gutters. As the pans or basins were very shallow, the heat of the sun soon caused the water to evaporate, and a

Then I saw a large number of shallow saltpans formed of clay...

crystallisation of excellent salt, tinged red by the clay, was the result. Many men and boys were employed in raking and heaping up the salt, and others were busy measuring it, selling it and loading it on to the hundreds of waiting camels, asses and mules.

Rais called together the drivers of the camels who had come with us from Stuka, and he paid each of them a small sum of money, which they immediately used to buy salt. Then they went to load the camels with the salt, after which, having wished us a prosperous journey, they set off back to Stuka with Bo-Mohammed.

Our numbers reduced, we remounted and descended to the plain. We now stopped for the night, because we were just too tired to continue, however close Essaouira might be. But Sidi Hamet said that he did not need to rest; he would press on to advise Mr Willshire of our approach.

As soon as it was daylight, we set off once more, and before long we arrived near a group of buildings. I asked Rais if we could buy some milk from the people living there. We waited as Rais rode off to the buildings, but he soon returned and told me that the people there were not willing to sell him anything.

This was a severe disappointment, as we were so cold and tired that I was sure we would not be able to ride much further that morning. Our minds were now dulled, and we were no longer motivated by fear. I said as much to Rais.

"Keep up your spirits, Captain," he replied. "Only a few hours more and you will be in Essaouira, if God Almighty continues his protection."

What did he mean? Did we need protection from new dangers? Or perhaps this was just a figure of speech. Anyway, maybe this was really our day.

We rode on, still in the early morning, passing along a narrow footway between high bushes, until we came to a long string of sandhills on our left. Next we started to mount the side of one of those hills and soon we came to the top.

Suddenly, the city of Essaouira was in view. I could express no emotion; I was stunned by the sight. There it stood, Essaouira, and outside it the island of Mogadore, which still kept the old name of the city. And even from this distance I could see anchored in the bay a brig flying the English colours.

The city where our redeemer was waiting, and a ship to take us to England. It was not necessary to say anything; I just stared at the view and felt the relief permeate my entire body.

"Take courage, Captain," said the good Rais, "there is Essaouira, and there is a vessel to carry you to your country and your family. If God pleases, you will soon see the noble Willshire, who will relieve you from all your miseries. I thank God that your sufferings are nearly at an end, and that I have been found worthy to be a servant of the Omnipotent to redeem you from slavery."

He gave thanks to the Almighty in Arabic, and then declared in Spanish, "May it please God to reward me by having preserved the lives of my wife and my children."

What a giant. No reward, no regard, no gratitude could be enough for this man overflowing with fidelity and courage. And yes, let the Almighty preserve his children; Rais should not die without leaving a copy of himself behind.

Now for the final steps. We proceeded down the sandhills towards the city, going very slowly, while bel Mooden and Sidi Mohammed went on ahead.

Soon we reached the walls of a fine building, a palace, about two miles to the south of Essaouira. The walls were over twenty feet high, and formed a square of about a hundred yards on each side. They enclosed a house at each corner, which rose one storey above the walls, each building being roofed with green tiles.

We stopped near the western angle of the walls, dismounted and rested on the grass. Rais told us to wait there while he went to find Mr Willshire.

"Well," I said to my men, "I think we're alive once more. We *will* return home."

"Yes, Captain," said Burns, "I didn't believe this would ever happen. It's just so good."

My other men just smiled and nodded. We must all have been thinking the same thoughts, experiencing the same emotions - so many emotions, but mainly relief and happiness.

The beauty of the view added to our contentment. A small stream of fresh water ran from the east near the northern wall, flowing and meandering slowly over the beach towards the bay. In the bay, small boats were moving gently, others were anchored near the city; probably men were fishing, but I could not see for sure. This, together with the sight of great numbers of men driving camels, cows, asses and sheep, and riding horses, all at a distance and travelling in various directions, infused in me a kind of sublime delight and a heavenly serenity that is indescribable.

I looked over the whole panorama from the island of Mogadore across to Essaouira, and there over the houses I discovered commanding this noble view the American flag fluttering gently in the breeze. The little blood remaining in my veins gushed through my heart and poured a flood of new life through every part of my exhausted frame.

Mr Willshire had raised the flag as a signal as soon as he had learned of our approach from Sidi Hamet. Then he had ridden to the eastern wall of this palace where, unknown to me, he had already met Rais.

I had expected Mr Willshire to come to us soon, but I had not realised that he was only yards away.

As I walked back to join my men, I heard Rais' voice say in Spanish "*Alli estan*" - "There they are".

We looked round and beheld our deliverer, who had at that moment turned his eyes on us. He started back one step in surprise. The blood drained from his face for an instant; but, recovering himself, he stepped forward and clasped me to his breast, exclaiming, "Welcome to my arms, my dear sir; this is truly a happy moment. I have been waiting for you since early September, when I learned of the wrecking of your ship."

Mr Willshire then took each of my companions in his arms and welcomed them to their liberty, while tears rolled down his cheeks. Then, raising his face to the heavens, he said, "I thank you, Lord, for your mercy to my friends." He could say no more; his whole frame was so agitated that he sank to the ground and rested on his knees.

I looked upwards in silent adoration, while my heart swelled with gratitude. Tears of joy streamed from our eyes. I saw Rais bel Cossim go to hide behind a wall to conceal his weeping.

We all had to exhaust these emotions before we could continue. After a short time, when we had all in some measure recovered, Mr Willshire said, "Come, my friends, let us go to the city; my house is prepared for your reception." We once more mounted the mules and slowly rode off towards Essaouira, coming down the hill and travelling along the gently curved beach at the edge of the wide bay to the south of the city. As we reached the bay, we could feel the brisk wind that is usually in attendance in Essaouira, and which causes the waters in the bay to be rough and choppy, like a miniature sea.

Savage and Clark were on one mule, Burns and Horace on another. They shared their mounts not because of a shortage of mules, but rather so that they could support one another. We travelled along the beach, and then entered the city at the Bab Maroksh, the Marrakech Gate. What a busy and noisy place it was. The gateway was crowded with Moors, Jews and negroes. The news of our arrival had spread throughout the city, and everyone was curious to see the Christian slaves.

The men and boys of the rabble were only just restrained by the efforts of the gatekeepers, and then several soldiers voluntarily escorted us to Mr Willshire's house.

As we dismounted, about twenty more soldiers arrived. One of them announced that it was the Bashaw's order that we should appear before him immediately. We had no choice but to obey, and Mr Willshire and his interpreter led us the short distance to the Bashaw's residence.

We entered through two large doors, and were then ushered into a hall that served as an audience chamber, where we were

ESSAOUIRA

...and then entered the city at the Bab Maroksh...

ordered to sit on the floor. There we saw before us a very respectable looking Moor of about sixty years of age. He was sitting cross-legged on a mat, drinking tea from a small cup.

The Bashaw called me forward, and asked me about my country, where our vessel had been wrecked, how many men had been on board and how many were still alive. He also wanted to know how much of our money had fallen into the hands of the natives and what cargo we had been carrying.

All his enquiries having been satisfied, he announced rather grandly that we were now free. He said that he would write to the Sultan, and hoped that we would be given permission to return to our country. The Bashaw then dismissed us, and we returned to Mr Willshire's house.

I was now a little confused; things were not going to be quite as simple as I had assumed. We still needed the Sultan's permission in order to leave this place. Yet another problem.

EXTRACT FROM WILLIAM WILLSHIRE'S LETTER DATED 10TH SEPTEMBER 1815, TO CONSUL GENERAL GREEN IN TANGIER, REPORTING HIS KNOWLEDGE OF THE WRECKING OF RILEY'S VESSEL

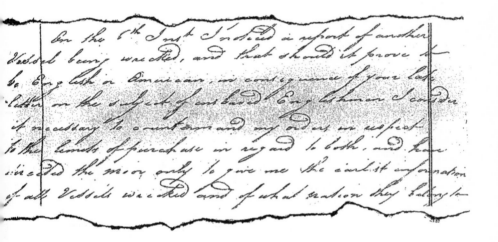

On the 6th Inst I noticed a report of another Vessel being wrecked, and that should it prove to be English or American, in consequence of your late letter on the subject of enslaved Englishmen I consider it necessary to countermand my orders in respect to the limits of purchase in regard to both, and have directed the Moor only to give me the earliest information of all Vessels wrecked and of what nation they belong to.

EXTRACT FROM WILLIAM WILLSHIRE'S LETTER OF 5TH NOVEMBER 1815 TO CONSUL GENERAL GREEN, REFERRING TO THE ENSLAVEMENT OF JAMES RILEY AND TEN OF HIS CREW

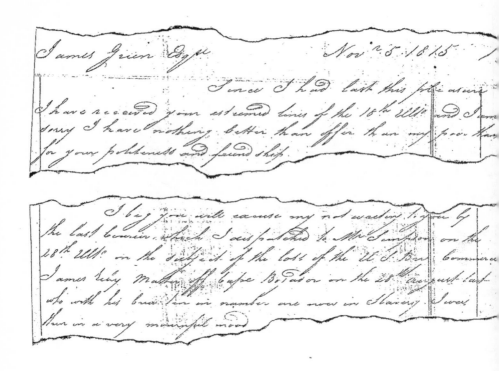

James Green Esq   Nov 5, 1815

      Since I had last this pleasure I have received your esteemed lines of the 18th Ult. and I am sorry I have nothing better than offer than my poor thanks for your politeness and friendship.

      I beg you will excuse my not writing to you by the last Courier, which I dispatched to Mr Simpson on the 28th Ult. on the subject of the loss of the US Brig Commerce James Riley Master off Cape Bajador on the 28th August last who with his Crew ten in number are now in Slavery. I was then in a very mournful mood.

EXTRACT FROM WILLIAM WILLSHIRE'S LETTER TO CONSUL GENERAL GREEN, REPORTING THE ADVANCE OF THE FIVE AMERICANS TOWARDS ESSAOUIRA

Every Christian whether Spanish Portuguese or any other nation, calls himself an Englishman in the hopes of imposing on the Natives, but they are in general too keen to e cheated, the reason is that Englishmen are treated with greater kindness. Should any English Crew unfortunately be thrown on these coasts, and be brought to me, which ould be done under the idea of being directly ransomed in pursuance of your orders, I hould find myself under the necessity of refusing until I had made an application to this Government. This circumstance would be soon spread through the Country even eyond Timbuctoo, and then instead of Englishmen being treated with some degree of indness, they would be looked and spurned upon, as Brutes only fit to till the earth. My eason for these remarks arises in consequences of the information I have obtained from he Moors who have brought up five of the Americans, men who are continually ravelling along the coast.

CHAPTER TWENTY-FOUR

Recovery and a farewell

As soon as we entered Mr Willshire's house, we were given some tea to drink. Then we were directed to a room where men were waiting to cut our hair and shave off our beards. The hair on our heads was in a very unpleasant condition. It was cut off as near to the skin as the horrid state of our flesh would allow.

Our squalid and emaciated frames were then cleansed and purified with soap and water, and our bodies were rubbed down with sweet oil. It was so enlightening to feel clean again, and the cleansing seemed to relax our limbs and remove so much of the stiffness. Next, our humane friend gave us some of his clothes to wear. The shaving, the washing, the clothes; all combined to invest in us a modicum of self-respect, despite the fact that we must still have looked a most pathetic collection of individuals.

Mr Willshire's cook had by this time prepared a meal consisting of beef cut into square pieces that were then rolled in onions and mixed with salt and pepper. The pieces were next put on iron skewers and laid horizontally across a pot of burning charcoal and turned over occasionally until perfectly roasted. They call this dish 'kubbub'. It is eaten hot from the skewers, and is indeed an excellent way of cooking beef.

We wanted to eat so much, but we knew we should not eat

more than was comfortable. So we ate sparingly of the meat and the accompanying wheatened bread, following it with exquisite pomegranates that sprayed cool water around our mouths as we crushed the seeds with our teeth.

Then Mr Willshire told me that he had arranged for a doctor to see us.

"Do you have European doctors here?" I asked.

"You're fortunate," said Mr Willshire. "The doctors we've had here have been a sorry collection of quacks and fraudsters; but two months ago a new doctor arrived, and he has quickly established himself as the only effective physician in the area. This new doctor is a Jew who was born in Russia and studied medicine in Moscow. He travelled through Germany, Italy and Spain, practising medicine in those countries before coming to live in Essaouira."

The doctor came later in the day. He examined all of us, and questioned me about the conditions we had experienced and the food we had eaten. He spoke in Spanish, and greatly impressed me by asking only questions necessary to enable him to decide how to treat us. When he had finished, he administered some medicine to each of us, which he said would help condition our stomachs for normal eating within a few days. The doctor also discussed with Mr Willshire the nature and volume of the food and liquid we should receive each day.

In the evening we were visited by two European residents of Essaouira, Mr John Foxcroft and Don Pablo Riva. Having congratulated us on our survival, they offered to do everything within their power to assist us in our return to America.

Mr Foxcroft explained to me a little of the history of the area. Apparently, most of the coastal towns were originally established by the Phoenicians, who built a network of harbours along the African shores, giving them access to Cornish tin, Spanish silver and African gold. They also traded in corn, oil, fish, dyes, timber and ivory, and at the same time introduced new skills to the native peoples, such as the pottery wheel, weaving techniques, masonry and metal-work. The Jews came with the Phoenicians. Later, their communities were greatly enlarged by refugees fleeing the devastation of their country, Judea, by the Romans; and, with the expulsions from Spain and Portugal, Jews form about twenty per cent of the population in most cities in the Sultan's lands.

Now Mr Willshire explained to his guests that we needed rest, and they immediately said goodbye and left.

My next recollection was three days later. Though my body had suffered greatly, my mind had been strong throughout our troubles and had supported me during all my trials. That strength of mind had compensated for the weakness in my body, and had also enabled me to encourage and keep up the spirits of my frequently despairing fellow sufferers. But now that the need for such strength of mind had passed, it collapsed and could no longer sustain me.

It was not just my mind. The sudden change of situation relaxed my very soul, and all my faculties fell into the wildest confusion.

Mr Willshire later told me that he had immediately called the Russian doctor, and the two of them had taken turns in looking after me, day and night. But everything they did seemed only to ferment the tempest that was gathering in my brain. I became delirious, and for three days I did not know who or where I was. When not raving in my delirium, I was bathed in tears and shuddered at the sight of every human being who approached, apparently fearing that they had come to carry me back to slavery.

Slowly, I returned to my senses, and eventually I was rehabilitated to my former self; relaxed, but exhausted.

Once more with my men, we rested whilst waiting for the Sultan's permission to leave. Throughout this period, Mr Willshire spared no pains or expense to procure for us every possible comfort.

Mr Willshire is a native of the city of London, about twenty-five years old, an elegant man with the most accomplished manners. He had lived in Essaouira for little more than a year, and managed a large mercantile establishment.

WILLIAM WILLSHIRE

I asked him about his business, and he told me that England was Morocco's main trading partner. Morocco imported cloth, iron, arms, china, tea, coffee, sugar, chocolate, tin and paper. In return, the English bought cattle, mules, beeswax, honey, silk, leather, ivory and ostrich feathers.

"It's not just trade that binds our countries together," he said. "We're an important ally for the Sultan, as he is always in fear of invasion by the Spanish or French. He has a particular loathing for the French, largely because of their revolution, which fills him with horror. Of course, good relations are important for England as well, because the Sultan's friendship is vital for the security of Gibraltar, which is crucial to our sea power."

Judging from the number of clerks and assistants in his employ, Mr Willshire was quite wealthy. He invariably had a religious service performed at his splendid mansion on the Sabbath, which many Europeans and ship's captains attended. He conducted the services himself, in the Anglican mode (or, as we now call it in America, the Episcopalian mode) with the most solemn devotion. Mr Willshire is committed to securing the freedom of all Christians in slavery in this country. As soon as he learns of a Christian slave from any nation, he despatches a Moor or a Berber to negotiate his redemption.

Mr Willshire had sent for dates, figs, pomegranates and all kinds of foods to restore every part of our bodies. He gave us the finest juices and occasional wine to drink throughout the day, until we began to have both an appetite for food and the constitution to accept it.

My men and I were bought shirts and trousers, jackets and shoes. We were fed the most nourishing soups and other kinds of food, and we all gained a considerable degree of strength. Although I knew that I had to overeat in order to regain my normal weight, I observed the instructions of the Russian doctor to increase my intake of food gradually, day by day.

Mr Foxcroft and Don Pablo Riva regularly sent food for us, and we were even brought some European food – pork, split peas and potatoes - by Captain Wallace of the English brig Pilot, whose flag we had seen flying when we first set eyes on Essaouira. Captain Wallace offered to take us on board his ship immediately, so that we could be taken to England, but we were unable to accept his offer, as the Sultan's permission had not yet arrived.

A few days after our arrival, a courier arrived at the house. He had been sent by US Consul General Simpson at Tangier, and he delivered to me a letter from Horatio Sprague. The letter expressed the soul of the writer.

My Dear Riley,

I will not waste a moment by unnecessary preamble. I have written to Mr Willshire that your draft on me for twelve hundred dollars, which he tells me is the cost of the obtainment of your liberty and of those with you, or more if necessary, shall be duly paid.

I have sent to him two double-barrelled shotguns to meet his promise to Sidi Hamet. In a short time after your receipt of this letter, I hope to have the happiness to take you by the hand under my roof again. You will come here by way of Tangier.

Your assured friend,
Horatio Sprague

I felt such joy and gratitude on reading this letter. I knew Mr Sprague only from my two-week stay in Gibraltar before our fateful voyage. For him to offer all means of assistance, it was sufficient for him to know that his fellow creatures were in distress and that it was within his power to save them.

Mr Willshire also read the letter, and was equally impressed by the man's generosity. He asked me what I knew of Horatio

Sprague. I told him that I did not know Mr Sprague well, but that I had been told about him by others; told sufficient to feel able to name him in my letter.

"He comes from Boston, Massachusetts," I said, "and had established himself as a respectable merchant in Gibraltar a little before the outbreak of the recent war. In the early part of that war, a number of American ships were despatched with provisions and other cargoes for Spain and Portugal. Many of those vessels were seized by British ships of war and taken to Gibraltar. The vessels and their cargoes were confiscated, and the crews were thrown on to the streets of Gibraltar without a cent in their pockets.

"Mr Gavino, the American Consul, would not aid them because, as he stated repeatedly, his functions had automatically ceased because of the war. Whether or not that was correct, it was a convenient argument, and it enabled him to avoid a mountain of work and expense.

"The American sailors were left without employment or the opportunity to return home. I know just how desperate that can be, as I suffered a similar fate when my vessel was seized by the French some years ago.

"But Mr Sprague was not looking for an excuse, even though he had no obligations, other than those of a decent man and a compatriot. He took the stranded American sailors under his protection and hired an old ship for them to live in. Then he furnished them with provisions and other necessaries and comforts for over a year, until they were able to find voyages home. In this manner, he supported as many as one hundred and fifty of his abandoned countrymen out of his own pocket, from pure philanthropy.

"Not only that. Mr Sprague, with the assistance of other Americans, also sent a considerable sum of money to Algiers to rescue from hard labour the officers and crew of the brig Sylvester, who had been enslaved after their ship was wrecked in a storm. Regrettably, Captain Smith and his men, having been freed, boarded the United States sloop of war The Epervier, which was bound for Norfolk, Virginia, carrying the peace proposals to end the war of 1812 between our two countries. But she was lost near Bermuda with all on board, thereby prolonging the hostilities for no good reason. But still Mr Sprague is willing to part with his money to save his countrymen."

I could see that Mr Willshire fully understood Mr Sprague's attitude. He told me that he looked forward one day to meeting this remarkable man. So did I.

Mr Sprague's letter was a great comfort, and seemed to be the penultimate step towards freedom. All we now needed was the Sultan's consent.

As we talked, I asked Mr Willshire how often he had redeemed Christian slaves.

"It's happened several times before," he said, "even though I've been here for only eighteen months. Mr Dupuis, my predecessor, redeemed some before I arrived. You see, the Honourable Company of Ironmongers in London are trustees of a bequest for the redemption of British nationals taken as slaves in Turkey and Barbary. They sent Mr Dupuis a fund of one thousand Spanish dollars to pay for the redemptions. If we hear of a British man who is enslaved here, we must first apply to the Sultan, who is obliged by treaty to redeem our people. Only if the Sultan refuses to do so can I use the Ironmongers' fund. If the slave is not British, then I seek an assurance that the slave or his country will repay me the costs of redemption."

We relaxed for several days, but then the nights became a problem for me. When I returned to rest and sleep had closed my eyes, my mind still retained strong impressions of my past sufferings and made them the subject of my dreams. I started to rise in my sleep, imagining that I was driving camels up and down the sandy hills near the desert or along the craggy mountains.

In the midst of my agonising toils, while groping around my room I would hit my head against something, and this would wake me up. Then I would throw myself on to my bed again to sleep

POST SCRIPT TO A LETTER FROM MR WILLSHIRE TO THE MERCHANTS RESCUED FROM THE WRECK OF THE SURPRISE, WHOM MR WILLSHIRE WAS TRYING TO REDEEM, INFORMING THEM OF THE TERMS OF THE IRONMONGERS' FUND

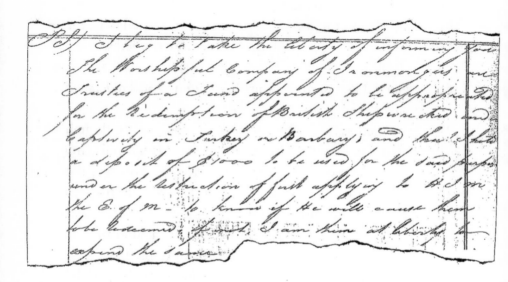

PS I beg to take the liberty of informing you The Worshipful Company of Ironmongers are Trustees of a fund appointed to be appropriated for the redemption of British Shipwrecked under captivity in Turkey or Barbary, and that I hold a deposit of $1,000 to be used for the said purposes under the restriction of first applying to HIM the E of M to know if He will cause them to be redeemed, if not, I am then at liberty to expend the same.

and dream, and relive those haunting scenes.

There was a grating in the window of my room, and on several occasions I awoke to find my hands trying to tear the metal away so that I might get out. However, with the passage of time, my mind became more composed and my strength increased. Soon I was behaving completely normally, I was able to leave the house and walk about the city, and I could once more sleep in peace.

By now the two double-barrelled shotguns sent by Mr Sprague had been delivered. Sidi Hamet used to come to see us on most days, and the time had now arrived for him to collect his gun and leave.

He came with Sidi Mohammed to say farewell. Sidi Hamet said that he wished to see his wife and children. I knew that he longed for the freedom of the desert. He swore by his right hand that once he had rested, he would gather a large company of men, and would set off to find the remainder of my crew. I told him that I would double the reward.

In my contentment, any mention of the lost men made my heart sink. The guilt of leaving them would forever weigh on my mind. I would never escape that shadow. But it was no use thinking about it; I could do nothing for them, and I still had to see to the four who were with me. Our own escape was not yet complete.

"My dear Riley," said Sidi Hamet, "I was once a bad man like Seid. But when I saw you, naked and a slave, with your skin and flesh burned from your bones by the sun, and I heard you say that you had a wife and children, I thought of my own former distresses, and God softened my heart and I became your friend. I did all I could to lighten the burden of your afflictions. I have endured hunger and thirst and fatigue, and have fought for your sake. Now I have the pleasure of knowing that I have done some good in the world. May the great and universal Father continue to protect you. You have been true and kind to me, and your friend has fed me with milk and honey. I will always in future do whatever is in my power to redeem Christians from slavery."

I handed Sidi Hamet one of the shotguns. It had already been agreed that the one intended for Seid should be given to Sidi Mohammed, who had done so much for us, purely out of the goodness of his heart. I handed the second shotgun to him.

Sidi Hamet and Sidi Mohammed took their leave of me by shaking my hand. They also shook hands with my companions, wishing us a happy return to our country. Then they set off for their homes.

I did not part from them without feelings of regret. Sidi Mohammed had done us nothing but good. Sidi Hamet had on occasion been cruel, but at most times he had been a kind master to me, and I owed him in large measure my life and my deliverance from slavery.

His memory would always be with me - not with the same fondness as Mr Willshire and Rais bel Cossim, but just as important. I was truly sad to see him go.

CHAPTER TWENTY-FIVE

An execution and a scheme

After Sidi Hamet had left, Mr Willshire took me aside, because he wanted to tell me of some recent events that would affect the speed with which we would obtain the Sultan's permission to leave.

"Mohammed ben Absedik has been the bashaw, or governor, of Essaouira for some time," said Mr Willshire. "In fact, throughout the reign of Mulay Sulimaan, the present sultan."

"Are you on good terms with the Bashaw?" I asked.

"Yes," said Mr Willshire. "It's impossible for a foreigner, or indeed anyone, to live in Essaouira without being on good terms with the Bashaw. Of course, I'm in a slightly better position than others, because I'm the British vice-consul, and I have also been appointed American agent as there are no Americans here to act as vice-consul."

"But I thought that Mr Renshaw was the British Consul," I said.

"We do not have a consul here, only a vice-consul. Mr Renshaw was the most important European merchant in Essaouira until he returned to England, but he was not the vice-consul.

"Mr Renshaw has a substantial trading house in England, which carries on business under the name of James Renshaw & Co. He came here three years ago and established an office with Mr Dupuis,

297

who was the British vice-consul. When Mr Renshaw returned to London, I came to Essaouira as his agent. I worked with Mr Dupuis under the style of Dupuis & Willshire, but several months ago Mr Dupuis decided to return to England for a short visit, and on his recommendation I took over his position as vice-consul on a temporary basis.

"Mr Dupuis was taken ill in Gibraltar on his way to London, and had to remain there for several months. When he was eventually able to leave in March of this year, his vessel was seized by the French, and he was imprisoned. With our victory over Napoleon at Waterloo, he will no doubt soon be released and allowed to complete his journey to London, but it's unlikely that he'll ever return to Essaouira; so now I'm permanent British vice-consul and American agent, and also Mr Renshaw's agent.

Mr Willshire went on to tell me that the bashaw was always powerful, and Mohammed ben Absedik had been particularly powerful. But, he told me ominously, things had changed.

"Some months ago there was an insurrection in the province of Duquella, and it soon spread to the provinces of Abdah and Seidmah. I was told that the trouble started following a false report of the Sultan's death, but there were probably some tribal problems or power struggles behind it all.

"Mohammed ben Absedik was also the governor of Abdah and Seidmah, and he decided that he would quell the insurrection immediately. He could make little progress with his own forces, so he appealed to the Sultan for assistance. The Sultan sent him an army of thirty thousand men. The Bashaw attacked with his new army, and a desperate battle took place. The battle ended with the death of over fifteen thousand of the rebels; the rest had no choice but to surrender. Surrender was hardly better than death. All the defeated people, their animals and property fell into the hands of the Sultan, or rather his black troops, who showed them no mercy. They seized the fugitives wherever they could be found, massacred many thousands, and marched the remainder with their families to the loyal provinces, where they were distributed as slaves.

EXTRACT FROM A LETTER FROM MR DUPUIS TO CONSUL GENERAL GREEN IN TANGIER

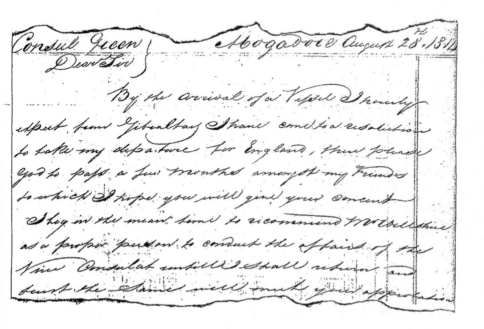

Consul Green   Mogadore August 28th, 1814
Dear Sir

By the arrival of a Vessel I hourly expect from Gibraltar I have come to a resolution to take my departure for England, thus please God to pass a few months amongst my friends to which I hope you will give your consent. I beg in the mean time to recommend Mr Willshire as a proper person to conduct the affairs of the Vice Consulat untill I shall return and trust the same will meet your approbation.

"With the war over, Mohammed ben Absedik returned in triumph to Essaouira, arriving a few days before you reached the city. He expected his power to have increased as a result of the victory, but he returned to a political disaster. While ben Absedik had been at war, news arrived in Essaouira of the death of the ben Slowy, the Sultan's first minister. Ben Slowy had been a man of enormous influence; he and Mulay Atay – he's the Sultan's princely tea maker, who's always in attendance on the Sultan - managed all the affairs of the Moorish Empire. Ben Slowy had been a friend of ben Absedik, and had procured and maintained his appointment as governor.

"With ben Slowy dead and ben Absedik at war, the enemies of the Bashaw seized the opportunity to transmit their complaints against him to the Sultan.

"While you were unwell, ben Absedik became aware of the cloud forming around him. He set out with a light guard and raced to reach the Sultan in Fez before his enemies could gain an advantage. Ben Absedik hoped to dispel the impending storm; but his time had passed. As he was heading north to the Sultan, the new bashaw was pressing forward in the opposite direction, accompanied by six hundred horsemen.

"The Bashaw had left his brother Hajji Hamet - Hamet the Pilgrim - in charge of the city. You've probably heard of the pilgrimage to Mecca, and how those who have accomplished it are entitled to the title 'hajji' or 'pilgrim'."

"Yes, I know that Muslims make such a pilgrimage," I said.

"They certainly do, but they didn't invent it," said Mr Willshire. "The pilgrimage to Mecca was an annual month-long event centuries before Islam. There was a shrine there that was visited by people of all religions long before the time of Mohammed.

"Mecca, which was then called Macoraba, was the ancient capital of the Qorashites, and was an oasis on the caravan route linking the Mediterranean with Arabia, Africa and Asia. It was a holy place for all, and the pilgrimage was undertaken by many faiths: Zoroastrians, Coptic Christians, Jews, Jacobite Christians and others. It was a tolerant city, and the home of the dark stone thought to have come from the sky.

"Abdul Qasim, who came to be known as Mohammed, announced that he had received the revelations of God through the Archangel Gabriel whilst meditating in the desert. Declaring Mecca to have been the first place created on Earth, he had all the statues in Mecca, except those of Jesus and Mary, destroyed. He proclaimed the dark stone to be one of the stones of Paradise that had been presented by Gabriel to Abraham, and the Kaaba shrine to be at the place of the altar built by Abraham and Ishmael, his son by Hagar, Sarah's handmaid.

"Mohammed hoped that the Christians and the Jews would accept him as a prophet; but when they did not, non-Muslims were banned from entering Mecca, and any caught there are sold into slavery. That's why only Muslims now make the pilgrimage.

"It takes three to four years to get to Mecca from Morocco and return, and the people go off in large caravans, each being obliged to go once in his life. Even a few women do this; when they return, they can wear a man's *haick* and walk in the streets, as they are considered holy women. However, the journey isn't only long, it's dangerous, so some towns in this area with holy sites have declared that five pilgrimages there are equal to one pilgrimage to Mecca. As a result, some people using the title '*hajji*' have never actually left Morocco.

"Anyway," continued Mr Willshire, "soon after ben Absedik had left, the new governor arrived. The Sultan's order was delivered to the gatekeepers, the gates were opened, and the new bashaw entered amid joyful acclamations from Moors, Jews and all other inhabitants of the city. These people had deluded themselves into believing that this new arrangement would be for the better. Within hours, they were ready to attend on the new bashaw and present their gifts, as well as their complaints against his predecessor.

"Then in the evening a new military commander arrived. He entered the town with an escort of three hundred black horsemen.

It all looked very threatening."

"What happened to the old bashaw?" I asked.

"I was told that Mohammed ben Absedik made his way to the Sultan's palace; but he was immediately put in irons and sent to prison. His property has been seized by the Sultan. As for his brother, well the pilgrim has been required to make a new pilgrimage. A company of guards is now taking him and his family to Fez. I don't think we'll see any of them again."

"But what does this mean for us?" I asked impatiently.

"Not good, I'm afraid," he replied. "The letter the old bashaw sent to the Sultan asking for permission for you and your men to leave this country is now worthless. We need a letter from the new governor."

"Will there be a problem in getting him to write such a letter?" I asked.

"It's too early to say," replied Mr Willshire. "I think that in time the new bashaw will write and give his recommendation. But first I need to make him my friend. He won't write the letter unless it's to his advantage or is in return for some favour."

I was distraught. How long would we have to stay here? Mr Willshire could see how I felt.

"You must stay calm. Let's wait for a few days and see how things develop. This is a very unpredictable time. Things may get better and you may get the consent. They may get worse, and then we may all have to take some risks. There's no point in deciding what to do now; it's impossible to predict what the situation will be in two weeks' time."

I explained these developments to my men, and we agreed that we would relax and take life easy for two weeks; then we would make a decision.

The next morning, Burns came running into the house with new information.

"I've been down to the port," he said. "A vessel has arrived from Gibraltar and is waiting to come in. Maybe we can get on board after they've tied up."

"Yes," I said, "I'll speak to Mr Willshire about it." Maybe Burns was right. Why wait? Let's take the first opportunity to get out.

I went to Mr Willshire and told him of the proposal. He said that he would try to find out when the vessel would come into port and when they intended to leave.

Mr Willshire returned later in the day with bad news. "Unfortunately, the vessel didn't come into the port; it's already left. You know the old adage 'New lords, new laws'? Well, the new bashaw has imposed a regulation under which no vessel that enters the port is to be supplied with more than a day's provisions. Also, they have to pay duty of one hundred per cent of the cost of the provisions for every day they remain here."

"My God," I said, "no vessel will ever come here again!"

"Wait," said Mr Willshire. "In the first place, these regulations will in time be eased. Secondly, ships will probably start to arrive with sufficient provisions on board, once reports of this new regulation spread."

He was right; but our predicament was now getting worse, despite our physical condition improving day by day. We were no longer slaves, but the city was becoming more and more like a prison.

I told my men that the vessel from Gibraltar had left, and I also passed on to them all that Mr Willshire had told me. They were disappointed, but there was no despair. I advised them to keep out of trouble, and to keep their eyes and ears open. We had to seek the best opportunity to get out of this place. Then we would take it.

Although things were worrying for us, the people of Essaouira were also having a bad time. The Moors, who had rejoiced at the fall of the old bashaw and the civil magistrate, or alcayd, soon changed their opinion and began to wish that they were back in power. All the Moors in the town had been considered to be imperial soldiers; as such, they had received a monthly payment from the Treasury. This was now stopped for the white Moors; but the black Moors, or negro troops, were to receive double.

New officers were appointed to all civil and military positions, and many of the old officers were seized and imprisoned, and their property was confiscated. Clearly, a reign of terror was beginning, and the Bashaw was dividing the city between the terrorised and the favoured.

The Christian merchants in Essaouira were obliged to make costly gifts to the new bashaw. All of them gathered at Mr Willshire's house to discuss the situation: Mr Willshire himself of Dupuis & Willshire; Don Estevan Leonardi from Genoa, but who was acting as the French vice-consul, and his nephew Don Antonio; Don Pablo Riva of Genoa; Alexander Court; and John Foxcroft.

They agreed that the situation was delicate; but while foreign trade in this region was largely limited to Essaouira, they had to make the best of it or else leave the country. For the time being, they would keep quiet, do as the new bashaw wished without complaining, and hope that in two or three months things would get better.

Two or three months! Our families were waiting for us. I was determined to be home by then, Sultan's consent or not.

The Jews also fared badly. They had been overjoyed at the recent change, but their joy soon turned to misery. Within a few days, they received an order to pay their *jizya*, or yearly tribute, to the Sultan. The gates of the Jews' town, the Mellah, were immediately closed on them, and none could leave until the money was paid.

In a total population of thirty thousand, there were about six thousand Jews in Essaouira, but some of them were very poor. Their rabbis soon convened them in their synagogues and apportioned the tax according to their law. They divided their people into four classes. The four principal Jewish merchants formed the first class; they were the families called ben Guidallas, Macnin, Abitbol and Zagury. These families lived in a very comfortable style and managed a great deal of the trade with England. They did not live in the Mellah, but were permitted to reside in the main town. The Guidallas even wore European clothing. These merchants were required to bear over half the tax.

The minor traders formed the second class; the skilled men were the third, and the poor the fourth. The rabbis and priests were exempt from payment, the other classes supporting them at all times.

The Jews of Essaouira were always the chosen intermediaries between the Moors of the interior and the European merchants. They stood outside the normal community, not only in their payment of extra taxes and their leaders' demands for funds for the upkeep of synagogues and schools, but also because they were administered by the Caid al-Yahud, the Governor of the Jews.

During this time, I visited the Jews' town several times. For three days, not a single one of them was allowed to leave the Mellah without the written permission of the Alcayd. Any others who tried to escape when the gates were opened in order to procure food and water for their hungry families, were beaten back inside.

On the fourth day, when the arrangements had been made by the priests and the elders, they sent word to the Bashaw, and the four classes were ordered to appear before the Alcayd to pay their shares. I knew all of this because Moses Nahory, Mr Willshire's interpreter and broker, was a Jew and was a member of the committee making the arrangements.

I wanted to see what happened, and I went with Moses Nahory to the Alcayd's house to watch the payments. The Jews soon arrived, divided into their various classes. As they came forward, they removed their slippers, took their money in both hands, and presented it to the scrivener. In this way, the first three classes paid their shares without much difficulty. Then the fourth class came forward. Those who could pay, did so; those who could not were beaten and thrown into the dungeons until their friends paid for them. It seemed an odd way to treat people the Sultan was relying on to deal with foreign trade. I felt that I was in a similar position to the Jews; I would try to survive here for the time being and I would put up with everything, but when I could get to my own home, I would leave instantly.

The next day, I was told that two vessels had arrived from London. One was commanded by Captain Mackay, the other by a Captain Henderson. I decided to go down to the port to meet them when they came ashore, and Rais agreed to come with me.

As we reached the port, I saw a large number of soldiers milling about. Something important was happening; there was an air of excitement, with people jostling to get ahead of one another. I asked Rais what was going on, and he told me that an execution was about to take place, accompanied by the maiming of some lesser criminals. He suggested that we stay and watch.

Within a few minutes, the Bashaw arrived and took his seat at the front of the square that the soldiers had forced the crowd to form. Next, the prisoners were brought forward, walking one behind the other, their heads bowed, their hands tied behind their backs.

The Cadi, the judge of Muslim law, read out the order for the punishments. Then he told the prisoners to prepare themselves, which they did by saying, 'Ashhadu alla ilaha Allah wa ashhadu anna Mohammed rasula Allah' – 'I bear witness that there is no God but Allah and I bear witness that Mohammed is his messenger' - and then reciting some prayers.

Next, the butcher came forward. That was when I witnessed the execution that started me thinking about how I had come to be here. Now I had finished recalling the whole of my life: childhood, the sea, disaster, the desert and redemption in Essaouira. Well, at least I had not passed out. I only hoped that the next part of my story would be less exciting. All I wanted was permission to leave and an uneventful journey back to Middletown.

But what now? The next few minutes would be memorable, if only for their hideousness. The execution had been completed, but there were still seventeen prisoners left. All knelt down in a row. They had not been condemned to death, but they were still to suffer appalling punishment; eight had been sentenced to lose a leg and an arm each, and nine to lose a hand.

The butcher began to amputate the legs at the knee joint by

306

cutting the flesh and sinews with his knife, which he sharpened from time to time on a stone. He then parted the joint by breaking it over his thigh. Having in this manner taken off the legs and thrown them on the mat, he proceeded to remove the arms at the elbow in the same clumsy manner.

I found myself freezing my emotions, and analysing what was happening in a very cold-blooded manner. Perhaps it was the only way to see this through. The butcher improved with practice, so that he carved off the hands of the last nine victims at the wrists in a very short time. As he finished with each man, the executioner's assistants cauterised the arteries by dipping the stumps into a kettle of boiling pitch called 'kitran', which they make from the sap of wild juniper trees.

All the sentences having been carried out, the assistants collected the various parts, and then carried the lifeless trunk, the head and the limbs to the market for display. The officials who had been present during the execution of the sentences appeared to be quite unconcerned; gaily conversing throughout the butchery. The Moors, who came to watch from mere curiosity, did not show the least sign of disapproval, nor any hint of horror. Indeed, many of them jested with the butcher, who seemed highly gratified with the part he was playing.

The entertainment was now over, and within minutes all the onlookers had gone. As Rais had told me, this butcher had been a willing executioner in order to receive the considerable fee for one life and twenty-five limbs. He left town the next night, abandoning his wife and seven children, but carrying most of the wages of death and amputation with him. His wife obtained an immediate divorce on applying to the Cadi and swearing that, as her husband had served as an executioner, she was afraid to live with him lest he should be tempted to commit some violence against her. Although it was easy for a man to divorce his wife, generally a woman could only divorce her husband on the grounds of impotence; fear of an executioner was a useful addition. So everything was sorted out and life went on.

Now the area around the port was empty, apart from a number of soldiers and the two of us. Rais was uncomfortable. He said that we ought not to remain here any longer, but should return immediately to Mr Willshire's house.

When I was back in the relative safety of Mr Willshire's residence, only Moses Nahory was there, apart from the servants. I had a long conversation with him, and found him to be full of interesting information about his people.

He told me that a Rabbi had recently arrived from Jerusalem to gather the tribute paid every year by all the Jews in Barbary towards the support of the Jews who are permitted to reside in Jerusalem by paying tribute to the Sultan of the Turkish Empire.

According to Nahory, the Jews believe that Jerusalem must be kept as a kind of possession until the time arrives, as predicted by the prophets, when the little stone is to be cut out without hands from the mountains of Jerusalem and is to fill the whole earth. This and other predictions, together with the miseries inflicted on the Jews by the merciless Moors, encourages them to support their spiritual leaders in Barbary and in Jerusalem.

I told Moses Nahory that I had learned how many of the Jews came here in the time of the Romans. He said that the dark age for the Jews after their eviction from their country was followed by a prosperous period for them in North Africa. As Islam conquered North Africa, all were required to become Muslims, except for the peoples of the book: the Jews and the Christians. The Jews were able to establish positions in trade, metalwork, jewellery and similar crafts.

In later times, Isaac Alfasi and then the philosopher-physician Maimonides were the intellectual leaders of the whole continent. Alfasi, meaning 'the man from Fez', compiled a compendium of legal decisions in the eleventh century. Maimonides, whose real name was Moses ben Maimon, was a twelfth century physician and writer on logic, religion, medicine and philosophy. But despite being people of the book, both had to flee this land to avoid the choice of conversion to Islam or death; Alfasi to Spain and

Maimonides to Saladin's court in Egypt.

Then, in the late fifteenth century the first compulsory enclaves, the *mellahs*, appeared, and, periodically, Jews in various towns were required either to convert or be killed; others were killed without even having that choice.

Moses Nahory said that he had been told that the word '*mellah*' came from the Arabic word for salt, '*melh*', because the first *mellah* was built in Fez Jdid, New Fez, over an old salt mine. But he preferred the story that it was because Jews were forced to put salt on the heads of those who were about to be executed, so as to preserve them for display.

The *mellahs* facilitated security and self-government, and the first one was created by order of the Sultan next to his palace in New Fez, so that he could protect the Jews. But the designated areas also facilitated persecution and taxation. The Jews had to pay a special poll tax, called the '*jizya*', plus a special land tax called the '*kharaj*'. This led to Jews not holding land, consequently excluding them from the main source of income, agriculture, and compelling them to buy food from the Muslims. Many were therefore forced to turn to commerce. So when in later years commerce became the principal source of revenue, the Jews were well placed, and they were resented for it. Also, confinement in the *mellahs* meant that the Jews had to educate their children in their enclaves; but instead of disadvantaging them, it resulted in a high literacy rate that gave them a further advantage in commerce.

There was another wave of Jewish immigration after the fall of Granada, when the Jews of Andalucia were expelled from Spain and settled in cities such as Fez and Rabat. In music, speech, dress, cuisine and architecture, these Jews had much more in common with their fellow Moors, who were largely Muslim Andalucians, than with the indigenous or Berber Jews, and this division between the white Jews and black Jews still exists.

The Sultans regarded the Jews as a vital resource of the state, and they often held important posts in the administration, although this in itself led to further envy and persecution. They were given useful rights in commerce to ensure that they could afford to pay the *jizya*, and they, as well as some Muslims, became know as the Tujjars al-Sultan, the Sultan's merchants. These stories fascinated me, and I asked Nahory to introduce me to some of his people.

On the following day, Nahory had more important information for us. He told me that a schooner had arrived from Gibraltar flying the British flag. The vessel was in fact Genoese, but her captain dared not fly that flag as the Barbary powers were at war with the King of Sardinia. This ship was carrying a cargo of dry goods, iron, steel and cotton to Mordechai Zagury, as well as bringing young Elio Zagury to visit his parents.

After Elio Zagury had been to see his family, Nahory brought him to call on Mr Willshire and to see me. Elio was a charming young man. He was dressed in the European fashion, and he spoke good English, having been educated in England. I told him our story, and he expressed great joy at our deliverance. He invited Mr Willshire, Savage and me (all of us being able to speak Spanish) to dine with him at his father's house on the next Saturday evening. We gladly accepted the invitation. I was eager to learn some of the Jewish customs, and I wanted to meet the Rabbi from Jerusalem, who was a guest at Mordechai Zagury's house.

The buildings in the Mellah were much like those in the rest of the town, although the alleyways were narrower and many of the houses featured the Star of David over the entrance, on the door, or in the woodwork on the balustrade of the balcony. The doors of their homes were generally painted blue, a colouring brought by the Jews who had escaped from Spain. We found the Zagurys' house in the main town, the Medina, close to the entrance to the Mellah.

On our arrival that Saturday evening, we met all the Zagury family. We also met two members of the Horeb-Elisha family who had accompanied the Zagurys on their walk home from prayers, and had called in for a few minutes before continuing to their own home in the Mellah.

The Jews' clothing is regulated by Moorish laws. The wealthier

... and many of the houses featured the Star of David
over the entrance...

men wear a shirt without a collar, and trousers that come tight below the knee. They wear a jacket made of green woollen cloth, with a collar and with sleeves to the elbow. On their feet they have black slippers, as the luxury of coloured slippers is forbidden to them by the Sultan's order. The women wear a wide muslin shirt with fine needlework, a white waistcoat and a green cloth dress that has a number of red woollen cords hanging down, a piece of silver at the end of each. The married women cover their heads with a flowing silk handkerchief. Those who can afford them wear amber and pearl necklaces and silver and gold bracelets; but they were very few, perhaps twenty in all Essaouira.

Then I was presented to the Rabbi, Abraham ben Nassar. He was a man of middling stature, dark complexion, short hair and a most venerable beard. He wore a brown striped mantle that buttoned close round his neck and fell loosely to his feet. His head was covered with a turban, and around his waist he had a brown silk girdle that was about six inches wide. In his hand he held a string of large beads, which he continually counted.

We conversed in Spanish, which he spoke fluently. I asked him about the city of Jerusalem and its inhabitants. From his answers I learned that the total population is now fifty thousand. They can easily be divided into four groups. There are thirty thousand Turks, many of whom are soldiers and officials. They are the majority, as they occupy the city and the surrounding lands. The remaining twenty thousand are Jews, Armenians and Greeks.

He also told me that a very brisk trade is carried on from Jerusalem, mainly by the Jews, with Persia, Constantinople and Jaffa. He said that his people are permitted to reside in Jerusalem by paying a tribute to the Grand Seignior, or Sultan, of the Turkish Empire, and that the language mostly spoken there by both Jews and Christians is Spanish.

Jerusalem is apparently well fortified by the Turks, and its walls are strong. All religious denominations are tolerated there upon making the required payment.

The Rabbi's journey to collect contributions for the maintenance of the Jews and their institutions in Jerusalem would take him to many countries. Out of the total fund brought back to Jerusalem, the yearly tribute is paid to the Grand Seignior; other impositions are paid to various Turkish officers, and whatever is left goes to support the community.

When I had finished with my questions, the Rabbi asked me about America, a country of which he knew very little. In fact, he thought that it was mainly wilderness or desert. I explained to him that we had many cities and towns, and that there were a large number of Jews in America, where they enjoyed the same privileges as people of other religions. He was surprised that they could live there without paying an extra tribute, but he accepted that what I said was true. However, he did not accept that the arrangement would be permanent. He said such a situation had existed in other countries, but when times were bad or a disaster occurred, the treatment of the Jews quickly changed.

I told him that he should go to America to see for himself, and he said that in a year's time, when he had completed his present journey, he would ask for permission to go to America. I warned him that our Jews were not as superstitious as those in Africa and Europe.

"That may be," he replied, "but if they are Jews, they must contribute towards the support of those of their people who live in the Holy Land, in order to prepare for the fulfilment of God's promise to restore Jerusalem to them."

"But how are the Jews here treated?" I asked.

"From time to time very badly, but otherwise in a way that allows them to survive as well as most people in this country," he replied. "You see, at first Mohammed and his followers were friendly towards us, and created customs similar to ours. Mohammed expected the Jews to accept his new faith; but when they did not, his attitude became hostile and the Jews in Medina were annihilated or expelled. By the end of his life, Mohammed had given up his hopes of converting Jews and Christians, and he ordered his followers not to take Jews or Christians as friends.

313

"Nevertheless, he still gave Jews and Christians a special category. They had their own books, and were therefore the peoples of the book. Everyone else was either a believer or an infidel. We are called 'dhimmis', the 'protected ones' - second-class citizens who may practise our religion privately, but do not have equal rights under the law.

"Jews were therefore not required to convert or die. However, that has not stopped us from being subject to that requirement from time to time, because they have invented an amendment that provides that as our Messiah has not arrived for over five hundred years, we must now convert. Before I go to Gibraltar, I shall visit Ifrane near Agadir to pray at the tomb of the fifty Jewish martyrs who chose to die by fire only twenty-five years ago, rather than become Muslims.

"So yes, the Jews here may prosper and live well, but a shadow always hangs over them, and they cannot be sure of their survival the next day."

The Rabbi certainly had a powerful belief and message, and I was glad to have had the opportunity for such a discussion. But now it was time to eat, and serious conversation came to an end temporarily. For dinner, the principal dish was *skenah*, a complete meal in a single large pot. This is prepared before their Sabbath, as the Jews may not cook on the Sabbath. *Skenah* is made of beef and marrowbones and a large quantity of beans baked in an oven for nearly twenty-four hours. It is very luscious and fattening, and it was so good that all talk ceased whilst we gorged ourselves. This *skenah*, with a few vegetables and a plum pudding, good bread and a Jewish spirit called '*maychayim*', which is distilled from figs and aniseed and bittered with wormwood, is the favourite meal of the wealthier Jews. The taste of the *maychayim* reminded me of the Irish *usquebaugh* or whiskey, and means in Hebrew 'the water of life', rather like other countries' *eau de vie* or *aquavit*.

Obviously I was not the first American ship's captain to be given a *skenah* meal, because others before me had brought back to New England the concept of baking beans rather than boiling

314

them, and baked beans had eventually become a Sabbath dish for Colonial Puritans, who copied the Morrocan Jews and baked the beans on the day before their Sabbath, so as to avoid cooking on that day. In fact, this has become so common that Boston is now known as 'bean town', although they bake their beans with molasses and bacon. Over recent years, baked beans have become a traditional American food.

When the table had been cleared, the Rabbi announced that it was time to consider our situation. He said that with such a varied collection of people and talents in the house, it was an ideal opportunity to find a solution to our confinement.

Everyone present knew the details of our story and circumstances. We all discussed the problems and the possibilities in a very lively manner, and finally agreed that waiting for the Sultan's consent to leave was pointless. That could take a very long time; it might never arrive; things might deteriorate dangerously while we waited.

I felt that the best thing to do was to go aboard one of the English ships the night before she was due to leave. Savage and Mr Willshire agreed, but the Rabbi would not have it.

"Wait," he said, "we have not finished thinking." He then spoke privately with Elio and his father, before announcing his recommendation.

"My friends," he said, "it is clear that you should leave as soon as possible. You came to this country by sea and we agree that you should leave by sea."

"Fine," I said. "We must take one of the English ships."

"No," he said. "That is too obvious. They will suspect that immediately. You must go on the Genoese ship that brought Elio. That ship is bound for Gibraltar with goods belonging to our host. He will arrange for you and your men to be carried on board."

"But we will be given passage on the English ships as well," I said.

"No doubt," said the Rabbi, "but you are not permitted to leave this country. If you and the English vessels disappear at the

315

same time, Mr Willshire will be in severe danger. The wrath of the Bashaw will fall on him."

"Of course," I replied. "We will do nothing to endanger Mr Willshire; but if we disappear at the same time as the Genoese schooner, will that be any better?"

"That depends on how it is done," said the Rabbi. "We must play a delicate game. First, you and your men will be seen very publicly in the town before the English vessels leave. You will go nowhere near those vessels. The English ships will depart, and you and your men will continue to be seen about the town. This will relax the Bashaw and his military officers. Then the Genoese vessel will be loaded, the captain will be paid by Mordechai Zagury, and the vessel will leave. Now there will be no ships in the port, and all will see that you are still in Essaouira. Once out of sight, the Genoese vessel will hold its position for two days. The following night, when no one will expect your escape by sea, the Genoese will come close to shore not far from the city. They will send a boat to collect you, and you will then be on your way to Gibraltar. Mordechai Nahory's friends there will take all of you to your friend, Mr Sprague."

"Wonderful," I said. "But what about Mr Willshire?"

"What is the problem?" replied the Rabbi. "You could not have left by ship, there were no ships in the harbour. You must have escaped to the north by land. You are not permitted to leave this country without the Sultan's consent, but you are permitted to leave Essaouira. You will have committed no crime, and Mr Willshire will be safe."

It all sounded too easy. Now our hosts amused themselves by singing songs in Arabic and telling stories, which they kept up with great enthusiasm until we left for the night. What a wonderful evening. In a very good humour, I prepared myself for a period of relaxation while we awaited the departure of the English vessels.

CHAPTER TWENTY-SIX

Flight and arrest

Waiting for the English vessels to leave and allowing myself to be seen around the windy town did not involve much effort. I decided that I would occupy my time by exploring the city and finding out as much as possible about it and its inhabitants.

The city of Mogadore, now called Essaouira by the Moors and the Arabs, stands on a peninsula projecting into the Atlantic. It is about eleven hundred yards long and eight hundred yards deep from the sea. The city walls are twenty feet high and six feet thick, and have cannons all along the summit.

Essaouira is divided into four parts, the buildings in each section being plastered or whitewashed and having flat terraced roofs. As this town has been built to a plan, many of the streets meet one another at right angles, most of them being quite short and narrow. The Kasbah, or fortress, is at the west side and forms the defence to the sea. This section is separated from the main town by a strong wall whose gates are shut at eight o'clock every evening, and not opened again until daylight. It is in this section that the high officials live, and where the treasury and arsenal are located. Mr Willshire and the other Christian merchants and consuls reside in this fortress area, and the four principal Jewish merchants are permitted to store their goods there.

ESSAOUIRA

English Consulate   Court   Mellah   Christian cemetery   Jewish cemetery

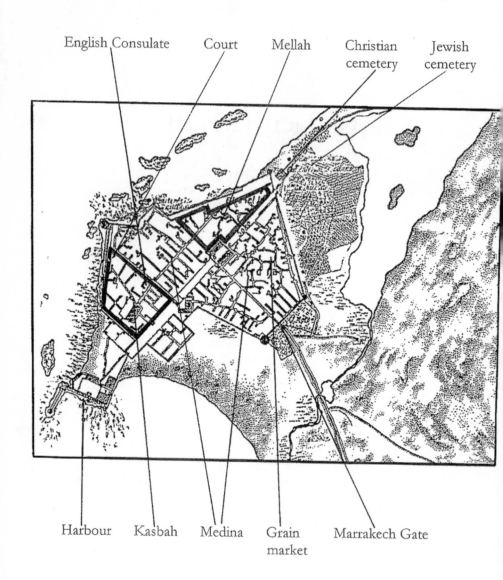

Harbour   Kasbah   Medina   Grain market   Marrakech Gate

The next section is the Medina, or main town, where the market is held. There is a square that is used as the grain market; it is surrounded by numerous shops owned by Jews and Moors. These shops have a door, but no window, and are so small that the shopkeeper can sit in the centre and still reach nearly every article in the shop. There are also places of manufacture nearby. They produce, amongst other things, large quantities of *haicks*, which are made of woollen yarn, spun by hand with an iron spindle. Some are taken to other towns for sale, but it is against the law to export them by sea. They also make scimitars and axes and knives, and many iron tools.

East of the main town is the area occupied by the blacks. Like the fortress and the Mellah, this part is walled in and has its gates shut every night. The negroes who are free enjoy nearly all the privileges of the Moors, being of the same religion. However, they are not allowed to intermarry with the Moors.

The fourth division is the Mellah, the Jews' town. It is separated from the main town by a high wall. The Mellah has only one gate, which is always strongly guarded by the Moors. This separation is common to most Moorish cities, and the Caid al-Yahud regulates the Mellah and settles all disputes concerning the Jews, other than those between Jews, which are dealt with by their Rabbis. At eight o'clock every evening, all the Jews except those in Mr Willshire's house, those who are permitted to live in the Medina and a few others must retire to the Mellah until the morning.

To the west of the town is the harbour, which is shielded from the sea by the islands; but they are really only several outcrops of rocks, although the biggest is large enough to accommodate an old Portuguese fort that now serves as a lookout tower. Vessels can safely anchor between the islands and the harbour for nine months of the year. But in December, January and February, fierce gales often prevail from the west and bring in such swells around the ends of the islands that the strongest cables may be broken and the largest vessels driven to the shore.

In fact, in the winter of 1814, an English brig anchored in the bay with a full cargo on board was swept on to the rocks and

Harbour   Isle of Mogadore   Small island with ruins
of Portuguese fort

The islands from the ramparts of Essaouira

totally destroyed. Another had her cables broken and was heading towards the harbour, at which moment her master and crew deserted her in one of the ship's boats in the hope of saving their lives. But the boat overturned in the storm, and they were all drowned or dashed to pieces. By an appalling irony, the parts of the cable still attached to the brig caught on some rocks, and in this manner she was held fast through the remainder of the storm, and the ship was saved.

On the other side of the bay stands the island of Mogadore itself, which now serves as a prison. It is heavily guarded and usually holds at least a thousand prisoners. These are not ruffians or thieves; at least not in the normal sense. Common criminals are not imprisoned in this country; they just lose their limbs or their lives, as I had seen the other day. They see no sense here in providing accommodation and food for criminals.

The people in the prison are all former alcayds, officials and military men who are out of favour. Those who survive are generally pardoned and restored to their posts after a few years of patience in their irons, when the wheel of fortune turns to their advantage. No new governor wants to change the system, realising that he may be the next to fall out of favour. In effect, the prison is a form of temporary exile, and communication with the mainland is forbidden without the Bashaw's consent, on pain of death.

Apparently, the island of Mogadore had a rather more glorious history many centuries ago, as it was renowned throughout the time of the Roman Empire for the manufacture of the imperial purple dye that they made from certain shellfish. But that stopped long ago.

As part of his scheme to reduce the influence of Agadir, Sultan Sidi Mohammed, the father of the present Sultan, arranged for the fortification, rebuilding and enlargement of Essaouira in 1760 according to the design of the French architect, Theodore Cornut who had been working in Gibraltar. Having been a pupil of the military architect Vauban who had designed the fort and ramparts at St Malo in Brittany, Cornut adopted a similar plan for Essaouira.

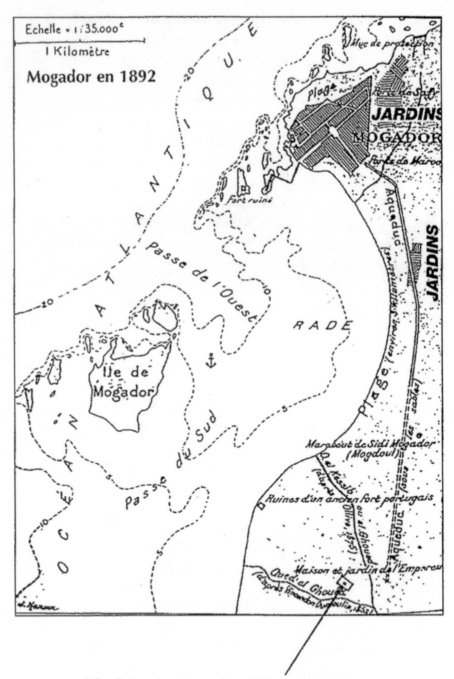

The Sultan's palace where Riley met Willshire

Sultan Sidi Mohammed also built the palace to the south of the town, which I shall always remember, for it was outside its walls that we first met Mr Willshire.

The Sultan then shut the ports of Santa Cruz, Saffy, Rabat, Azamore, Dar el Beida and others, and ordered the principal merchants in those towns to go to Essaouira, most of them being Jews who were promised the Sultan's protection.

Trade was encouraged by the Sultan. Large quantities of wheat were exported to Spain and Portugal. Other exports included olive oil, sheep's wool, almonds, dates, beeswax, gums, aniseed, cumin, pomegranates and animal skins. Imports were principally iron and steel, raw cotton, cloths, silks, tea, sugar, spices, gold and silver ornaments and timber.

Essaouira prospered, and there were at one time thirty Christian business houses conducting trade. The duty on imports was ten per cent, and the administration sensibly allowed the importers a short period of credit, so that they could raise the money for the payment of the duty from sales. This is the duty to which the Sultan is entitled under the Koran as his tithe, or tenth, for the Sultan is their religious as well as temporal sovereign. Indeed, a sovereign's authority can in the long term survive only if the people accept that he has been appointed by God.

The whole country flourished during the Napoleonic wars, with cattle being sold to the English fleet and grain to the French, the Jewish merchants in Essaouira handling the Sultan's sales of the grain he acquired by taxation.

But things changed with the accession of Sultan Sulimaan, who was extremely suspicious of all the Christian countries, especially France with its revolution. He did all he could to limit contact and trade. The easiest way to do this was to increase duties, and then the Sultan prohibited the import of certain items and the export of others, such as wool, wheat and olive oil. As a result trade has been depressed in recent years, and most of the Christian establishments have closed down.

It is the policy of the present Sultan, whose power is absolute, to keep the people as poor as possible, so that they cannot rebel. A rebellious army cannot be supported without money, nor kept together without the hope of plunder.

When the people murmured, they were told that it was a sin to trade with men who did not follow the true and only holy religion on earth; that their prophet had strictly forbidden such traffic as it would be liable to corrupt their morals and defile them in the sight of God; that this sin had been committed and that God was now taking vengeance on the sinners.

These were arguments that carried great weight with the superstitious Moors, and they were aided by the plague, which was raging with dreadful fury, ultimately carrying off a large proportion of the citizens of most cities and towns. In Essaouira it caused the death of over half the town's population in 1799 and 1800.

It was in this way, walking about the city and talking with some of its inhabitants, that I carried out the Rabbi's advice to make myself seen every day. Rais helped by introducing me to numerous people, although, of course, I could not speak to the women, as they are seldom seen in the streets. Those that do go out are required to be completely covered by their clothing, which goes over their heads and is held by their hands on the inside so as only to permit them to peep out with one eye, unlike the Berber women who show their faces. Of course, the Berbers wear *haicks*, their blankets; but the other men mostly wear *djalabas*, long flowing tunics with a hood that usually flops unused on the wearer's back.

Then a courier from the Sultan arrived in Essaouira with an instruction to the Bashaw. He was ordered not to allow any Moor to serve a Christian or a Jew, or to live in their houses, on pain of the severest penalty.

This letter was no sooner read than the news flew to every part of the city. As a result, Rais bel Cossim and bel Mooden, who had spent a great deal of time in Mr Willshire's house, dared not return, even to take their leave. The life of a Christian before this was hardly safe without a Moor in company to ward off the insults

EXTRACT FROM A LETTER DATED 22ND DECEMBER 1815 FROM WILLIAM WILLSHIRE TO CONSUL GENERAL GREEN IN TANGIER, COMPLAINING ABOUT THE PROHIBITION ON EMPLOYING MOORS

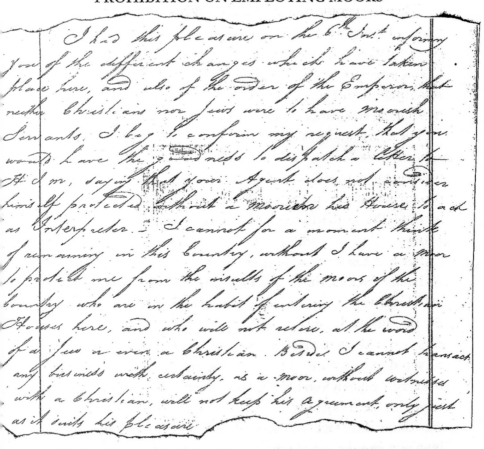

I had this pleasure on the 6th Inst. informing you of the different changes which have taken place here, and also of the order of the Emperor, that neither Christians nor Jews were to have Moorish Servants. I beg to confirm my request that you would have the goodness to dispatch a letter to HIM, saying that your Agent does not consider himself protected without a Moor in his house to act as Interpreter – I cannot for a moment think of remaining in this Country, without I have a Moor to protect me from the insults of the Moors of the Country who are in the habit of entering the Christian Houses here, and who will not retire, at the word of a Jew or even a Christian. Besides I cannot transact any business with certainty, as a Moor, without witnesses with a Christian, will not keep his agreement, only just as it suits his pleasure.

of boys and those of the Moors who were vicious or fanatical. Now it was positively dangerous.

New orders were also given to the guards at the port not to allow anyone other than the officers and crew to go on board any vessel without a special permit from the Bashaw. This order seemed to have been made with us in view, and the whole air of the city became very threatening.

I could see that Mr Willshire was extremely upset to have lost the support and protection of Rais.

"Yes," he said, "Rais has been a companion, servant, adviser and protector for me. I've been able to rely completely on his word and his courage. The Moors are an extraordinary people. They're as brave as men can be, believing that even if they venture up to the very mouth of a cannon, they cannot die one moment before the time appointed by fate, nor in any manner other than that which was predestined by the Almighty before they were created. It's wonderful to have such a strong belief; but this means that one can't negotiate or reason with them, for nothing can change what has been decided."

At last, Captains Mackay and Henderson came to dine with Mr Willshire and to say goodbye. They had decided to leave the next day. Sorry as I was to see them go, this was a welcome first step in our plan of escape.

In the afternoon, I went with Mr Willshire to pay a visit to Don Estevan Leonardi, an old man, Genoese by birth, who had been living in Essaouira for a long time, and who had exercised the functions of French vice-consul for several years.

He received us with the compliments of the season and congratulated me coldly on my redemption from slavery. After we had refreshed ourselves with a glass of wine, he told me that five years ago he had received a letter from Suse, written by a Frenchman and brought to him by an Arab. The letter stated that the writer and his companion had escaped from a prison in Tenerife a few weeks before, where they had long been confined as prisoners of war and been treated with great harshness and cruelty by the

Spaniards. They had escaped and stolen an open boat in the night, and had steered to the east towards the coast of Morocco, seeking to regain their liberty with the help of a French consul. The wind had carried them to the coast of Suse not far from Agadir, and after great sufferings and hardships, they had been seized as slaves and stripped naked.

The letter concluded by begging Mr Leonardi to ransom them and save their lives. "But," said Mr Leonardi, "I had no orders from the Consul General to expend money on behalf of his Government."

So Mr Leonardi sent a message to the Consul General asking for instructions and stating that the price for the two slaves was four hundred Spanish dollars. "The messenger returned after thirty-five days, saying that I could only spend one hundred dollars per man," continued Mr Leonardi. "When I told him this, the Arab left in disgust.

"I sent another messenger to Tangier, and he returned with an instruction that I might pay the four hundred dollars demanded, but by now the Arab was so angry that he increased the price to five hundred dollars. These negotiations continued for almost a year," said Mr Leonardi, "but I have had no message for some time, so I suppose the two men are now dead."

How fortunate that Mr Willshire had received my letter, rather than this man who was so concerned that he might not recover the extra few dollars. For that trifle, two men spent the rest of their lives in slavery.

After we returned to Mr Willshire's house, Elio came to tell me that we should prepare ourselves, as the Genoese vessel was due to leave the day after the English ships. There would then be no foreign vessels in the port, and the scene would be set for our departure.

We continued to spend most of our time wandering around the town, making sure that everyone could see that we had remained after the three vessels had gone.

Two days after the Genoese vessel had put to sea, Elio came to the house and told me that after the gates had been closed that evening, we must all be outside the city where the beach met the city walls. We were to wait there until the Genoese boat came to collect us. Then we were to board it without delay, ensuring that we were not seen by anybody.

My men were very excited at this news; literally counting down the hours until our departure. I was also excited, although I was concerned at the difficulty of remaining unseen. But first I had business to attend to. I took a pen and paper and drew a bill on Horatio Sprague for the amount spent by Mr Willshire in obtaining our redemption and in buying clothes for us. Mr Willshire had given us many items of his own clothing, but he would not accept any payment for them, nor for board or all the other expenses he had incurred while we had been his guests for almost two months. I protested, but Mr Willshire would not be paid, and it was right to allow him to do what he believed was honourable.

The evening of our escape. We left the house with Mr Willshire, my men and I dressed in dark *djalabas*, our heads hooded. We made our way through the Bab Maroksh, and furtively crept towards the sea. Then we crouched under some small trees growing at the top of the beach, and waited for the Genoese boat to arrive.

We hid there for what seemed an age. After some hours had passed, we saw a figure shuffling towards us; he was humming and talking to himself. What was he doing here? The gates had been closed long ago. He came right up to the trees, and immediately discovered us. He started to ask questions; I told him to go away. Mr Willshire offered him money, but still he persisted. Then I saw the Genoese boat gliding silently towards the shore, its presence disguised by the numerous small boats leaving for the night's fishing. Mr Willshire could wait no longer; he stood up, took hold of the idiot and bundled him back towards the gate.

Now the man started to scream fearfully. Suddenly, I heard steps running towards us. I told my men to get to the boat quickly, but as they ran, crouching all the while, soldiers arrived to answer the idiot's screams. He pointed at Mr Willshire, who was instantly seized by the soldiers. I ran to assist; I knew we had to attract the soldiers' attention so that they would not see my men climbing into the boat.

Everyone was shouting - the idiot, the soldiers, Mr Willshire. Looking at the soldiers, I called to my men, who were behind me, "Don't stop! Get to the ship as fast as you can. Wait for me in Gibraltar. I'll make my own way there", in the safe assumption that none of the soldiers could understand English.

I worked out what was happening very quickly. Some days earlier, I had been told that every Moor who is born an idiot, or becomes insane, is considered a saint and treated with the greatest attention and respect by everyone. He is clothed and fed and taken care of by the whole community. Do what he will, he cannot commit a crime in the eyes of the law.

The soldiers were enraged that the idiot had been manhandled. In the most abusive language, they ordered Mr Willshire and me to return to Mr Willshire's house, and then they drew their scimitars, threatening to cut us down.

Mr Willshire's spirit could not accept this indignity, and he rebuked the soldiers in a very resolute manner, shouting defiance to them and to the Alcayd. He told them that if they did not withdraw, he would avenge himself instantly by complaining to the Sultan, and then they would lose their heads.

By now I could tell Mr Willshire that the boat had left with my men, and was out of sight. All shouting ceased, and the two of us were escorted through the Bab Maroksh, and we made our way back to Mr Willshire's house.

But the soldiers were still furious, and they ran to the Alcayd, complaining to him that Mr Willshire had beaten them, that he had called them foul names, and that he had defied the power of the Sultan.

Soldiers were sent after Mr Willshire. They arrived soon after we reached the house, and their officer insisted that we go straight to the Alcayd, and it could either be voluntarily or else by force.

Mr Willshire told him that first he had to wait for his interpreter, and then he would go. Within a short time Moses Nahory was brought to us, and we went to the Alcayd's residence.

The Alcayd reprimanded Mr Willshire for having cursed the Sultan, and advised him to settle the business by giving some money to the soldiers, otherwise they would send a report to the Sultan.

With the help of Nahory, Mr Willshire defended himself so well that his accusers began to lower their voices a little. He said that he had a letter from the Sultan that ordered all bashaws and alcayds to safeguard his person from insults and treat him with the respect due to the vice-consul of a great and friendly nation. He also complained that the recent order had deprived him of the aid of a Moor, to which he was entitled under the terms of the Sultan's letter.

Mr Willshire added that he would write to the Sultan with an account of the insult and the villainy of the Bashaw's soldiers, and he would not pay anything to anyone.

The Alcayd was visibly irritated by Mr Willshire's hostile stance. He said that he was under a duty to safeguard Mr Willshire and the other Christians in the town, and he wished them to be respected, but they should show respect themselves. All the same, he told the guards that Mr Willshire was under the Sultan's protection and that they must never lay a finger on him; but if they thought that he or any of the Christians living in Essaouira intended to board one of the ships in the port, they must prevent the ship from leaving until they had notified the Alcayd. He would then decide whether to issue the necessary permit or seek the Sultan's consent.

This seemed to me to be a perfectly satisfactory conclusion, but unfortunately the Alcayd was enjoying the sound of his own voice too much, so he continued. He told the soldiers that they had done a great wrong, and if they repeated it in the future, he would dismiss them. The soldiers were very angry, and their officer said that it was intolerable for a Moor to be insulted with impunity by a Christian dog. They would report the Alcayd to the Cadi immediately, and they did not fear the Alcayd's power. If necessary, they would appeal directly to the Sultan, and all would have to abide by his decision.

The situation was now very fragile. The soldiers turned to leave, their officer saying that they were going to the Cadi. The Alcayd told them that if they did not obey his instructions, it would cost them their lives. He ordered them to return to their duties straight away, promising that he would hold an enquiry into what had happened, and he would have justice done to them and to Mr Willshire. For the time being, the affair was over.

We returned to Mr Willshire's home. In the morning he took great care to send presents to the Addals, the Alcayd's four assistants, to ensure that they would advise the Alcayd that what the soldiers had done was wrong.

Things were now getting dangerous. But as I worried about the situation, I could relax and smile when I thought of my men on board ship, safely on their way to Gibraltar.

My smile quickly vanished two days later, when Mr Willshire and I were summoned to appear before the Alcayd at the courthouse to hear the result of his so-called inquiry.

"I will no longer concern myself with Vice-Consul Willshire and the misunderstanding with our soldiers," announced the Alcayd. "The truth has led me to more serious matters. The young man whom our soldiers bravely rescued has told me what happened, and I now understand why your former slave friend was dressed in a *djalaba.*"

What on earth was he talking about? What nonsense had been contrived against me? I said nothing; there was nothing I could say. I waited for the charge.

"You were seen leaving a mosque; that is why the young man tried to apprehend you," said the Alcayd, pointing at me with his arm outstretched.

Of course it was nonsense, there were no mosques outside the city walls. But what if I had been in a mosque; what sort of crime was that? I soon found out.

"You, a Christian, entered a mosque without a cadi or other authorised guard," the Alcayd continued, his voice rising to a shriek. "You have one day to decide. Either you must change your religion by having your head shaved, undergoing the operation of circumcision and confessing that there is but one God and that Mohammed is his only prophet; or alternatively, you will suffer instant death. Return to Mr Willshire's house and remain there to consider your decision. You will be guarded and may not leave the house until you are brought before me tomorrow to announce your choice. Now go!"

I was dumbfounded. What was happening?

"This is nonsense," I said to Mr Willshire, "and I intend say so."

"You can't," he replied, "because you'll be treated like the Jews and any other non-Muslims - you may not give evidence to contradict what has been said by a Muslim."

"But you spoke out when we were first brought before the Alcayd," I said.

"Yes," said Mr Willshire, "but I wasn't speaking as a Christian, I was speaking as a vice-consul with a letter of protection from the Sultan. Let's keep calm. I'll see what I can do for you, but this is not the time for argument."

So we were marched back to Mr Willshire's house. Once inside, he confirmed that the sentence was the usual one for this crime.

"There's no point in waiting for the Sultan's consent to leave," he said. "If at any time you can escape, you must do so. This wretched fellow has found a way to make his peace with the soldiers, give me no reason to complain to the Sultan, and justify everything that he and the soldiers have done. You are the victim."

"What can be done?" I asked.

"I don't know," said Mr Willshire. "If only I could talk with Rais again, we might find a way of dealing with this. We need a miracle. You've survived through so much, maybe you can have just one more piece of good fortune."

I felt that I had already had my fair share of divine assistance. It was time to look for the first opening, and then make a run for it.

That night I did not sleep at all well. The knowledge that guards were posted all around the house created a tension that stifled me. What would I say the next day to the Alcayd? I had regained my pride and did not wish to lose it again; nevertheless, I might have to take the easy but dishonourable option. What good would a proud corpse be to my family?

Late the next afternoon, I was taken to the courthouse, accompanied by Mr Willshire, who said that he would demand that nothing was done until he had sent a message to the Sultan and received a reply. He was really earning his hundred pounds a year salary as British vice-consul.

After Mr Willshire had made his demand, the Alcayd announced his decision. The Sultan would indeed decide my fate, but Mr Willshire was not to send a message; the Alcayd, not Mr Willshire, would report to the Sultan, and while his response was awaited, I would be confined in the prison on the island of Mogadore.

I was taken down to the port and put on a small boat with six guards. Mr Willshire told me not to worry, something would be done. Of course he did not explain what he would do to help me; he had no idea. But this man had saved me before; surely he could do it again.

Once on the island, I was marched to the prison, and then into a large dark cell with a blanket on the floor to serve as my bed. From the barred window I could see the city all day and all night, as well as vast numbers of seabirds and the occasional falcon, free to come and go as they pleased. But rather nearer to my window, I saw scattered about the island the bones of prisoners who had been left to die here.

The cell was large enough for me to walk to and fro, and for three days I survived tolerably well. Food and water were brought to me twice a day; but apart from the sounds of the guards and the birds, everything else was silence.

Then, on the evening of the fourth day, I had visitors. It was Rais bel Cossim and bel Mooden. Rais shouted to me through the door, "Riley, we have come to see you, and we have brought you food and clothes."

The door was opened, and they came in, dragging a large sack. The guard closed the door behind them. Rais and bel Mooden both hugged me, overjoyed to see that my condition had not had a chance to deteriorate during my short spell of imprisonment.

"What's happening?" I asked.

"You are leaving this place now," replied Rais.

"Why?" I said. "Is that the Sultan's decision?"

"No," said Rais, with a very serious look, "the Sultan's decision will never be made, because it will never be asked for; at least not while the present Bashaw and Alcayd are in power. But fortunately, the Sultan's recent order has been revoked and I have been able to see Mr Willshire once more. We have made an arrangement with the governor of the prison, for which he and his men have been well rewarded. You will leave tonight under cover of darkness. We will land to the south of the city, where Mr Willshire is waiting for us. He will explain everything."

"But what will happen when the Alcayd discovers that I'm not here?"

"We have thought of that," said Rais. "Probably the Alcayd will be happy to let you rot here; but if he ever asks for you, he will be shown your skeleton in your cell. In this sack we have the body of a thief who was executed in the town yesterday; soon there will be only bones left. Come on, let's go."

They left the corpse for the guard to deal with. The door of my cell had been unlocked whilst we talked, and all three of us hurried along the passage, out of the prison, and down to Rais' boat. No one questioned us, no one stopped us; they had all taken care to be out of sight.

Everything happened so quickly. I felt a rush of blood as the fresh air filled my lungs, and we drifted quietly away from the island of Mogadore and towards the mainland a short distance to the south of Essaouira. My escape had begun.

EXTRACT FROM A LETTER DATED 9th JANUARY 1816 FROM WILLIAM WILLSHIRE TO CONSUL GENERAL GREEN IN TANGIER, CONFIRMING RILEY'S DEPARTURE FROM ESSAOUIRA

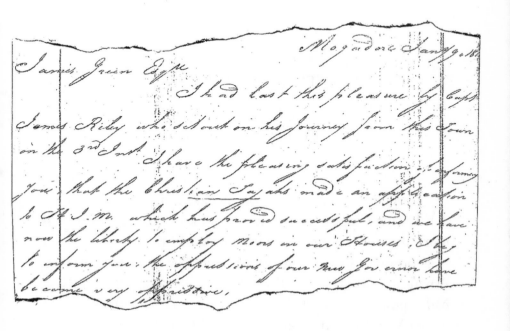

Mogadore January 9th, 1816

James Green Esqre

I had last this pleasure by Capt James Riley who set out on his Journey from this Town on the 3rd Inst.

I have the pleasing satisfaction of informing you that the Christian Sagahs made an application to H.I.M. which has proved successful, and we have now the liberty to employ Moors in our Houses. I beg to inform you, the oppressions of our new Governor have become very oppressive ...

CHAPTER TWENTY-SEVEN

A new profession

Mr Willshire was waiting on the shore, and he came to the water's edge to help us beach our little boat. He explained to me that Elio Zagury was travelling overland to Tangier. It had been arranged that I would go with him and be delivered to the American Consul General there, Mr James Simpson, the man who had appointed Mr Willshire as the American agent in Essaouira.

Bel Mooden said goodbye to me. Then he pushed the boat into the sea, climbed on board and headed back to the port. Rais, Mr Willshire and I travelled on mules for about two hours beyond the far end of the bay and the Sultan's palace. There we found Elio Zagury and five others waiting for us. Elio's companion was David Horeb-Elisha, whom I had met briefly at the Zagurys' house. There was also a Jewish servant, two Moors who were the muleteers and an armed man on horseback who was to be our guide and guard. Mules would be slower than horses, but there was no choice, for under the Moorish laws, Jews were forbidden to ride horses and camels.

January 3rd. It was time for me to leave my saviours. William Willshire and Rais bel Cossim; these two men, their faces, their voices, their memory would be with me for the rest of my life.

The knowledge that I would probably never see them again was painful. With a final goodbye, we looked into each other's eyes. "Thank you, thank you for everything," I said to both of them. We shook hands; then they turned, mounted their mules and headed back towards Essaouira.

The rest of us set off, riding inland and then towards the north. For a long time, all was total silence. I was thinking only of Mr Willshire and Rais. Two exceptional men; fate had been so kind to place them in my life.

But there would be more time to think of them in years to come. Now I had to get to Tangier. We proceeded along a path; not very quickly, but making steady progress. Our heavily armed guide led us; he was a fine looking fellow, half negro and half Moor, who had formerly been in the Sultan's army. As far as the Sultan is concerned, if a man possesses talent and bravery, his colour is disregarded.

Riding on in the dark through a dreary landscape, we came to a place called Omlays, or the Three Springs. There we found a number of other travellers watering their camels, mules and asses. We pitched camp for the night. Elio had brought a box containing tea, coffee and sugar, and the mules also carried coals for a fire, a selection of cooking utensils and a good supply of provisions.

We made some tea and ate *couskusu* for our late supper, then drifted off to sleep. Our guard and the muleteers slept outside the tents on the ground, wrapped only in their *haicks*. This is what the Moors and Arabs prefer to do when travelling, and they find it curious that people of other nations do not adopt this method. In fact, they carry this preference so far that many of the male inhabitants of the cities sleep on the flat tops of their houses, rather than on their mattresses under cover.

At daylight on the fourth, we struck our camp. After a breakfast of coffee and eggs, we set off once more. Before we left, Elio told me that when we came across other travellers, he intended to introduce me as the Sultan's doctor. He would say that I was returning to Fez after journeying south to treat one of the Sultan's

337

favoured officials. That would explain what a Christian was doing in these parts.

We travelled a little way inland through uneven ground and many groves of argan trees, which were loaded with the oil nut in various shades, from deep green to bright yellow.

Although the sea was now out of sight, we could still hear the roaring of the troubled ocean as it dashed against the coast. It sounded so threatening, and we continued to hear it until we were well inland.

Then, at sunset, we came to a village of about twenty stone houses, all one storey high. There were also many huts built only of reeds and sticks, and there was a small mosque in the middle.

Near this village, which was not walled in, we set up our tents. As soon as we had done so, a great number of unarmed Moors, probably two or three hundred, came to look at us and find out who we were. One of them brought a message from the leader of the village saying that we were welcome, and apologising for being unable to supply barley for our mules, as in each of the last three years their entire crop had been destroyed by locusts. However, we were given a loin of good mutton, two dozen eggs and some *couskusu*, so we ate well and then sent a message of thanks.

I asked Elio who this man was, and he told me that his name was Mohammed Il Factesba, that he was treated as a saint by the Moors, and that he taught young men to read the Koran. He usually had over three hundred students at any one time, and he did not just teach them, he also supplied them with food throughout their stay, for which he would accept no payment. His wife and daughter prepared meals for all those men without any assistance. Nobody understood how he could afford such generosity, so they treated it as one of his miracles.

My title, the Sultan's English doctor, soon reached the saint, and he sent a messenger with a request that I come to see him as soon as possible. Elio and I went immediately, and we were welcomed by a withered old man seated on a mat outside a house, his back resting against the wall.

The saint invited me to sit down near him, and then he asked Elio about me. Elio kept to the Sultan's doctor story, and this seemed to please the saint, who said that he was a friend to Christians and to men of every religion, for we were all children of the same heavenly Father and ought to treat each other like brothers. He then said that God was great and good, and he continued rather mysteriously by telling me that God had been very merciful to me and I ought to be thankful for the rest of my life. Did this man know the truth about me? If he did, it was amazing but worrying.

While I was looking at the saint, I was trying to work out just how much he knew and what the consequences might be. I was conscious that he was talking to me, but I was not listening to a word he was saying. Then I realised that he was describing some ailment that he wanted me to treat. Of course, I was a doctor, so I would have to be prepared for this wherever I went. I told the saint that my Arabic was not very good and could he please repeat his story, speaking very slowly.

He said that he was lame and could not walk, and that this had been caused by a stone falling on one of his feet. This had left him an invalid for four months, after which he had recovered sufficiently to ride his mule; or so he thought. But as soon as he mounted the mule, he had fallen off and caused further injury to the damaged foot, which had then become useless. All this had happened a year ago, and within the last few months his other leg had also become affected, so that he had now lost the use of both legs.

The saint said that he had no complaints about his lameness, because he knew that it came from God and was a punishment for his sins. But now he hoped that the Almighty would be merciful and pardon his offences, permitting him to walk again so that he could take proper care of his guests and do more good in the world.

Obviously he was relying on me as the agent of God. So I examined him. His legs were very thin and feverishly hot. There was no wound or broken skin, so there must have been some internal break or other disorder, particularly as the joints were very swollen.

I asked him if he had ever applied medication to his legs. He said that he had consulted a man eminently skilled in curing illnesses, and on this man's advice he had bound some skins with writing on them around his legs, and had also kept his legs wet with oil. But neither of these applications had helped. I was relieved; I could hardly do any worse.

The saint saw me thinking. He said that he knew some men were endowed with the gift of healing, and he hoped that I had such a talent; adding that he would be satisfied if only I could do something to ease the pain. Well, I would be delighted if I could. I told him that I would do everything in my power to help him, but I needed time to consider what should be done. So, assuming the air of a learned physician, I held my chin in my hand and retired to my tent with a very thoughtful expression.

My principal concern was how to get out of this predicament; but at the same time, I really did want to do something for the saint.

Elio came back to help me. First we made a paste out of some fruit, coffee and sugar. I sent Elio to give the paste to the saint, with instructions to spread it over his legs, hoping that this would buy us some time.

About half an hour later, Elio returned and told me that even if I did nothing else, the saint would be grateful to me.

It was now time to see the saint again. I knew that the first thing to do was to criticise the previous adviser, so I said that he must stop using the oil immediately. Instead, he should rub his limbs frequently with cloths to promote circulation of the blood. He was also to bind up his legs in fine salt every night to reduce the fever. I instructed him to try to walk every day, using his legs as much as possible, if necessary with two men supporting him. Finally, I prescribed a drink to be made by boiling the roots of several herbs in water.

His gratitude was really quite embarrassing. I retired to my tent and just hoped that God would do whatever my ministrations failed to accomplish.

Now I had a reputation. Many Moors came to us, asking me to prescribe something for their various disorders. I asked Elio and David to bring me one of every herb or plant that was available here. They brought quite a number, and as each patient described his symptoms, I pointed to one of the herbs or plants as the remedy.

One of my patients was a grey-haired old man. *"Tabib, tabib"* - "doctor, doctor" - he whispered as he put his head under the cloth of my tent. My guard pushed him away, but the old man would not be stopped, so I let him come in.

I asked the man to tell me the nature of his problem, but he was too frightened to speak, and kept looking about all the time to ensure that he was not seen. He would not say anything while my guard was present, so I asked the guard to wait outside, which he reluctantly did.

"Now, what is it?" I asked.

"My problem is serious, doctor," he said. "I have had three wives. The first two have died; they loved me very much, and everything was good. My new wife is very young and fat, but despite all my efforts she is cold and will not return my love."

This was not my area of expertise. The man was obviously besotted with his new wife, being particularly impressed with her fatness, which I knew these people preferred. Indeed, spice shops in Essaouira sold a much sought-after mixture of *ktiraht, sogat* and almonds, all crushed and mixed in honey, which was guaranteed to make women fat. I told the man that his case was a very difficult one, and to prescribe a remedy required some reflection. So I asked him to go away and to come back in an hour. I used the time to take a short nap.

The man returned with two of the saint's pupils, and they sat down awaiting my advice. I told him how much I sympathised with his affliction, and that there were several things he had to do to deal with such a distressing disorder; a single remedy would not suffice. First, I recommended that he should instruct his young wife to do no more work. He must speak to her sweetly at all times and feed her on beans baked in an oven and swimming in beef marrow, which I remembered as the *skenah* I had eaten with Elio's family. I also prescribed plenty of soft-boiled eggs and rich spices in her *couskusu*. Then I told him that he should eat with her at all meals, and chew opium from time to time. But most importantly, he was not to spend the night with her more than once in every two weeks. He promised to obey my instructions, though he did not seem to relish the last piece of advice.

My patient left me with a shower of blessings for my kindness, and gave me twelve silver *dirhams* and two dozen eggs in payment. The two pupils then joined in prayer and chanted over sacred poetry for about an hour, begging God to help the old man and the saint.

This done, I spoke with Elio and told him that we ought to move on before my remedies were put to the test. He agreed, and told me that we would leave as soon as the mules were loaded.

An hour later, I ended my medical practice. I took my leave of the saint, and we set off towards the north. We travelled on, passing several destroyed and deserted towns, which had been ruined by the plague or dismantled by order of the Sultan.

It was Friday, and I was aware that the Jews were obliged by their religion to stop and rest on the eve of the seventh day, their Sabbath. I suggested to Elio that as we were now on a plain where flocks of sheep were quietly grazing on the rich herbage, this would be a good place to stop and obtain some meat. Elio told me that this was not a safe place, and anyway he and the other Jews would not be able to eat any of the sheep, as they could only eat meat of an animal killed by one of their priests. I was surprised that a man educated in England should be so superstitious, and I said so to Elio.

"You must understand," he said, "that, like the Muslims, we cannot eat meat unless all the blood has been removed. 'I will set My face against that soul that eateth blood' says the Bible. So we have specially trained men who slaughter animals in accordance with our rituals, a way that causes the maximum loss of blood, and what is left they remove by washing and salting. Also, our butchers are required to reserve a piece of each slaughtered animal for the poor. But in Essaouira they are talking about changing that, and instead they want to have a tax on every purchase of meat, which the butchers will collect and hand over to our elders, who will use the money not just for the poor, but also to pay for schooling, for our hospital and for the upkeep of the synagogues."

So we carried on towards the city of Safi. Walking along the top of the cliff, we soon saw the city in the distance. But first we approached a large dome-shaped holy house or *koubba*. Our guard told us that even though we would not come within half a mile of the *koubba*, the Jews had to dismount and pass the house barefooted, as it was built over the remains of a great saint. Everyone who was not a Muslim had to pass in this way. However, as I was a good man and a Christian, I could ride past provided I paid one *dirham* to the saint towards keeping the house in repair.

I did not much relish this method of having money stolen from me, and I told the soldier as much. He said that every Christian had to pay, and that he would be asked to hand over the money when we reached the gates of Safi.

Despite his assurance, I was convinced that this was only a trick to extort money; but there was no way to get out of it, not even if I offered to take off my shoes and walk. So I paid him the *dirham*, telling him that I would set it down as a debt due to me by the saint, whom I presumed would have no objection to repaying me in the next world.

"No problem at all," said the soldier. "The saint was a fair man, and he will be certain to repay both capital and interest, and he will also intercede to procure your admission to Paradise as part of the bargain."

Having finished this nonsense, we continued towards Safi. We entered the city at the eastern gate, and made our way to the house of friends of the Zagurys.

Safi is a small town, and there is no *mellah*. The Jews live amongst the Moors. I could see that conditions were very bad. There was hardly any trade, for although Safi used to be a leading town, the port was closed several years ago by the Sultan to the benefit of Essaouira. The Jews here are hard put to survive, and I could not but pity their condition.

The central street is one continuous *souk*, or market. The public buildings are three mosques, each with high square towers. The Jews have several small rooms, their synagogue, for the purpose of worship.

Safi's inhabitants are supplied with good water by a brook that washes the northern wall of the city. All the cattle and sheep that are owned by the inhabitants are brought into the city every day before nightfall. They are driven out again in the morning, but they leave all their dirt behind and it just lies there. The filth in the streets was in many places over nine inches deep, so that it was impossible to get through the mire without being besmeared with it almost up to the knees.

It was Friday evening, and Elio, David and I joined Elio's friends for their Sabbath dinner. There were twenty people present. Before eating, they brought forward a cup shaped like a tankard and a plate with white bread into which some herbs had been chopped and mixed before baking. They all stood up and formed a circle around the supper dish, which consisted of boiled fowls.

Then they began to chant their prayers in Hebrew as fast as they could speak. This lasted about fifteen minutes. As I was ignorant of the Hebrew language, I could not join them.

When they had finished, they all said 'Amen', and then the patriarch of the household broke the bread into pieces, ate one, and gave a piece to each person present, who likewise ate it. After saying a few more words in Hebrew, they passed round the cup and each took a drink. It was wine made by steeping raisins in water, and it tasted rather sour. After the cup had gone round, all turned to the east and bowed three times. Next, each shook the others by the hand, stamping their feet at the same time, and this terminated the Sabbath evening ceremony.

Everyone washed their hands, and then the boiled fowls were cut into pieces and the parts shared out. Their bread was made of barley-meal, and they dipped it in the dish containing the liquid from the boiled fowls, to which some vinegar had been added.

I took part in these rituals as far as I was able, and we all had a very full meal. But I was eager to leave this decaying city as soon as possible.

CHAPTER TWENTY-EIGHT

A swarm and Rabat

We rested on the Saturday, and left Safi early on the morning of Sunday, 6th January. We travelled on uneven ground, frequently passing droves of loaded camels and mules, as well as several groups of tents, which they call '*douhars*'.

Riding on for some hours, we came to a beautiful valley. All over the land there were oxen, sheep, goats, camels, horses and asses. I saw many men busy tilling the rich soil, sowing wheat and barley. Near the middle of the valley we stopped to eat. As I sat there, I suddenly noticed what looked like a massive cloud of thick smoke rising over the hills to the north-east.

"My God, Elio," I cried, "there's a monstrous fire over there! Look, it's coming towards us."

"No," said Elio, "there is no fire. Those are locusts."

The cloud was advancing towards us at enormous speed. Without having seen one of these flights, a man can have no idea of the horror aroused by its approach. All the workers in the valley stopped and stood aghast; dismay was painted on each anxious face. They knew that they were helpless. Every field would be destroyed; the devouring plague was unstoppable.

As the flight approached, it suddenly flew low, and came to

ground some way to the north of us, only a few of the locusts actually reaching the area where we were standing. We mounted our mules and rode on, but soon we found the whole surface covered with locusts as thick as they could stand, all busy with their work of destruction.

Most of the locusts were too intent on their fanatical eating to move out of the way, and as a result many were trampled to death by our mules. However, thousands rose as we passed along, filling the air like a swarm of gigantic bees. In their frenzy, they flew into our faces and bodies.

Elio's friend, David, distributed silk handkerchiefs, which we used to cover our faces; but it was still necessary for us to hold our arms across our faces as we proceeded. It took several hours to ride through this horde of destroyers, which, when on the wing, truly sounded 'like the rushing of horses into battle', as described in the Bible.

After we had passed the swarm, we stopped and looked back at them. They covered a space of about eight miles long and three miles wide. The people of the valley could only stand and watch, waiting for the locusts to fill themselves and then move off as one body with the wind.

To see a year's work ruined in a moment would be enough to fill the strongest man with despair and cause him to abandon his fields. But the people here consider the swarm as just chastisement from Heaven either for their own or for their nation's sins. As a result, when a crop is destroyed, they accept the punishment and immediately get to work, sowing the same ground again.

I picked up a few stragglers to inspect the extraordinary creatures. The largest African locust is over three inches long and nearly one inch wide. He has the most voracious appetite of any insect in the world, and devours grass, grain, the leaves of trees and every green thing with indiscriminate avidity. This winged insect resembles at first sight the largest grasshoppers to be found in America. It is only when you look closely that you can see how different they are. The locust's head is like the face of a miniature sheep, and it is crowned with two long and tapering protuberances that turn backwards like the horns of a goat. Attached to his mouth is a pair of feelers used to gather the herbage about him, which he nips off, making a violent chomping noise.

He has four wings, the hind pair being quite transparent. The locust stands on six legs, with two claws on each foot, which are divided something like the hoof of a sheep. He is stout about the neck, breast and body, the hind part of which is forked and armed with a bony substance, with which he can dig a hole in the ground.

But the worst feature of these creatures is the way in which they swarm. They travel in flights, and each flight is thought to have a leader, called the Sultan Jeraad – the King of the Locusts – who directs the movements of his followers.

I heard it said in Essaouira that the Berbers who live in the Atlas Mountains have the power to destroy the flights of locusts that come from the south and the east. They do this by building large fires at the appropriate seasons on the ridges over which the locusts are known to fly. As the Atlas are high and the peaks covered in snow, the insects become chilled when flying over them. On seeing the fires, they are attracted by the glow and the warmth, and the swarm plunges headlong into the flames.

Apparently, the Sultan used to pay a considerable sum of money every year to these tribes to keep the locusts out of the north and west of his dominions. During the time when the Sultan paid that sum, not a single locust was to be seen in those lands. However, about six years ago the Sultan refused to pay the annual sum any longer, because there had been no locusts for so long that he thought he was paying for nothing. Within months, the locusts returned, and they have continued to lay waste to the country ever since. For the Sultan to start paying the Berbers again would be to admit to his mistake, so all are resigned to the annual plague.

But the people's hatred and fear of locusts is only partly because of the destruction of their crops. Far worse, they blame the locusts for the plagues of cholera that visit this country every few years, killing tens of thousands of the people. As the locusts fly west, they reach the Atlantic Ocean and continue until they are too far from land to return. They fall into the sea, dying in their millions, their remains drifting back to the shores and forming mounds of decomposing and rotting bodies. These are claimed to be the origin and breeding ground of the cholera.

The only small benefit, not to say revenge on the creatures, is that all the peoples of Barbary consider the locusts to be very good food. Why not – the insects feed only on the greenest crops. They are caught in large numbers and thrown, still alive and jumping, into a pan of boiling argan oil. There they hiss and fry until their wings are burned off and their bodies are cooked. Then they are poured out of their body shells and eaten. I had tried this delicacy in Essaouira; it resembles, in both consistency and flavour, the yolk of a hard-boiled egg.

We travelled forward and out of the tormented valley, ascending a hill to our right. Just as it was becoming dark, we came to a *douhar*, or encampment, surrounded by a stone wall. At first, the chief of the *douhar* would not allow us to enter; but when he was told that I was the Sultan's doctor, he quickly agreed to let us in.

Once we were inside, I soon regretted both my false description and our admission to this place. We were told that we must take great care because the men and women were suffering from venereal disease. As if that was not enough, I was then asked for advice on treating the disorder.

I said that I had no more medicine with me, but I recommended that they should all drink plenty of milk and observe a light diet. In addition, I suggested that they took a root which looked like sarsaparilla, and which I knew to be common in the area, and make a drink of it. I said that they must follow this advice for ten weeks, after which they would see the benefit. It was possible that my advice would be helpful, but anyway I would be far away in ten weeks' time.

Having stayed the night, we were only too happy to leave at first light without waiting to eat. We travelled hard for two days,

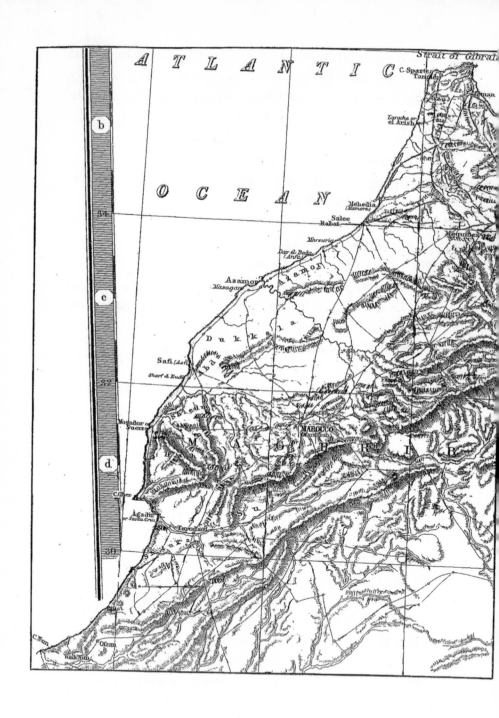

Principal towns on Riley's route north

passing Mazagan and Azemmour. There was a great movement of people here, for workmen and craftsmen were required in Azemmour as the Sultan was having the town rebuilt and changing its name, appropriately, to El Jadida – The New.

Stopping only for meals and sleep, we continued at a good pace, and two days later we passed Dar el Beida, a walled town of about two miles in circumference on the edge of a broad bay. This was the former Berber town of Anfa, named after 'anafa', the Arabic for the aniseed that grows nearby; but for some centuries the town has carried the name of Dar el Beida, the House of the White [Princess], after the shrine of the pale-skinned daughter of its patron saint, who drowned near the town on her way to visit her father. However, much of the town was destroyed in 1755 by the same earthquake that devastated Lisbon. The town is slowly recovering, and has some Spanish traders in residence. They have translated the town's name into their own language, and call it Casa Blanca.

Next we passed Afidallah and Sebuilah, and, after another day's journey, we finally saw in the distance the city of Rabat, or 'the Castle'. We approached it by the water's edge, walking along the beach. At the other end of the water was home – but so far away. All I could hear was the roar of the waves breaking on the shore, waves no more than four or five feet high, yet their noise filled my ears, the sound of one set of waves not yet having ended before the roar of the next set took over.

Mr Willshire had given me a letter of introduction to Mr Abouderham, the English vice-consul here, who had formerly been the Secretary to Consul General Green in Tangier, so we headed straight for his house. When we arrived, Mr Abouderham welcomed us warmly and gave me a room and everything else needed for my comfort, while Elio went with the others to the Mellah. Salvadore Abouderham is a Jew from Leghorn, but as a vice-consul he did not live in the Mellah. His house is in a street in the Medina where all the consuls and European merchants were required to live. It is a fine thoroughfare, linking the Kasbah and

351

On the west, facing the sea, is the Kasbah...

the Mellah, quite unusually over twenty feet wide, with villas on both sides, built one against the other.

The next day being the Jews' Sabbath, we would not be leaving. Mr Abouderham went to one of the synagogues in the Mellah with the other Jewish men. The Jewish women, their hair long and black, braided and greased with argan oil, put on their finest clothes and stained their fingernails and the insides of their hands and fingers yellow, and put on their jewellery. I used the time to wander around the city.

Rabat is situated at the mouth of the River Bouregreb, on its left bank. It is defended to the south by a double wall and several batteries of cannon. On the west, facing the sea, is the Kasbah, or fortress, and along the river to the north there is a very high and steep cliff, a wall and a number of batteries of canon.

Rabat and Salle are both ancient towns, and stand on opposite sides of the estuary. Rabat was at one time the imperial capital, but rule was transferred to Seville and later to Maroksh (Marrakech or Morroco City as the Europeans call it), then Fez. When the Muslims were expelled from Spain, they were given Rabat by the then Sultan. The two towns soon became an independent corsair state, concentrating all their efforts on piracy and bringing terror to the waters of the Mediterranean and the north-east Atlantic. Ships and towns were raided wherever opportunity arose. Hundreds of men in villages in Ireland, south-west England and France were abducted for sale into slavery, as were sailors of all nations.

Relief was obtained when European countries agreed to make annual payments to the corsair states. American sailors were protected by the British tribute while we were a colony, but once we became an independent country we lost that protection, and American sailors were seized in large numbers. An annual tribute for the future was agreed, as well as a ransom of $4,000 for the release of every imprisoned sailor and $1,400 for every cabin boy. But Congress would pay only $200 of each prisoner's ransom, so the rest of the money had to be raised by the communities where the sailors came from. I could remember listening to the lists of New England sailors being read out in church every Sunday, with an appeal for money to pay for their redemption, until all had been paid for in full and had returned. The payment even had to be made for the bodies of the thirty-seven who had died in captivity.

President Jefferson was appalled that the ransoms we paid to Algiers, Tripoli, Tunis and the corsairs in Morocco totalled nearly one-fifth of the Government's income. He said that it would be cheaper to build a navy. So that is what we did. When the war of 1812 was over, the American navy attacked the corsairs in Morocco, and the Europeans followed suit. After a violent French assault on Rabat, the Sultan took control of Rabat and Salle and ended all remaining piracy. From then onwards, carpet-making became the main trade.

Rabat is a crowded city with a population of about fifty-two thousand Moors and eight thousand Jews. Vast quantities of *haicks* and other woollen and cotton cloths are made here, as well as leather goods and coarse earthenware, and, of course, carpets. The city carries on a brisk inland trade, and some of its inhabitants are quite prosperous. The shops along the streets are mainly cubicles, some no more than eight feet wide and ten feet deep; some completely open, others with a half-wall and a ledge at the front.

Most of the streets are narrow lanes, with children rushing around, men going about their business, stallholders waiting for custom, old men just leaning against a wall or sitting on the ground, one hand extended, awaiting alms.

As I walked along, I saw loaded mules and donkeys struggling slowly along the alleys delivering goods, their owners shouting at everyone to make way, their voices audible over the general hubbub that filled the air. I could distinguish a dozen or so words from each conversation before it dissolved back into the general din.

Mr Abouderham was a well-educated man who spoke fluent

French. He took me down to the river. This area is the principal naval yard of the Sultan, where his ships are built, but there are no vessels of commerce here. We went to the shipbuilding area and saw one frigate under construction. She looked to be about five hundred tons and had positions for thirty-two guns. I was told that she would soon be ready to sail to Larache, where their ships of war are fitted out, probably in two or three months' time.

The problem would be to get the vessel over the bar at the mouth of the river, which was heaped with sand. It was so shallow that this had to be done when the ship was half-built and not too deep in the water. They would have to remove as much weight as possible from the ship, and then position her sideways at the bar at high tide in mild weather. The vessel would then be steadied by means of cables and anchors, and allowed to rest there until the yielding sand was washed away. Finally, the arrival of the ebb tide would force her over the bar and into the open sea. Then she would be taken to the deeper waters at Larache for completion.

To explain the value the present Sultan sets on his ships of war, Mr Abouderham told me of the manner in which he disposes of them. Apparently, the Bashaw of Tripoli had recently sent the Sultan of Morocco a beautiful girl as a present. She was a Circassian, a people from the Caucasus who have been expelled from their lands and now live in the Turkish Empire. She possessed charms with which the old Sultan was so enraptured that he asked the ambassador who had escorted her from Tripoli what he could send to his friend the Bashaw in return for this jewel. 'I have nothing but wheat,' said the Sultan, 'of which the Bashaw your master can have as much as he pleases. But I would rather send him something more valuable, as he has made me such a superb present and I wish to return the compliment in a handsome manner.'

'Your majesty has some frigates, I believe,' said the ambassador.

'So indeed I do,' replied the Sultan, 'and they give me much pleasure. Go to Larache and choose one from my navy. I will have the vessel prepared in the best manner and sent to your master as soon as possible.'

The ambassador did not hesitate. He went in haste to Larache, frightened that the Sultan might come to his senses and change his mind. He chose a fine new frigate of thirty-two guns. It was immediately fitted out and was now ready to sail to Tripoli. The Sultan never for one moment doubted that he got the better part of the exchange.

Having wandered around Rabat, I told Mr Abouderham that I would now like to visit the town of Salle. However, he advised me not go there, warning me that the people of Salle still retained their ancient prejudices and ferocity, and no Christian could enter the town without being in imminent danger of losing his life.

That was enough for me.

CHAPTER TWENTY-NINE

A performance and a voyage

Sunday, 13th January 1816. Our guard and one of the muleteers came to bring me to the Mellah to see Elio, so that we could arrange our departure.

The Mellah was only five minutes' walk from Mr Abouderham's house. Soon after we had entered the Mellah, I saw a large crowd of people, Jews and Moors, clustered around a single-storey building that stood alone. They were pushing and shoving one another to get nearer to the house. When I asked the guard what was happening, he told me that Moorish serpent charmers were about to amuse the crowd with a display that would involve the sight of two of the most venomous creatures on earth attacking a human being.

Everyone who wanted to watch had to pay one *falus*, their bronze coin. I paid my fee and hurried towards the building so that I could look through one of the windows.

"Make way for the Sultan's doctor!" I heard the guard shouting. As a result, I was given a whole window to myself. I looked in. The room was about twenty feet long and fifteen feet wide, the walls were plastered, and the floor was paved with tiles. There was one door, and it had a hole cut in it that was about seven inches square, with a grating over it.

In the room stood two Arabs with long bushy hair and beards. These were men who came, so I was told, from a particular race who could charm snakes. There was a wooden box, about four feet long and two feet wide, on the floor near the door, and it had a string fastened to a slide at one end. The string led through a small hole in the door.

Now the two men, who were dressed in *haicks*, went through some sort of religious ceremony. Then they hugged each other, and one left the room, closing the door firmly. I could see him looking into the room through the grating in the door.

The man remaining in the room started to develop the most dreadful distress. He was breathing heavily, and his chest heaved violently. He put his hands to the sides of his head and cried out very loudly, '*Allah hooakbar!*' three times.

Then he went to stand near the wall opposite the door. Suddenly, the string was pulled, the slide was raised, and a snake crept out of the box. It was about four feet long and about eight inches - like a man's arm - in circumference. Its colours were beautiful: deep yellow, purple, cream and black with brown spots.

As it came out, it looked about the room. It saw the man, stopped and stared at him, its small green eyes sparkling like emeralds. Then it raised its head two feet above the floor and darted at the defenceless man, seizing him between the folds of his *haick* just above his right hip bone, hissing most horribly. The man let out a shriek, and then another serpent came out of the box.

This one was black, brightly shining and twice as long as the first snake, but little more than three inches in circumference. As soon as it had left the box, it fixed its fiery red eyes on its intended victim, thrust out its forked tongue, and curled itself into a coil with its head, which was surrounded by a heart-shaped hood, erected a full three feet above the floor. It sprang like lightning at the screaming man, opening its mouth wide and thrusting its fangs into his neck near the jugular vein, while its body wrapped three times around him.

The man yelled in the most hideous and pitiful manner, and started to foam at the mouth. Then, with his right hand, he grasped the second snake, trying to tear the reptile from around his neck, while with his left hand he grabbed it near its head. But strain as he might, he could not break its hold.

By this time, the first snake had twined itself around the man's legs, and was repeatedly biting him about the lower parts of his body, making apparently deep incisions. Blood flowed from every wound and streamed all over his *haick* and skin.

The blood in my own veins chilled at this sight, and it was with the greatest difficulty that I kept on my feet; but I could not tear my eyes away.

Despite the man's greatest efforts to wrench the snakes away, they twined themselves even tighter, restricting his breathing. Then he fell to the floor, rolling over and over in the most inconceivable agony, smearing blood about every part of his body, until he ceased to move, apparently dead.

At that instant, I heard the shrill sound of a whistle. Looking towards the door, I saw the other man with an instrument in his mouth. The snakes listened to the music - which surprised me, as I had thought all snakes were deaf - and their fury seemed to dissipate by degrees. They disengaged themselves from the apparently lifeless man and crept towards the box. Once they had made their way inside, the slide came down and they were locked in.

The second performer now ran across the room to aid his companion. He had a phial of black liquid in one hand and an iron chisel in the other. He tried to open his colleague's mouth, but the man's jaw was firm and his teeth were locked together. So he thrust the chisel into the man's mouth and prised the teeth apart, which allowed him to pour some of the black liquid down his throat.

Then, holding his colleague's lips together, he applied his mouth to the man's nose and blew air into his lungs. Next, he poured a little of the black liquid into each of the wounds; but still there was no sign of life.

El Efah

El Buskah

I was convinced that the man was dead. His neck and veins were very swollen, and all colour was drained from his face. Then his partner knelt behind him and put his arms around the man's chest, alternately squeezing his torso and releasing it. After a time, he started to breath, and five minutes later he was standing up. The swellings on his neck, body and legs gradually subsided as both men washed the wounds with water, occasionally applying more of the black liquid.

A clean *haick* was then wrapped around the injured man, but his strength had been so exhausted that he could no longer stand. His colleague helped him to lie down next to the wall, where he fell into a deep sleep.

The show was now over, and the crowd drifted away. I stayed behind to speak to the participants. I asked the second showman what kind of snakes they were, and he told me that they called the thick and beautiful serpent 'El Efah', and the long, black, heart-headed one 'El Buskah'.

I thought that the poisonous fangs must have been pulled out of the jaws of these formidable reptiles, and I said so to their keeper. He confirmed that the poison had indeed been removed.

"So how did they make those swellings on your friend's neck and body?" I asked.

"Although the poison has gone, they still have teeth," he explained, "and the poison in their breath and spittle is enough to kill anyone they bite. After being bitten by such a serpent, with or without its poison, there is no outcome but death."

"But your friend lives," I said.

"Yes," he replied. "No man can survive unless he is one of the Aisawie, the people endowed by the Almighty with the power to charm and manage serpents."

"And you are one of them?"

"Yes," he said, "both me and my friend."

I then went to see Elio. He had concluded his business in Rabat, and we agreed to set out the next morning. In the meantime, I took my leave of Mr Abouderham. He told me that he knew that

I was not the Sultan's doctor, and advised me not to waste my time wandering around towns and increasing my knowledge, but to get out of this country as soon as possible.

"Have you forgotten your family?" he asked.

"No, of course not," I replied, a little shamefaced. "I'll leave tomorrow." He was right; I must press on and think of nothing but getting on board a vessel to America.

Elio and the others collected me in the morning, and we set off in good spirits. I felt that we had now reached much more civilised parts, and Europe could not be far off. We journeyed through some fine country, nearly all of it cultivated.

Early in the afternoon, we passed to our left a fresh-water lake that was about two miles long and half a mile wide, and soon afterwards we arrived at the bank of the River Mediah. On the left bank of the river, near its mouth, I saw the old Portuguese town and fortress of Mamora, although the town was completely in ruins. The fortress is situated on a high hill that overlooks the town and the surrounding countryside.

Elio told me that we had to cross this river by boat. Fifteen camels with their loads and masters could be taken on each crossing, but I saw waiting ahead of us a queue of at least five hundred loaded camels, as well as numerous mules and asses. They were carrying mainly wheat and barley, and were going to Tangier and Tetran, where breadstuffs were said to be very scarce and dear. Our soldier said that we would have a long wait, because the boatman made only six crossings a day. Looking at the mass of humans and animals in front of us, it would be at least a week before it was our turn.

I told the soldier to go to the boatman and tell him that I was the Sultan's doctor and we could not wait, but had to be taken across the river without delay. My 'profession', plus the offer of three silver *dirhams* to the boatman, had the desired effect. He told us to come to the water's edge and board his boat. But those who had been ahead of us were not so eager to see us go past them. A great cry went up, and several men drew their scimitars and started to advance. Then I saw some way back in the crowd, the two serpent entertainers. I called to them to come forward with their mules and cross the river with us. When they reached us, they knew exactly what to do. They untied the wooden box from one of the mules and lifted the slide. The two snakes quickly slithered out into the open and moved towards the men who were coming at us. The men's eyes opened as wide as plates, and they turned and ran.

Now the camels and mules also saw the evil serpents approaching, and a great whinnying and moaning ensued as the beasts strained to get away. All was chaos. We quickly boarded the boat with the boatman and his workers, the snakemen recovered the two snakes, ushered them into their box, ran on board, and we were off.

Having alighted on the other side of the river, we thanked the snakemen, they thanked us, and we went our separate ways. We mounted some sandhills, still travelling to the north, and in the late evening we erected our tents next to a *dourham*, where we bought some milk and eggs for our supper.

It rained hard with heavy squalls of wind all night. It was as if the elements were announcing that I was approaching my goal; something momentous was not far off.

When we left on the morning of the fifteenth, the storm had passed and all was serene. I looked around at the surface of the land, carpeted with violet and pink flowers not more than an inch or two in height, which seemed to have sprung up during the night.

The countryside on our right was a low morass, partly covered with water, which soon grew into a lake of considerable size. We travelled all day along its left side; the surface spotted with countless aquatic birds. I heard shooting at one time, but it was only some men trying to procure a Barbary duck dinner.

In the afternoon, we saw the ridge of the mountains that lie behind Fez. At first, they were scarcely visible on the distant horizon, and looked like the tops of high islands when one approaches from the sea; but later we could see them in all their majesty stretching from the Atlas to the Straits of Gibraltar, forming one of the famed Pillars of Hercules.

We spent the night at another *dourham* near the edge of a lake, and on the morning of 16th January, we went down a bank to the sea and passed round the former outlet of the lake, which was now dammed high with sand.

Continuing our journey until about noon, we came to some large trees. This developed into a forest, and we travelled through it, emerging only after quite some time. At sunset, we reached the walls of Larache.

As we entered the town, I saw some friars in the street. Discovering that I was a Christian, they invited me to stay with them for the night. They took me to their dwelling, a fine house surrounded by gardens. The principal friar came out to meet me. After I had told him the main points of my story in Spanish, he said that he would give me lodging for the sake of charity, and led me to a well-furnished room.

He told me that he had lived in Essaouira for some time, and he asked me many questions about that city and his acquaintances there, some of whom I had met. The bell now rang for prayers, and I was allowed an interval for rest. Then I was called to join the priest for supper. He gave me wine, which he said was made from grapes grown in their own vineyards, and an excellent meal of duck cooked with apricots and cinnamon, accompanied by salads dressed in the Spanish fashion.

This priest, whose name was Juan Tinaones, told me that he had lived in Barbary for almost ten years: four years in Essaouira, three years in Rabat, and over two years here.

He had agreed to be secluded from the civilised world for all that time under an arrangement made with the Court of Spain. The Court supports those priests of good character, approved by the Archbishop, who are willing to spend ten years in Barbary as missionaries, and then pays them a stipend of three thousand Spanish dollars a year for the rest of their lives.

I asked him what use he could be here to the cause of

Christianity, because he would be executed if he so much as attempted to convert a Muslim.

"No use at all," he admitted, "but still we are entitled at home to be regarded as missionaries who convert heathens."

"But for what purpose?" I asked.

"When the ten years have expired," continued this priest, "we are permitted to return to Spain, where we are received as beacons of piety who have rendered vast service to the Christian world. Everyone seeks the honour of our company, and the yearly salary allows us to live in comfort. But more importantly, in return for the ten years of privation and severe gospel labours, we are granted absolution for the rest of our lives."

I thought that the wine had loosened his tongue rather too much. But despite all the advantages he had listed, I would not be willing to stay here for ten years, whatever the reward. I asked him if he would bless me. In reply, Padre Tinaones asked me if I was a Catholic. I answered in the negative.

"That is a pity," he said, "for unless you become one, your precious soul will always be miserable."

On that note, I went to my room to sleep. In the morning, Elio called for me and I said farewell to Padre Tinaones. He would accept nothing for the board or meal; but he said that in return there was something he wished me to do when I reached Tangier.

"About one and a half years ago the Sultan's vessel of war, The Essaouira, captured a Russian ship and brought her to Larache. The Emperor of Russia has not made a treaty with the Sultan, and has no consul in Tangier. As a result, the vessel's cargo was disposed of as prize and her officers and crew, ten in all, were thrown into prison."

"Are they still here?" I asked.

"No," said the padre. "The Sultan let them lie in prison for a year, waiting for a Christian power to claim them. No claim was made, so the Sultan has transferred them to his prison in Tangier. You must try to arrange for their removal to a Christian country."

I promised that I would do all in my power to help them as

soon as I reached Tangier.

We wanted to leave Larache immediately, but it was impossible to cross the river at that time, so we went into the town to wait for conditions to improve.

Larache, or El Araich, is another former corsair base, and is built on the bank of the River Loukos, near its entrance to the sea. The town is spread along the bank and is half a mile in length, but is very narrow. It is strongly walled, and has two gates.

I was told that this was the only safe port the Sultan had for fitting out his large cruisers, from where his ships can reach the sea fully loaded with their armaments. On our side of the river was the frigate that Mr Abouderham had told me about, and which was ready for its voyage to Tripoli.

The tides here run very rapidly both at flood and at the ebb, and that was why we had had to wait before crossing. But now we could go to the ferrying place. When we got there, I saw an old brig lying half sunk. This was the Russian ship whose crew had been imprisoned.

On the opposite bank, I could see the Sultan's navy. It consisted of a frigate of about seven hundred tons with thirty-two guns on the main deck, and The Essaouira, a beautiful vessel with eighteen guns, which had been built in England. The Essaouira had been presented to the Sultan by a man named Macnin, whom I remembered as one of the principal Jewish merchants in Essaouira.

These two vessels and the new frigate at Rabat constituted the whole of the Sultan's naval force. However, even with such a small navy, the Sultan is confident of his power. It is the Sultan's position that he is at war with every nation that has not made a treaty with him and does not have a consul at Tangier to make the customary presents on his annual holidays.

According to this system, he sends his vessels to sea when it pleases him. If they find a ship bearing the flag of a nation with which the Sultan is at war, they bring her in as prize and keep the crew as prisoners or slaves. That is what had happened to the Russians.

As we were waiting to cross the river, I turned and saw David running towards us, waving his arms. When he arrived he could hardly speak; he was extremely agitated. I told him to recover his breath before he said a word.

"Riley," he said finally, still gasping for air, "there are six soldiers on horseback looking for you."

"Who are they? Are they from Essaouira?" I asked.

"No, not from there," he replied. "These men are the Sultan's soldiers. They're looking for the man who says he is the Sultan's doctor, and that means you."

"But what do they care about the Sultan's doctor?" I asked.

"Your escape has been so perfect, but just one mistake," said David. "You see, you're a Christian, but the Sultan's present doctor is a Jew. They know there's some mischief."

"What am I to do?" I asked.

"You cannot continue with us," said Elio. "You'd be caught long before we reached Tangier. David will stay here with you, and we'll go on ahead and try to draw the soldiers away."

"I can then follow with David, when it's safe," I added.

We agreed, shook hands, hugged each other and said farewell. David and I made our way along the river as the others boarded a small craft that would take them to the other side. I saw them disembark and start to climb the high hills as they headed off to the north and Tangier.

David and I sat down on the ground for a rest. Then I had a thought. If the road to Tangier was dangerous, why not the sea? I suggested to David that perhaps a way could be found for me to board a ship bound for Tangier or Gibraltar.

"You may wait a year for such a voyage," said David. "The only vessel leaving here is that one going to Tripoli."

"Very well," I said, "I'll go to Tripoli."

"Yes," agreed David, "you'll be safe from the Sultan's soldiers and you'll be in the Mediterranean. That will give you many opportunities to reach Europe."

But the question was, how was I to board the ship? Certainly not as the Sultan's doctor; that ruse had run its course. David and I discussed various possibilities, but all were fraught with danger. The only way forward was to get on board as a stowaway. There would be just a skeleton crew on board, sufficient to sail to Tripoli, no more than that. For sure, I would find plenty of places to hide.

David and I wandered furtively down to the vessel, which was tied up at the quayside being loaded with provisions and other essentials for the voyage. We hid in an alleyway between two buildings, with the side of the ship in view. David told me that he would go and buy some food for me, and he hurried away. I sat down, leaning against one of the buildings, my head lowered, pretending to be asleep. About two hours later, David returned with a sack containing two cooked chickens, bread, fruit and flasks of water.

We waited until sunset, the time for prayer. Whilst the area was deserted, I said goodbye to David, ran to the vessel and along the gangplank, clutching my sack of provisions. I scurried across the deck towards the stern, then quickly made my way down to the lower deck, and from there to the hold. Here I lifted a hatch and found myself a hiding place. This is where I would stay for the time being. Now David was free to cross the river with our two mules and chase after his companions.

I soon fell asleep. When I awoke, we were out at sea, sailing briskly to the north. It was wonderful to be on board again, enjoying once more the motions of a vessel ploughing towards the Mediterranean. I should have been afraid, because if I was discovered then death, prison or slavery were the only possibilities. But for now I would savour the freedom of the ocean.

From time to time I had the courage to climb out of my hiding place and make my way to the lower deck to peer out to sea through the cannon ports. For two days and nights I stayed there, sleeping, resting, gazing at the ocean, eating my provisions and occasionally exercising my limbs so that I should not get too stiff.

The following day we turned due east as we passed Cape Spartel, heading into the Mediterranean. We kept near to the coast of Morocco, and I knew that we would soon be passing Tangier. Why wait for Tripoli and possible discovery? I was getting off here.

I waited until all was dark and quiet. Probably not more than three or four of the crew would even be awake. I made my way up as I had originally climbed down, and reached the main deck. Then I crawled to the stern and, looking over into the waters, I saw to my great relief that, just like the Commerce, this vessel was trailing a stern boat behind her, attached by a thick rope.

In a second I was over the side and clinging to the rope, struggling along it in the same manner as I had crawled along the rope for my rendezvous with the savage on the first beach. No one was watching; why should they? There was nothing to look at behind the ship.

Soon I was sitting in the small boat, bobbing along in the sea, being dragged forward by the warship. I still had one memento of my days in slavery – the knife Sidi Hamet had given to me before we set out for Essaouira all those weeks ago. I cut away at the rope for an age, until at last it was severed and I could watch the warship sail away into the dark.

I raised the sail and made for the coast. I would have preferred to be heading in the opposite direction, towards Gibraltar; but that was too far and too dangerous in these waters in such a small craft.

Before dawn, I had beached my boat on the shore, some way to the west of Tangier. I slept for a short time on the sands, and on awakening I started my march to the town.

As I progressed, I saw more and more men and animals on their way to Tangier, making their way to the western gate. I joined the procession and easily merged into the throng. Increasing my pace, I passed others who were held back by the loads their animals carried, until I saw, not more than fifty yards ahead of me, Elio and his party. I rushed towards them, and we greeted each other with great joy. Naturally they were astonished to see me, and Elio asked me to explain what had happened.

When I had finished my story, I sat once more on my mule, and we all continued towards the city.

I looked to the north beyond the shore as the early morning haze cleared, and there I saw the Bay of Tangier, the Straits of Gibraltar and, to my delight, only ten miles away, the coast of Spain - Europe.

A torrent of sensations rushed through my mind. It was filled not only with joy, but also with the recollection of all the distresses I had suffered since leaving Europe, as well as the great deliverances.

We travelled on towards Tangier, but I was so agitated that I could not keep myself steady, and I actually fell off my mule no less than three times during the five-mile journey. As I had not fallen off once before on our travels from Essaouira, our soldier assumed that I was ill, and I could not convince him to the contrary. He insisted on dismounting from his horse and walking alongside me until we reached the city. I suppose it was fair recompense for the money he had extracted from me.

It was still the early morning when we arrived at the gates of Tangier. We all went immediately to the American Consulate, where we were most hospitably received by Mr James Simpson, the American Consul General, who introduced me to his wife, and told me to consider his house as my home.

I said goodbye to the soldier and the muleteers, and shared my remaining coins amongst them. Before he left, I also gave the soldier a note for Mr Willshire, thanking him again and informing him that I was safe at last.

Elio and his companions went to stay with friends in the Jewish quarter, Tangier not having a formal *mellah*, while I took up Mr Simpson's kind offer and remained in his house.

It was 21st January 1816. A short trip to Gibraltar and then a journey by sea to America – then I would be home.

CHAPTER THIRTY

Three continents

Whilst I was in Tangier, Mr Simpson introduced me to Mr James Green, the English Consul General, and to Mr Olof Agrell, who was the Swedish Consul General. I was especially pleased to see Mr Agrell, as we had met many years before, when I was in St Petersburg.

I told Mr Agrell about the crew of the Russian vessel, still languishing in prison in Tangier. Mr Agrell went with me to see the Governor, who told us that the crew were in fact natives of what had once been Swedish Pomerania, and no one was interested in redeeming them. Mr Agrell explained that although Sweden used to own West Pomerania on the south Baltic coast, his country had transferred it to Denmark two years ago in exchange for Norway, and since then Denmark had transferred it to Prussia in exchange for Lauenberg.

Nevertheless, Mr Agrell agreed to redeem the crew for the sum of two thousand Spanish dollars, even though they had been captured under the Russian flag and owed no allegiance to Sweden.

We went to collect the crew from the prison, and brought them back to Mr Agrell's house, where they would stay until they were collected by a Swedish vessel of war. The captain told me that their ship had in fact been an English merchant vessel, but they had been flying the Russian flag to avoid capture by American cruisers. Their subterfuge had backfired on them when they had been spotted by the Sultan's ship, and they could not convince anyone that their ship was English, not Russian.

Tangier was taken from the Moors by the Portuguese in 1441, and they gave it to King Charles II of England as a dowry for Catherine of Braganza when she became his queen. The English kept the city for only twenty years. They deserted the place after enduring continual attacks from the Moors, but not before they had destroyed its fortifications and blown up its basin to lower the water level so as to prevent it being used as a harbour by their enemies.

The city is built on the west side and near the mouth of the bay to the east of Cape Spartel, rising like an amphitheatre. There is little trade between Tangier and Europe, despite it being so close to Spain. The trade that exists is chiefly carried out by the Jews, and is principally the supply of cattle and provisions to the English garrison in Gibraltar.

Tangier is a warren of narrow lanes, which are mainly crooked and badly paved. Seen from the bay, the town looks very handsome; but it is poorly built. The houses are in general small, one storey high, brightly whitewashed and with flat terraced roofs.

However, there are also some very fine buildings in the town, including the Spanish, Swedish, Dutch, French, Danish and Portuguese consular houses. The old English consular house has been abandoned because of its poor condition, but they are now building a very elegant one that is said to have cost the British government ten thousand pounds sterling so far, and they expect it will cost another ten thousand to finish it.

The American government does not have a consular house as such in Tangier. Mr Simpson had purchased a plot of land on which to build a new American Consulate, but our Government would not send any funds to pay for it. Instead, Mr Simpson bought for his own use a building that is attached to the Swedish consulate and which used to be its kitchen. He uses one room as the consular office to save the expense of renting separate premises. The house is so small that when Mr Simpson's children visit, they have to take lodgings in the Jewish quarter. In order to protect his family from the ravages of the plague, Mr Simpson built with his own money a house on Cape Spartel, a few miles from Tangier, which he called Mount Washington; but he had to let it fall into ruin, as his consular salary was rarely received. As a result, he had been obliged to borrow funds from friends in Gibraltar and from other consuls in Tangier.

Although it is only a small city, all the Christian consuls are required to live in Tangier, rather than in Fez where the Sultan resides. Consequently, they must travel whenever they have an audience. But in Tangier they have established their own diplomatic calendar, and the consuls keep up a sort of etiquette of celebrating the anniversaries of memorable events for their countries as well as their national holidays. They also take turns in holding dinners to welcome a new consul or bid farewell to a departing one. These continuous celebrations are extremely expensive, but have become absolutely necessary to impress upon the Moors respect for the nations that the consuls represent.

The consul generals are usually men of importance and ability. They earn a large salary, because they are not allowed to engage in any commerce. The salary is also a reward for excluding themselves from the society and comforts of the civilised world, and for living in constant jeopardy, being always under the shadow of religious fervour and the Sultan's whim.

They have to send to Europe for all their clothing and their children must go to other countries for their education. Mr Simpson himself has been American Consul General for many years, although he was in fact born in Scotland. He left the office of American Consul and a lucrative commercial establishment in Gibraltar in 1796, and went to Tangier to serve our country when the new Sultan threatened war against our commerce. He succeeded in negotiating peace and confirming our treaty with the Sultan, and has stayed here ever since.

Dressed in European clothes, I was now an American gentleman, the guest of the Consul General. I was not a former slave or the Sultan's doctor, and I had nothing to fear from the officials in Essaouira or the Sultan's soldiers.

My stay in Tangier was truly a period of relaxation and recovery. I spent all my time eating and conversing with Mr Simpson and his friends, and being shown around the city. Eventually I felt totally recovered, physically, mentally and now also socially.

But the time had arrived for me to leave this continent. I saw Elio several times, and he said that he would arrange for me to be transported to Gibraltar. I asked him about the Sultan's consent, but he told me not to worry – there would be no problems.

On 28th January, Elio sent a note to Mr Simpson's house informing me that he had organised my passage the next day aboard a vessel that had been hired by a man named Torrel. This man was taking his family and three other Jewish families to Gibraltar. They were unwilling to conform any longer to the mode of dress that all Jews in Moorish Barbary had been ordered to adopt, nor did they wish to pay the extra tax recently levied on them by the Sultan. As a result, they had no alternative but to leave the country. They would also be taking Mr Simpson's oldest son, John, and his wife to Gibraltar after a short visit from Italy.

The next morning, Elio came to collect me. I thanked James Simpson and his wife for their kindnesses, and went to the Jewish quarter. There, Elio handed me over to my last guardian in Africa, Mr Torrel. Now it was time to say goodbye to Elio. Here was yet another person to whom I would always be indebted. We hugged one another, and he waved goodbye as I left for the port.

I walked with the four families and the Simpsons out of the gates of the city and towards the ruins of the old mole to board the boat. The Jewish families were carrying all their possessions, and were accompanied by a large number of their friends who wished to assist them and to escort them to the boat, and then say their farewells.

The four departing families went on board, and the Simpsons and I joined them. It was about eight o'clock in the morning when we were finally ready to leave, but then there was a delay. The captain was ordered to await a letter that the Governor wished to have delivered to Gibraltar. Everyone feared that there was something more to this, and for three hours we waited in dread that we would never get out of this place.

Then the Jewish families who were waiting to see their friends off were attacked by the Moors in charge of the port. Without ceremony, they attacked the Jews with large sticks, applying the weapons so unmercifully that many of the Jews, both men and women, were beaten to the ground, where they were struck again to raise them to their feet and drive them back to the city. No wonder they wish to leave. Macnin should take his vessel back.

Now the Governor's letter arrived; was it really a letter, or had it been a ruse to give time for the beatings? Anyway, now we set off with a light breeze directing us towards Europe.

At last; at last I had left the continent and was in sight of Gibraltar. I breathed in deeply, filling my lungs with the air of freedom. I looked back at Africa. I had met some good men there: Rais, Mr Willshire, Sidi Mohammed, Elio, Mr Simpson, and others. But the scene of inhumanity and oppression I had just witnessed left me in no doubt that I should thank God I was leaving.

We had a smooth and uneventful journey, and arrived safely in the Bay of Gibraltar in the early evening. As I looked at the city from our vessel, a spiritual presence seemed to hover over the scene, and it filled my heart with bliss. Unfortunately, we could not get into the town before the gates were closed, so we had to remain on board our vessel for the night. But no matter; we were in Europe.

On the thirtieth, we were visited very early in the morning by a boat from the health office, and were then permitted to land. I climbed ashore to be met by Horatio Sprague and my four crew members. We greeted each other with unrestrained jubilation. We were all free and safe. The American Consul, Bernard Henry,

HORATIO SPRAGUE

was also there to welcome me.

I stayed with Mr Sprague for three days, awaiting the departure of a ship that would take me home. During that time, Clark and Burns left on board The Rolla, commanded by Captain Brown of Newburyport, which was sailing for America via Cadiz.

While I was in Gibraltar, I was told how Mr Sprague had received Mr Willshire's letter informing him of my captivity. Horatio Sprague generally spent the Sabbath in Algeciras, a Spanish town about ten miles from Gibraltar on the opposite side of the bay. He returned to Gibraltar on the Monday morning, and went straight to a meeting with Mr Henry, Mr Kennedy from Baltimore and some other American businessmen.

Mr Willshire's letter was delivered to Mr Sprague during the meeting. He read it to himself, and then read it aloud to the others. Mr Henry suggested that a subscription should be opened and sent to all the American consuls in the Mediterranean, inviting them to assist in raising the money for our redemption as soon as possible.

Horatio Sprague would have none of this. He had decided straight away to pay the money himself. Mr Sprague sent a trusted young man out with orders to purchase two double-barrelled shotguns, while he hastily wrote a reply to Mr Willshire.

There was only one double-barrelled shotgun for sale in the garrison, and the young man bought it for eighty dollars. Mr Sprague then took that gun and his own gun, and rode back to Algeciras. There he despatched a courier to Tariffa with the guns and his letter, ordering that they be sent by boat to Tangier to the care of Mr Simpson. He had enclosed a note to Mr Simpson requesting him to forward the letter as fast as possible to Mr Willshire in Essaouira, to be followed by delivery of the guns.

Mr Sprague had paid the bill I had drawn on him in Essaouira to repay Mr Willshire the cost of our ransom. As if he had not done enough already, he now gave us provisions for our voyage home.

The ship, Rapid of New York, commanded by Captain Robert

Williams, was now in port ready to sail. Having thanked Horatio Sprague with all our hearts, Savage, Horace and I went on board and started our voyage home.

We set sail on 2nd February 1816 with a fair breeze, and the next day we were safely outside the straits and heading for the Atlantic. After beating about for several days near Cape St Vincent at the extreme south-west point of Europe with heavy gales of wind from the west, we steered towards Madeira, and then headed north-westwards and finally due west.

Finally, on 20th March 1816, I set foot on American soil and was received with great demonstrations of joy. I hastened to Middletown to my wife and children and my parents. Our hearts beat in unison at last.

I had so many plans and ideas, such happiness.

But my remaining shipmates in Africa...

I have spent my days, thus far, amidst the bustle and anxieties incident to the life of a seaman and a merchant, and being now fully persuaded that the real wants of human nature are very few, and easily satisfied, I intend henceforth to remain, if it is God's will, in my native country.

I have been taught in the school of adversity to be contented with my lot, whatever future adversities I may have to encounter, and shall endeavour to cultivate the virtues of charity and universal benevolence. I have been dragged down to the lowest level of human degradation and wretchedness; my naked frame exposed without shelter to the scorching skies and chilling night winds of the desert, enduring the most excruciating torments, and groaning, a wretched slave, under the stripes inflicted by the hands of barbarian monsters, bearing indeed human form, but unfeeling, merciless, and malignant as demons; yet when near expiring with my various and inexpressible sufferings; when black despair had seized on my departing soul, amid the agonies of the most cruel of all deaths, I cried to the Omnipotent for mercy, and the outstretched hand of Providence snatched me from the jaws of destruction.

Unerring wisdom and goodness has since restored me to the comforts of civilised life, to the bosom of my family, and to the blessings of my native land, whose political and moral institutions are in themselves the very best of any that prevail in the civilised portion of the globe, and ensure to her citizens the greatest share of personal liberty, protection, and happiness; and yet, strange as it must appear to the philanthropist, my proud-spirited and free countrymen still hold a million and a half, nearly, of the human species, in the most cruel bonds of slavery, many of whom are kept at hard labour and smarting under the savage lash of inhuman mercenary drivers, and in many instances enduring besides the miseries of hunger, thirst, imprisonment, cold, nakedness, and even tortures.

This is no picture of the imagination: for the honour of human nature I wish its likeness were indeed nowhere to be found; but I have myself witnessed such scenes in different parts of my own country, and the bare recollection now chills my blood with horror.

Adversity has taught me some noble lessons: I have now learned to look with compassion on my enslaved and oppressed fellow-creatures; I will exert all my remaining faculties in endeavours to redeem the enslaved, and to shiver in pieces the rod of oppression; and I trust I shall be aided in that holy work by every good and every pious, free, and high-minded citizen in the community, and by the friends of mankind throughout the civilised world.

The present situation of the slaves in our country ought to attract an uncommon degree of commiseration, and might be essentially ameliorated without endangering the public safety, or even causing the least injury to individual interest. I am far from being of opinion that they should all be emancipated immediately, and at once. I am aware that such a measure would not only prove ruinous to great numbers of my fellow-citizens, who are at present slave holders, and to whom this species of property descended as an inheritance; but that it would also turn loose upon the face of a free and happy country, a race of men incapable of exercising the necessary occupations of civilised life, in such a manner as to ensure to themselves an honest and comfortable subsistence; yet it is my earnest desire that such a plan should be devised, founded on the firm basis and the eternal principles of justice and humanity, and developed and enforced by the general government, as will gradually, but not less effectually, wither and extirpate the accursed tree of slavery, that has been suffered to take such deep root in our otherwise highly-favoured soil: while, at the same time, it shall put it out of the power of either the bond or the released slaves, or their posterity, ever to endanger our present or future domestic peace or political tranquillity.

James Riley

EPILOGUE

WHAT HAPPENED TO ALL OF THEM?

(1) The crewmen who were left behind

When James Riley returned to America, only four of his crew, Horace Savage, Aaron Savage, Clark and Burns returned with him.

Antonio Michel had been murdered on the first beach, and the cook, Dick Deslisle, had been left by his master to die in the desert.

There remained in captivity Robbins, Porter, Williams, Barrett and Hogan.

Robbins and Porter

After his meeting with Riley, Robbins journeyed north-east with his new master, having been told that they were heading for Essaouira. But before he got anywhere near that town, he was sold to Hamet Webber, a trader in blankets, tobacco and powder.

Fed on a diet of camel's milk, *llash* and occasional camel meat, Robbins regained much of his strength. He and Hamet Webber travelled on and joined other desert travellers, amongst whom he once again met Porter. Robbins' job was to look after the camels, and his latest master treated him well most of the time, providing him with clothes and allowing him to sleep in his tent.

Over the following weeks, Robbins became used to the way of life of the tribesmen as they transferred from one caravan to another, moving into the mountains and passing through cultivated land.

Eventually, one evening, Hamet Webber told Robbins that they were going to Essaouira. But only three days later his hopes of redemption were again dashed as he was sold to Bel Cossim Abdullah, who was heading south to Widnoon in the land of Suse. They arrived there some weeks later.

Robbins now became virtually a resident in the capital of the northern desert of the Sahara, a town about thirty miles from the sea, serviced by a stream of fresh water issuing from a spring in the mountains that separate the town from the Atlantic.

After a short time, amazingly, he yet again met Porter, who had completely recovered from all his troubles and was now the slave of a wealthy merchant. Porter was respectably dressed and living in Widnoon as well as possible for a slave in such a place.

He told Robbins that he had been allowed to send a message to the English vice-consul in Essaouira, and that his master, Abdullah Hamet, had received a letter from the vice-consul making proposals for Porter's ransom, and asking him to tell Porter that Captain Riley had arrived in Gibraltar with four of his men.

Robbins, Porter and a Spaniard were the only white slaves in the town, as a few days before Robbins' arrival in Widnoon, the crew of the British brig Surprise of Glasgow had been taken from the town by Sidi Ishem to hold for ransom. Both Robbins and Porter lived and ate well, although they would often be reminded that they were still slaves. Once, for not being available when required, Robbins was heavily beaten by Bel Cossim Abdullah, who also hit him on the side with a stone, which caused Robbins severe pain for over two months.

In July, Robbins came across another Christian slave, an American called Thomas Davis. His vessel had been wrecked in May, and he and others from his vessel had been enslaved by Sheikh Ali, the father-in-law of Sidi Hamet and the man who had tried to steal Riley and his companions from Rais bel Cossim. Davis had been sold by Sheikh Ali to a trader who was now living in Widnoon. In December, one of Davis' shipmates, John Brown, arrived in Widnoon, having been taken there by Sidi Ishem, who had acquired him after a battle in which Sheikh Ali had been killed. Brown was bought by Davis' master.

Sidi Ishem lived not far from Widnoon, and visited the town from time to time. Robbins often saw him there, accompanied by a bodyguard of mounted warriors. He was always treated with the greatest of respect and revered by all the townsfolk. Sidi Ishem spent most of his time scouring the country with over a thousand mounted men, spreading terror wherever he went, and robbing the caravans that were bound for Fez and Marrakech.

It was about this time that Robbins first heard the name of William Willshire as the English vice-consul to whom a great number of former Christian slaves in Africa were indebted for their redemption. One morning, Porter came to see Robbins. He brought with him a letter from Mr Willshire saying that the terms of Porter's ransom had been agreed. Porter soon left for Essaouira, where he was redeemed and put on board a vessel bound for the United States. Robbins had given Porter a letter to give to Mr Willshire, but no reply was received.

Robbins continued his stay in Widnoon, working for his master. Then, on 16th February 1817, a Berber approached Robbins in the town, handed him a piece of paper and asked him to read it. It read:

"To any Christian slave,
You are requested to sign this paper at the bottom, mention the name of your vessel, the place and date when it was wrecked, and from what nation you come. Then return the paper to its bearer."

The paper had no signature.

Robbins questioned the man, who told him that he had been sent by William Willshire, who had, with his assistance, ransomed from Sidi Ishem seventeen men from the British brig Surprise.

Seizing the opportunity, Robbins took the Berber to Bel Cossim Abdullah, who informed the man of the amount required for Robbins' ransom. Then Robbins wrote his note on the paper and gave it to the Berber, who immediately departed.

In due course, the man returned with the required money, paid the ransom and set off with Robbins. Before leaving Widnoon, the Berber collected the Spaniard, whose ransom was also paid. But he refused to ransom Brown and Davis, claiming that they were pirates.

Robbins and the Spaniard followed the same route as Riley along the coast, through Agadir, and eventually reaching Essaouira. Outside the town, they were greeted by William Willshire. The Spaniard was delivered to the Spanish vice-consul and Robbins was taken to Mr Willshire's house where, to his surprise, he found Brown and Davis, who had arrived two days earlier with another of Mr Willshire's messengers.

On 22nd March 1817, Robbins, Brown and Davis left Essaouira by mule with the soldier who had been Riley's escort, again following in Riley's footsteps and reaching Rabat seven days later. There they were looked after by Mr Abouderham, and after two days' rest, they pressed on and reached Tangier on 5th April.

Then they travelled to Gibraltar, where Mr Henry, the American Consul, told them that it was too expensive for them to live on shore. The three of them therefore had to stay on board the US brig Spark until they could get a passage to America. They asked Mr Henry for some clothing, but he told them that what they were wearing was sufficient, adding that if they were given work on board, they could buy clothing with their pay. Robbins sent a note to Mr Simpson, and following his intervention they were given clothes and a little money by Mr Henry; but he would do no more for them.

In the absence of help from Mr Henry, they were fortunate to come across Captain Stanward of the ship Hero bound for Boston, who agreed to give them passage home. They sailed on 30th April, and arrived in Boston on 30th May 1817, over a year after Riley's return.

Then, Robbins worked his passage on board the schooner Pearl to Saybrook, from where he travelled on foot to his home town of Wethersfield.

Porter had reached America three months before Robbins. They both returned to the sea and lived out their lives as sailors, Robbins' extraordinary life finally ending at the age of seventy-three.

Williams, Barrett and Hogan

Robbins saw Williams and Barrett at the fishing grounds near Cape Mirik, before he travelled to Widnoon. Both had regained their health, despite still being slaves.

When Robbins was redeemed in Essaouira, William Willshire told him that he had learned that two Christian slaves were living on an island far to the south-west, near a fishing area. Presumably they were Williams and Barrett. Mr Willshire sent a messenger to try to find them, but he was unsuccessful.

No more was ever heard of them. The same can be said of Hogan, who was so nearly bought by Sidi Hamet, and missed his freedom for the want of an extra blanket.

(2) Those who came back with Riley

Burns, Aaron Savage and Clark

All three returned to the sea and spent their lives on board American vessels ploughing the oceans.

Horace

Horace Savage also went back to the sea, and quickly earned promotion after promotion. On 24th February 1823, he married Jane Hastings in Hartford, and their daughter was born in 1828.

He continued with his life at sea, eventually captaining his own vessel. Then, in 1849, Captain Horace Savage and his wife went to live in Matamoras, Mexico, where he became a prosperous merchant.

Having made his fortune, in 1856 Horace and his family returned to America and settled in Wethersfield, Connecticut, not far from his place of birth, Cromwell. He remained in Wethersfield until his death in 1881. So, nearly dead at the age of seventeen, he lived on until he was eighty-two years old.

(3) Captain Riley

Back in America, Riley spent some time with his family, quickly recovering his strength. Before doing anything else, he re-named his second son, and also the son born just three days before his departure for Gibraltar, whom he had never seen until his return from slavery. Their new names? Horatio Sprague Riley and William Willshire Riley.

Now it was time for Riley to become active again. First, he was invited to Washington, where he met James Monroe, the Secretary of State, who was to become President a few months later. Monroe promised that everything possible would be done to seek and rescue the crewmen still in African slavery, and that provision would be made for whatever might be demanded in exchange for them. The Administration also paid $1,852-45 to Riley to compensate him for the sum he had paid Mr Sprague, who had paid that sum to Mr Willshire, who had in turn paid an equivalent amount to Sidi Hamet.

After he returned home from Washington, Riley received a letter from Consul General James Simpson in Tangier, asking Riley to represent him in claiming the balance of the fees and expenses due to him for his services over the past twenty years. Riley's efforts were in vain. The salary claim was denied, and the expenses would not be considered until full documentary evidence was submitted. By the time the documents arrived, Simpson was dead.

Riley then decided that his mind and body would benefit from a journey through the western states. So he travelled alone on horseback to Kentucky, Ohio and Illinois, and then to Canada. After a journey of over 4,000 miles, he returned home. There he set about writing his recollections of his time in Africa. At first it was thought to be a work of fiction, but with the confirmation of the crewmen who had returned, it was eventually accepted as true. One person who took Riley's Journal seriously was Abraham Lincoln. When asked what books had most influenced his thinking, Lincoln named the Bible, Aesop's Fables, Plutarch's Lives, Bunyan's Pilgrim's Progress, Benjamin Franklin's Autobiography and Riley's Journal.

But memories of slavery were still at the forefront of Riley's mind. In 1819, Missouri, a slave state, applied to join the Union. Public opinion in Ohio was strongly against Missouri's admission, and Riley played a role in the debate.

Writing to the Governor, he could barely restrain his anger: *'...all wishing to prevent by all means in their power the further extension of that crying evil alike inhuman and disgraceful in a country like ours...have agreed to meet and explain...their detestation of the principle and practice of enslaving mankind and their abhorrence of the attempt now making [sic] at Washington to extend and perpetuate this...abominable enormity.'*

His anger turned to rage as he continued with the memories of his agonies in Africa, *'When the subject of slavery is brought forward...every nerve and sinew about my frame is strongly affected, the blood thrills quickly through my heart to the extremities, my former suffering among barbarians rushes across my mind like a torrent, my whole body*

388

is agitated in a powerful manner, the situation of my late mate and shipmates who if still living are still groaning in wretchedness and slavery in Africa...overcome by this crowd of sensations which torment me almost incessantly, I endeavour to shake them off by sleep and laborious employment, but all in vain...' Then returning to the purpose of his letter: *'...It is high time that the inhabitants of the non slave-holding states should rise in their strength and put a stop to...these accursed practices...'*

However, Congress pulled back from requiring the abolition of slavery in Missouri, and agreed to accept the state provided they imported no more slaves – but even that was too much. So, Missouri was admitted without restriction, though against the votes of Ohio's representatives; the only concession being that slavery was to be barred north and west of Missouri for ever.

Although the compromise settled matters temporarily, the North's hostility to slavery would eventually lead to the Civil War, for it was seen by the South as a threat to their cotton-based economy, which relied on slave labour.

In December 1819, Riley was appointed deputy surveyor by the US Surveyor General, and travelled to survey lands purchased from the Indians. Whilst carrying out his surveying duties, with the earnings from his Journal Riley purchased some land at a rapid in the St Mary's River adjoining the Indiana line, called the Devil's Raceground. He dammed the river, intending to construct a mill, and also built a log cabin into which his family moved in January 1821.

One year later, Riley began to plan and lay out a town on his land, on which several families soon settled. Roads and bridges were constructed and houses built. Riley named the town 'Willshire'. Today, Willshire, Ohio has about 1,400 inhabitants and includes Riley Street, Williams Street, Hogan Street, Green Street, Simpson Street, Sprague Street and Liberty Street.

Riley was elected to the Ohio State legislature in October 1823, and participated in the revision of the entirety of the state laws. He was particularly involved in the formulation of a canal policy

The cover of The Willshire Recipe Book, showing a replica of
the log cabin built by Riley (later used for the first school),
and the present school.

and a system of common schooling.

But in 1824, the effects of Riley's tortures in Africa finally started to catch up with him, and his health began to fail. In January 1826, he was attacked with an inflammation of the brain. With rest this eased, but he still suffered excruciating pain in the back of his neck that could only be alleviated by the use of opium. Riley was taken to New York in July, where he lived with his older brother, Asher, and was treated by Professor Valentine Mott, the most eminent American surgeon of his day. By the end of the year, Riley had recovered. He could walk once more, no longer needed opium and was restored to full health, except for deafness in his right ear.

With his health improved, Riley started once more to express his views on slavery. He joined Americans in hailing the Latin American revolutions as *'the triumph of the principles contained in our Declaration of Independence'*, but went on to say that the *'Declaration would remain unfulfilled until we can with truth proclaim liberty throughout all the land to all the inhabitants...'*

Riley's views were more liberal than those of most Americans, yet even he did not demand instant abolition, because he feared that freed slaves would not be able to survive, and that former slave-owners would lose their property and inheritance. He joined those who wanted a gradual and orderly freeing of slaves in America, and the return of the majority of the slaves to Africa. It was this movement, which its supporters believed was the only way to win a national consensus, that led to the founding of Liberia as a west-African state for freed slaves.

In May 1828, Riley's family joined him in New York. But in New York he had been reunited with the sea. Although he had resolved never to leave his native land again, by November the irresistible pull of the siren's song had become too great; Riley had to return to the oceans. After a voyage to the Caribbean and back, he purchased a half-share in the brig James Monroe, and travelled several times to Virginia and the West Indies.

Then, in 1831, Riley sold his half-share, and along with some associates, purchased the packet brig William Tell.

Short voyages on the William Tell were a start, but it would never be enough. After running aground again on the Florida reefs and damaging his vessel, the William Tell was refitted, and then James Riley was ready to let history repeat itself and sail once more for Gibraltar.

Fifteen years after leaving that place, Riley stepped ashore in Gibraltar to meet one of his deliverers, Horatio Sprague. Before he left Gibraltar, Riley asked Mr Sprague to find out whether, considering the manner of his escape, it would be safe for him to return to Essaouira.

When Riley was once more in New York, he wrote to the Secretary of State urging the appointment of US consuls at all foreign ports and asserting that the time had arrived when only US citizens should be appointed US consuls. In particular, he directed his anger at Bernard Henry, the consul in Gibraltar who had been so unhelpful to Robbins.

He complained that Mr Henry had not been available when Riley was last in Gibraltar because he was an Englishman and was spending some months in England. Riley also demanded that in future US consuls should not be allowed to engage in commerce, but should spend all their time in dealing with their consular duties. Mr Henry had '*become quite rich...and it would seem that he might be allowed to spend his time and money quietly in merry England, without...the trouble of making a brief visit annually to his far off consulate in order to gather up his fees...*'

In Mr Henry's place, Riley recommended Horatio Sprague. One month later, the Secretary of State wrote to Riley confirming Sprague's appointment by the Senate.

James Riley again sailed for Gibraltar, and delivered to Mr Sprague the official notice of his appointment, receiving in return the welcome confirmation that it would be safe for him to go to Essaouira, the old Bashaw and the Alcayd having long since died.

After unloading his cargo and spending some time with Mr Sprague, Riley knew where he had to go next. He left for Essaouira and once more saw his saviour, William Willshire. The two met as long lost brothers. By then, Willshire had married and had a young family: a son Leonard, a daughter Sara, a younger son Alexander and two small girls.

Now in Essaouira together, Riley and Willshire became business partners, purchasing a cargo of goatskins, gums, wool and almonds with which Riley sailed back to New York.

In May 1834, Riley again set out for Gibraltar and Essaouira. However, he could not go ashore in Gibraltar as it was in the grip of a cholera epidemic. He sailed for Essaouira but, having visited Gibraltar, he was not allowed to land there either, so he headed for Tangier. There he was told by James Leib, the US Consul General, about the lion and two horses in Leib's custody that were a gift from the Sultan to the President. Leib was irritated by the cost of feeding the animals, and had asked Congress for authority to sell them. In reply, he was told to send the animals to America. Instead, Mr Leib explained to Riley that as the President was not permitted to receive gifts from a foreign power, he had arranged for the lion to be accepted by a New York zoo, and he wished Riley to sell the horses. So Riley bought them himself for $300, and took all three animals on board.

Riley now made for Essaouira, where he was permitted to land on 3rd August. He purchased more goods with Mr Willshire, and sailed for New York on 23rd September 1834. Vast multitudes crowded the wharf in New York to see the lion and also the two horses, which Riley expected to sell at a profit. A Mr Holland Nicholl offered Riley $5,000 for the horses; but before the sale could be completed, a US marshal seized the animals as the property of the United States.

A bitter and lengthy dispute ensued. At one time, Riley agreed to accept $2,500 in settlement. But in the end the horses were sold by the marshal for $2,065 and Riley received nothing, the Government declaring that Leib's sale was invalid as he had acted without authority.

Riley's co-owners of the William Tell now sold their half-share to A.C. Rossiere & Co., with whom Riley maintained a prosperous and friendly business relationship for the rest of his life. His new partners gave him the command of another of their ships, the brig Americas, and Riley made for Essaouira on 3rd May 1835, which he found in a parlous state, having just seen the end of an epidemic of cholera that had reached the city despite all precautions.

Further voyages between New York, Gibraltar and Essaouira, led to extremely profitable business for Rossiere, Riley and Willshire.

The treaty between the United States and Morocco was due to expire in 1836, so in 1835 Riley volunteered to represent his country in the negotiations for a new treaty. His anger at not being appointed was exacerbated when he received only $3,000 compensation for his share of the loss of The Two Marys, out of the sum obtained by Congress from France.

Riley's disgust was increased when he learned that the Government's appointee to negotiate the new treaty with the Sultan was Mr Leib, the man who had caused the problems with the two horses. In the event, Leib refused to go to Fez to negotiate with the Sultan and his advisers, afraid that the Sultan would be angry that he had sold the horses and even more afraid that the Sultan might give him two more horses – that would involve him in more feeding costs. So he sent a vice-consul to Fez to conduct the negotiations and then to sign the treaty in Meknes, Leib deigning to endorse his approval in Tangier two weeks later.

But now Riley's health began to fail again. He started to suffer from a chronic inflammation of the bladder, which caused him extreme pain on every sudden movement. In late 1836, when once more in Essaouira, it became too much and Riley had to remain on shore whilst his vessel returned to New York. He stayed in the town throughout the Autumn and Winter. Riley was advised to see a specialist in France, and on 23rd March 1837 he left Essaouira for France via Gibraltar.

The voyage was eventful. At midnight they were struck by a

squall and all sails were let run and were flapping like mad. "For God's sake, don't run ashore!" Riley shouted at the captain. But this time they avoided the rocks and reached Gibraltar.

Riley then made his way to Montpelier, where he was to consult Professor L'Allemand. The Professor had his own technique. He refused to give any medicine by mouth; his treatment was *'cauterisation energetique'*. He thrust a hollow tube into Riley's bladder, without first applying a sedative or taking any other precaution. Then he used the tube to fill that organ with nitrate of silver dissolved in alcohol.

Riley was carried back to his rooms. For one week, he could not move from his bed. After three weeks, he was told by the professor that he should go to Vernet-les-Bains in the Pyrenees Mountains, where he was to bathe forty times in the hot sulphur baths.

Upon reaching Vernet, Riley discovered that the professor was a part-owner of the baths and the hotel. Here he met other patients of the professor, who had suffered from a variety of illnesses, including liver complaints, lumbago, rheumatism and coughs. All had received the same silver treatment and all had been told to stay in Vernet.

Riley left Vernet on 16th June, not yet able to walk. At first, he travelled in a cart pulled by a donkey, later in a horse-drawn carriage. By stages he reached Marseilles, from where he took a boat to Gibraltar and then to New York, which he reached in September 1837.

In his absence, world trade had suffered disasters in 1837; but in view of the vast profits made in the Essaouira trade, Rossiere & Co. and Willshire had survived, although their wealth, as well as Riley's, had been greatly diminished.

Having recovered from his 'treatment', Riley reached Essaouira again in late 1839. A grand cavalcade of Moorish dignitaries and mainly Jewish merchants from Essaouira and Safi was to make a journey to the Sultan in Marrakech to pay their respects and tributes. Riley and Willshire decided to join it together with Willshire's son, Leonard.

When they reached Marrakech, finally at the age of sixty, Riley was presented to the Sultan, Mulay Abdir Ahman, a man aged about forty. He had come to the throne on the death of his uncle Mulay Sulimaan in 1822, even though Mulay Sulimaan had thirty sons. "You are welcome to our capital," the Sultan said to Willshire and Riley. Then to Willshire and Leonard Willshire, "Is that your son? God bless him". And finally, "Rais Riley is also known to me through your goodness - he is welcome."

After a brief conversation, the Sultan gave Riley a lioness as a gift, and Willshire and Riley then returned to Essaouira. Now Riley informed Willshire that he had decided that it would soon be time for him to end his travelling and go home and live out the remainder of his life with his family. He told Willshire that, having resided in Essaouira for over twenty-five years, he also ought to return to Christian lands. He suggested that Willshire should settle in the United States, and assured him that having redeemed so many Americans, for which Congress had passed a vote of thanks to him, he would be welcome in his country. Willshire agreed that it would soon be time to close his business interests and leave Africa.

Riley returned to America, and arranged for the purchase of a house by William Willshire, after which he would make his last voyage to Essaouira to collect Willshire and his family and transport them to their new home.

But before proceeding to Essaouira, he made for the Danish-owned island of St Thomas in the Caribbean to deliver a cargo. Shortly after setting sail from New York, Riley became unwell and retired to his cabin. His condition deteriorated; in truth, he had never recovered from the excruciating treatment he had received in France three years earlier.

He struggled for a week, but on 13th March 1840, he finally lost the life he had fought so hard to preserve. His crew had hoped to arrange his burial when they reached St Thomas seven days later, which would be the twenty-fourth anniversary of Riley's return from slavery, but on 18th March 1840 the hot weather compelled them to commit his remains to the deep.

(4) Sidi Hamet

There is no evidence that Sidi Hamet was instrumental in the redemption of any other Christian slaves. All that is known is that William Willshire was told some years later that Sidi Hamet had been slain in battle.

(5) Rais bel Cossim

Rais continued to live in Essaouira as William Willshire's agent and friend. However, on 30th June 1825, he was taken unwell after praying at sunset. He was carried home, and expired an hour later.

(6) Essaouira

In 1844, the French were at war with the Algerian Emir, Abd el Kader. The Sultan of Morocco sent men to assist his neighbour. In retaliation, the French despatched a squadron commanded by the twenty-five year old Prince de Joinville to bombard Tangier from the sea.

De Joinville was the third son of King Louis Philippe, and was more famous for having brought Napoleon's remains to France from St Helena.

On 4th May 1844, the French vice-consul in Essaouira, Monsieur Jorelle, wrote to his Minister in Paris: *'If your Excellency considered it proper to support my representations with the presence of a warship, this would give weight to my endeavours and would have the added advantage of protecting the French and even the Europeans residing in Mogadore against the hostile disposition of Spain against Morocco'.*

In reply, he was told that the warship visit would provide more than a 'presence'. He was instructed to advise all the European consuls to make sure that they and all their countrymen left Essaouira by the end of July. But Monsieur Jorelle did not inform any of them. Instead, he quietly slipped out of Essaouira on a French vessel, accompanied by his family and the other French nationals.

Having dealt with Tangier, de Joinville and his squadron sailed south to attack Essaouira, and the Arabs of the desert swarmed to the town to assist in its defence. During a sporadic shower of shot from the sea for two days and nights, the Arab defenders, enraged at the French attack which they were powerless to prevent, and unrestrained by any authority, launched an indiscriminate attack on the inhabitants they had been summoned to defend, and plundered the entire city. As there were no French there, they attacked the Jews and foreigners and destroyed their homes and businesses. Adults and children were murdered; others were driven from the town. Many of the Jewish women were kidnapped and taken to the desert, never to be seen again.

Then, on 15th August 1844, a unit of five hundred French soldiers landed and stormed into the empty town. The French promptly left and sailed home, de Joinville being rewarded by promotion to vice-admiral.

The Sultan was appalled by these events, and gave ten thousand ducats for the relief of the survivors. As far away as England, a subscription raised £1,674 from the Portuguese Jewish congregation in London 'and several Christian gentlemen'.

The French shot had caused limited damage, but the ravages of the 'defenders' resulted in the burning and destruction of much of Essaouira. It took several months to rebuild the town. In time some of the surviving Jews returned, their numbers eventually swollen by those coming from other towns, but Essaouira never recovered its importance. Having controlled almost half of Morocco's foreign trade, its position was completely taken over by Casablanca and Agadir.

(7) The Jewish families Riley met in Essaouira

Zagury

People with the name Zagury, meaning 'from Zagora', a town at the edge of the desert, moved on to other countries, some reaching prominent positions in France and Brazil. Others remained in Morocco, where a Zagury descendant was, after 1945, the leader of the Jewish community in Casablanca.

Macnin

For a time, the Macnins maintained their status. Meir Macnin, known as 'the Sultan's Jew', was appointed Moroccan ambassador to England in 1828. But in time, they also left.

Horeb-Elisha

The Horeb-Elishas fared better. Named after the mountain, Mount Horeb, otherwise known as Mount Sinai, where Moses was given the Commandments and where Elisha became the pupil of Elijah, the Horeb-Elishas became heavily involved in trade with England. In order to regulate that trade, young Horeb-Elisha was sent to Manchester by his father. He stayed, and the family anglicised their name by moving the hyphen one letter to the left; thus, Hore-Belisha. Eventually a grandson, Leslie Hore-Belisha, entered the Government, and was Minister for War in 1939. However, he is best remembered for his time as Minister of Transport, when he introduced the flashing orange lights at pedestrian crossings, which are known to this day as 'Belisha Beacons'.

But the prejudice his forefathers had endured in Morocco was repeated in England. Hore-Belisha annoyed Prime Minister Chamberlain by suggesting conscription and increased spending on the armed forces at a time when Chamberlain was negotiating with Hitler. So Hore-Belisha was demoted to Minister of Information. But the Foreign Secretary, Lord Halifax, said it was 'inappropriate to have a Jew in charge of publicity'. A Foreign Office Minister added, 'Jew control of our propaganda would be a major disaster.' With those comments from his own party, Hore-Belisha resigned; *dhimmis* were not restricted to Morocco. Parties to celebrate the Jew's resignation were held in gentlemen's clubs in London, one MP toasting the move to a more appropriate friendship with Aryan cousins.

After the war, Hore-Belisha was given a minor position by Churchill, and was later enobled as Baron Hore-Belisha of Devonport.

In one of his last interviews, the man called the English Dreyfus told the journalist not to research the name Hore-Belisha, but to look for Horeb-Elisha in the Mellah in Essaouira.

General

Following the French assault in 1844, the enraged Arab defenders destroyed most of the Jewish businesses, and many of the Jews in Essaouira were murdered. They had not expected the attack, unlike the Jews in Tangier, of whom forty per cent left for Cadiz, Gibraltar, France, London and Manchester before they could be killed.

But even of those who returned to Essaouira, the young men knew that their futures lay elsewhere. Large numbers went to Rio de Janeiro, Caracas and other parts of South America, where they developed the rubber trade. Indeed, an old cemetery in the Amazonian delta contains the grave of a Zagury. But with the collapse of rubber prices when cheap rubber from south-east Asia was introduced at the beginning of the twentieth century, many moved on to the United States or elsewhere in the Americas, or back to their families in Morocco, where a large proportion remained until they could emigrate to Israel forty years later.

Those who left the Moroccan towns provided other countries with the first Jewish senator in the US, the inventor of fizzy drinks in America, several French Resistance leaders, a UK Government Minister, a President of the State of Israel, and numerous musicians, composers, painters, historians, poets, authors, doctors and religious leaders.

(8) The Consuls

James Simpson

James Simpson had been appointed American Consul in Gibraltar in May 1794, and two years later he was sent to Morocco to replace Thomas Barclay, who had died on his way to seek the new Sultan's re-affirmation of his predecessor's treaty with the United States. Simpson succeeded in that task, and was appointed American Consul General in Tangier.

Despite all Riley's efforts, Congress refused to increase Simpson's salary from $2,000 per year to $4,000 per year. John Quincy Adams, the then Secretary of State, said that such an increase was against the law. Riley took the matter up with former President Jefferson, complaining that the US Consul General in Algiers was paid $4,000 per year; but he let the matter drop when told that Congress would soon raise consular salaries to $3,000 per year.

Simpson continued in his office until he died of apoplexy on 8th March 1820.

James Simpson did not live to see the new consular building for which he yearned. It was only in 1821 that Sultan Mulay Sulimaan gave the United States one of the most beautiful buildings in Tangier as its consulate. This building remained the US consulate until 1956, and even now, as a museum and study centre, it is the oldest diplomatic property owned by the United States abroad.

Horatio Sprague

Horatio Sprague continued in office as US Consul in Gibraltar until his death in 1848. He was succeeded by his son, also named Horatio Sprague.

The son was involved in another remarkable story. On 5th November 1872, a vessel set sail from New York bound for Genoa, with ten people on board. On 13th December, she was towed into Gibraltar harbour by the British brigantine Dei Gratia, having been found drifting east of the Azores in perfect condition, but with not a soul on board.

As she was a US registered vessel, it was Horatio Sprague's duty to report on the mystery and the various investigations - all of them inconclusive. The name of the vessel? The Mary Celeste.

In a unique sequence of events, when Horatio Sprague junior died in 1901, he was succeeded as US Consul in Gibraltar by his son, Richard Sprague, who held the office until his death in 1943 – giving the family an uninterrupted appointment lasting over a century.

(9) Messrs Renshaw and Dupuis

Dupuis only reached London in 1816, following his illness in Gibraltar and subsequent capture and imprisonment by the French. Although he later prepared to return to Essaouira, Renshaw terminated their business relationship before Dupuis' departure. After applying unsuccessfully for numerous consular posts, Dupuis was appointed British Consul in Ashanti in West Africa, returning to London in 1824.

Now Dupuis went to war with Mr Renshaw, claiming that Renshaw owed him considerable sums as a result of their former business relationship. This became a violent dispute, with Joseph Dupuis putting his case in a series of vitriolic letters of up to twenty pages in length. Some of Dupuis' letters reached a stage where it seems that he was quite possibly deranged.

'...It is true I knew you when you were entitled to that homage – both as regarded the seigniority of your station, and the private virtues and qualifications for which I deludedly gave you credit – and, if I should ever know you again so qualified (to the extent of conviction) be assured that I will publicly proclaim my misconceptions; even though the confession embrace an acknowledgement of having calumniated a man whose pretensions would ostensibly aspire to the rank of friend and benefactor. But, until that day shall arrive, I can only recognize you in the character of a foe, and you best know with what truth I may add, an acrimonious and vindictive one.

'...And you are the man who would have it believed that I owe you respect!!! For what? Is it for your dissimulation, treachery, violations of word and covenants enmity or rapine? Or is it because with worldly sophistry you would now endeavour to cover mountains of infamy with the specious application of a few words of deceptive tenderness and affected benevolence?'*

But of course ending:

I am Sir, your obedient Servant,
Joseph Dupuis'

Dupuis claimed that he was Renshaw's partner and entitled to a share of all his profits in the business. He contended that he had been underpaid and cheated; that the house in Essaouira belonged to him; that Willshire had stolen the Ironmongers' fund; and that Renshaw owed him vast sums.

The matter went to arbitration. Mr Cocks, the arbitrator, rejected all of Mr Dupuis' claims, and found that when Dupuis left Essaouira he was in debt to Mr Renshaw in the amount of £199-6s-7d. At the arbitrator's suggestion, Mr Renshaw agreed that the sum could be paid by instalments over two years.

Dupuis now wrote repeatedly to the Foreign Office, begging for a new appointment. In the end they gave in, and appointed him vice-consul in Tangier. But when the Consul General retired and Dupuis was not promoted, he started a conspiracy with the Governor and the French Consul General, with the purpose of having the Governor insist on his appointment as consul general. Dupuis was recalled to London in disgrace. The Foreign Office verdict on his conduct was that 'his head was somewhat affected'.

(10) The Ironmongers' Fund

The Worshipful Company of Ironmongers developed from a fifteenth century guild. In 1723, one of its members, Thomas Betton, a turkey merchant who had himself experienced the calamity of bondage in Barbary, left £26,000, half his estate, to be administered by the Company as a fund for the redemption of British slaves in Turkey and Barbary. Today, the fund has an annual income of about £130,000 that is applied in grants to schools and the elderly and for the relief of poverty.

(11) The Essaouira vice-consulate

After Mr Willshire's return to England, Mr Dupuis applied to be re-appointed vice-consul. He was rejected. When William Willshire's chief clerk, William Grace, returned to Essaouira, he was the first European to come back to the town, and he was promptly appointed vice-consul.

Not one to give up, several months later Mr Dupuis wrote to the Foreign Office, informing them that the British vice-consul had drowned when his ship was wrecked on returning from a business trip to Gibraltar, and asking to be appointed vice-consul in his place. The Foreign Office rejected the application. Mr Dupuis then wrote to apologise, saying that the British vice-consul had not drowned – it was the vice-consul of another country - and could he be appointed vice-consul in Santa Cruz instead. As there was no vice-consulate there, he was again rejected.

(12) William Willshire

After the financial decline of 1837, William Willshire's business recovered. By 1840, his fortune amounted to some $200,000, and he was ready to leave Essaouira. Through the agency of James Riley, he purchased a beautiful home in New York at a cost of $16,000.

But when Riley died, Willshire abandoned his plan of moving to America, and the property in New York was sold.

Willshire remained in Essaouira, and his business continued to prosper until the 1844 attack by the French fleet.

As the French warships stood out at sea, preparing for their attack, two English ships, HM frigate Warspite and the steam vessel Hecla, arrived to rescue the European residents. De Joinville was astonished that there were Europeans still there, as he had expected the French vice-consul to have ensured that they had all left. He agreed to delay the attack until the Europeans were on board the British ships.

But the Bashaw would not let them leave. Mr Willshire started a lengthy negotiation, and eventually all were allowed to leave except for the merchants who had an account with the Sultan for the payment of import duties on goods that were as yet unsold. The duty was not payable until the goods were sold, but nevertheless the Bashaw would not permit those merchants to leave until he had the Sultan's written authority. He also insisted that their families remained in the town. After further efforts, Mr Willshire obtained permission for the children of those merchants to leave; but Mr and Mrs Willshire and four other merchants and their families had to stay in the town, and they were joined by two of Mr Willshire's staff, who remained voluntarily.

The attack started, and Mr Willshire's house was severely damaged. Fortunately, the Europeans were sheltering in one of Mr Willshire's warehouses. In the ensuing outbreak of ferocity and cupidity by the Arabs of the desert, Mr Willshire's fortune was sacrificed. His warehouses were plundered, his dwelling robbed. His life was threatened, and he and his wife were manhandled, with scimitars held at Mrs Willshire's throat to silence her as the thieves searched them for valuables.

After two days and nights of terror, they were able to escape to the shore despite the Bashaw's prohibition, as the Bashaw and his soldiers had been the first to flee. They found some pieces of wood, and one of the English merchants fashioned a raft on which he paddled to the nearest French ship. The French sent a small boat to the beach and rescued the Willshires and their companions, delivering them to the British vessels.

The Willshires were carried to England, utterly destitute. They reached London on 4th September 1844.

William Willshire never returned to Essaouira to recover his property, such as it was after its destruction. Poor Mr Willshire, his virtues unrewarded, found himself with no home, no business and no money.

He asked the Foreign Office to claim compensation on his behalf from the French and Moroccan governments; but they rejected the request, saying that neutrals could not claim compensation for losses in war. Of course, the French were now allies, and the safety of Gibraltar precluded any steps that might offend the Sultan.

Now penniless, Mr Willshire asked for a new consular appointment. At first he was refused, but then the British consul in Adrianople died, and in 1845 the post was offered to Mr Willshire. Just as the Foreign Office continued to call Essaouira by its old name of Mogadore, so Mr Willshire's new consulate was called Adrianople (an anglicised version of its former name of Hadrianopolis after the Roman Emperor Hadrian), despite the fact that the Ottomans had changed the town's name to Erdine in 1361.

The Willshire's time in Adrianople in north-west Turkey, near the border with Greece, was a time of poverty, sickness and misery. Mr Willshire frequently asked for an increase in salary (initially £60 per year) and a transfer. The salary request was occasionally granted, the transfer always refused. Again and again he complained of his misery and the effect the climate had on his and his wife's health; but to no avail.

After five years of dejection and despair, his letters became desperate. But the Foreign Office was not interested. On one occasion the only reply was an instruction from Viscount Palmerston to 'write larger and in a more upright hand'.

In 1850, Mrs Willshire contracted typhus, the children had fevers and Willshire himself had an operation for a cancerous malady in his back; but still they refused a transfer.

Finally, he wrote saying that if they would not transfer him, could he retire on a pension so that he might end 'his banishment from civilised society'. In reply he was informed that his post did not carry a pension.

He pleaded again and again, but was told that the Treasury would not treat him as an exceptional case. Then someone in the Foreign Office had a bright idea. If the consulate was closed, the Treasury might agree to the cost of a pension for Mr Willshire in return for the ending of all expenses in Adrianople. Palmerston proposed it, and the Treasury agreed.

On 18th August 1851, a letter was written to Mr Willshire by the Foreign Office confirming Palmerston's decision to close the consulate at the end of the year, when Willshire could at last retire and return to London on a pension of £100 per year.

The reply from Adrianople informed Palmerston that William Willshire had died on 4th August.

Willshire considered himself to be only a humble instrument in the hands of the Supreme Being, but to others he was, as Riley's son described him, an honour to his nation and an ornament to mankind.

(13) Willshire's letter – Antonio Michel

It was Riley's recollection that when he escaped from the first

WILLIAM WILLSHIRE'S NOTE OF HIS LETTER TO CONSUL GENERAL GREEN IN TANGIER, ADVISING HIM OF AN OLD MAN BEING FOUND ON THE WRECK

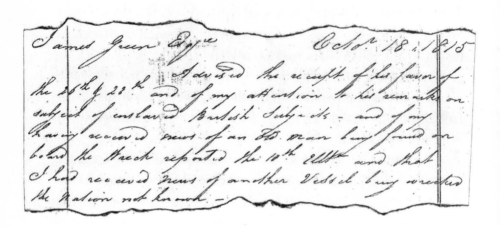

James Green Esqre   October 18, 1815

Advised the receipt of his favour of the 26th & 28th and of my attention to his remarks on subject of enslaved British Subjects – and of my having received news of an old man being found on board the wreck reported the 10th Ult* and that I had received news of another Vessel being wrecked the nation unknown –

*See extract from Willshire's letter of 10th September on page 283 beach, he was told that Antonio Michel had been killed. He looked to the beach to see the natives dragging Antonio's body away.

When Archibald Robbins returned to America, he told a different story. He said that Captain Riley had misunderstood what had happened, and he should not blame himself for Antonio's death. On the contrary, when the natives dragged Antonio away he was still alive, and many of the crew thought, as they struggled from disaster to disaster, that Antonio might well be the only one who would survive.

Now, 190 years later, William Willshire's copy of his letter to Consul General Green in Tangier, found in the depths of the Public Record Office in Kew, London, lends support to Robbins' version. Willshire says that an old man was found on board the wreck. Did Antonio Michel escape from his captors and try to return to his colleagues? Who was it who found him on the wreck? What happened to him after that? Was it indeed Antonio? We shall never know.

(14) Slavery in the United States

Abraham Lincoln had declared that Riley's *Journal* was one of the six books that had most influenced his thinking. It was the only one of the six books that dealt with the horrors of slavery. The *Journal's* inescapable message was that the evils and immorality of white slavery could not be distinguished from the evils and immorality of black slavery. Lincoln read Riley's *Journal* when he was a youth, and he quickly became a staunch abolitionist.

When Lincoln, a man now committed to the anti-slavery cause, was elected President, the southern states seceded from the Union, and the violent and bloody internecine conflict soon followed. The Civil War cost America hundreds of thousands of lives and a wound to the country that has not yet healed.

Slavery was not the only issue between the sides, but it was an important one, and it may well have lit the fuse. Whatever people were fighting for, one of the results of the North's victory was Lincoln's Emancipation Proclamation in 1863 and the 13th Amendment to the Constitution in 1865, which ended slavery in the United States.

Although he had been dead for over twenty years, if anyone's soul went marching on, it was Captain James Riley's.

THE END

RILEY'S FAMILY

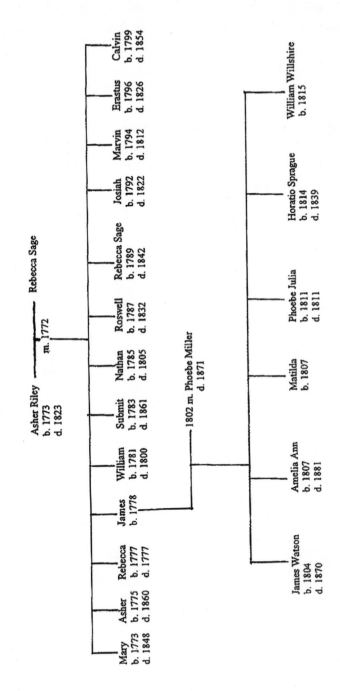

Asher Riley
b. 1773
d. 1823

m. 1772

Rebecca Sage

Mary
b. 1773
d. 1848

Asher
b. 1775
d. 1860

Rebecca
b. 1777
d. 1777

James
b. 1778

William
b. 1781
d. 1800

Submit
b. 1783
d. 1861

Nathan
b. 1785
d. 1805

Roswell
b. 1787
d. 1832

Rebecca Sage
b. 1789
d. 1842

Josiah
b. 1792
d. 1822

Marvin
b. 1794
d. 1812

Erastus
b. 1796
d. 1826

Calvin
b. 1799
d. 1854

1802 m. Phoebe Miller
d. 1871

James Watson
b. 1804
d. 1870

Amelia Ann
b. 1807
d. 1881

Matilda
b. 1807

Phoebe Julia
b. 1811
d. 1811

Horatio Sprague
b. 1814
d. 1839

William Willshire
b. 1815

RILEY'S CHILDREN

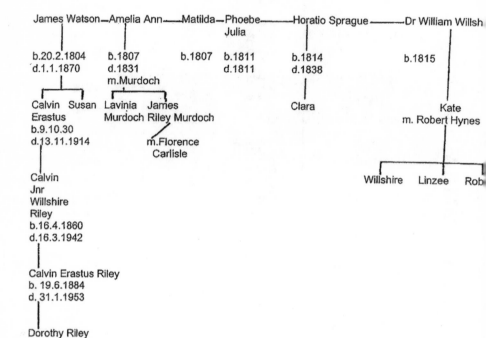

James Watson—Amelia Ann————Matilda—Phoebe————Horatio Sprague————Dr William Willsh

Julia

| | | | | | |

b.20.2.1804   b.1807   b.1807   b.1811   b.1814   b.1815

d.1.1.1870   d.1831   d.1811   d.1838

m.Murdoch

Calvin Susan Lavinia James   Clara   Kate

Erastus   Murdoch Riley Murdoch   m. Robert Hynes

b.9.10.30

d.13.11.1914   m.Florence

Carlisle

Calvin   Willshire   Linzee   Rob

Jnr

Willshire

Riley

b.16.4.1860

d.16.3.1942

Calvin Erastus Riley

b. 19.6.1884

d. 31.1.1953

Dorothy Riley

[still living in Ohio]

APPENDIX

1.   The Fateful Voyage

2.   From the wreck to the desert to Cape Nun

3.   Cape Nun to Essaouira

4.   Essaouira to Tangier

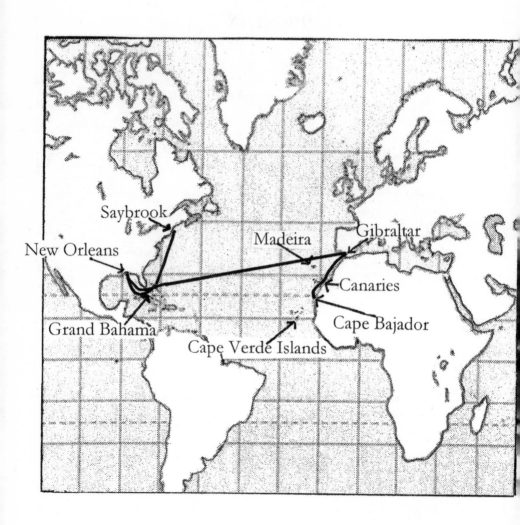

THE FATEFUL VOYAGE

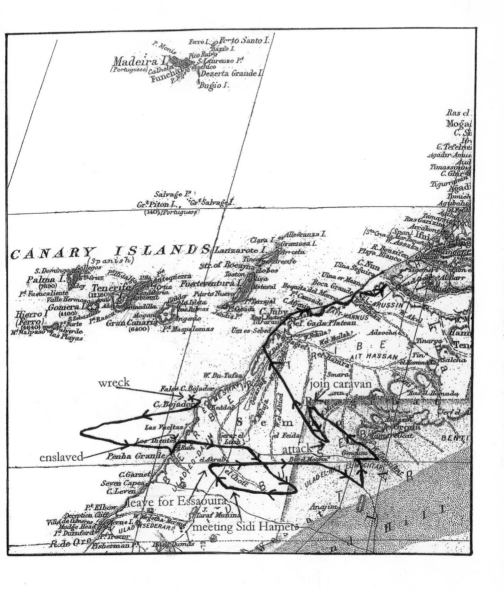

FROM THE WRECK TO THE DESERT TO CAPE NUN

CAPE NUN TO ESSAOUIRA

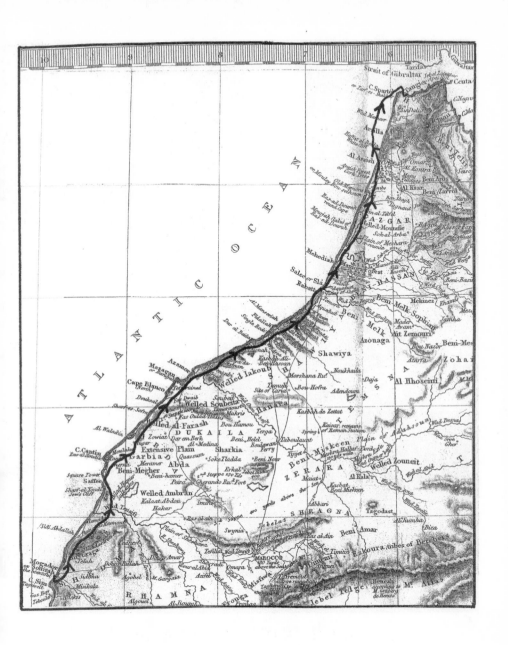

ESSAOUIRA TO TANGIER